CW00566917

## About the Author

Mitch Jago was born in Canada and educated at Ilford County High Grammar School for Boys in Essex. He joined an apprenticeship for oil and gas piping designers in the seventies, then went on to command leadership roles occasionally, managing teams of a hundred or more engineers and designers based in multiple, global offices.

Mitch has been fortunate to have travelled extensively throughout his career and for the third (and last) time, is married to Erica after they met while he was on an assignment in South Africa.

His interests outside the piping circles include cooking, golf, chess, photography and movie music while he might be seen at any given time in Stratford, East London cheering on his favourite football team, West Ham United.

He has two children and four grandchildren and continues to support global energy projects from his base in England.

# Drawing Boards to Docking Stations

**Mitch Jago**

# Drawing Boards to Docking Stations

Olympia Publishers
*London*

**www.olympiapublishers.com**
OLYMPIA PAPERBACK EDITION

**Copyright © Mitch Jago 2023**

The right of Mitch Jago to be identified as author of
this work has been asserted in accordance with sections 77 and 78 of the
Copyright, Designs and Patents Act 1988.

**All Rights Reserved**

No reproduction, copy or transmission of this publication
may be made without written permission.
No paragraph of this publication may be reproduced,
copied or transmitted save with the written permission of the publisher, or in
accordance with the provisions
of the Copyright Act 1956 (as amended).

Any person who commits any unauthorised act in relation to
this publication may be liable to criminal
prosecution and civil claims for damage.

A CIP catalogue record for this title is
available from the British Library.

ISBN: 978-1-80439-312-3

This is a work of fiction.
Names, characters, places and incidents originate from the writer's imagination.
Any resemblance to actual persons, living or dead, is purely coincidental.

First Published in 2023

Olympia Publishers
Tallis House
2 Tallis Street
London
EC4Y 0AB

Printed in Great Britain

# Dedication

To my dearest grandchildren, this is what Grandad was up to.

The Sikorsky S76 helicopter rose above Dyce airport towards a thick cloud base and corrected its course out to the oil field. I had mixed feelings about this next two week offshore rotation. On one hand I was sad to be leaving my young son again, soon to be re-acquainted with a couple of hundred chaps in the middle of the ocean.

On the other hand, I had spent the last two weeks quarrelling with my wife so things had to get better, even if it would mean getting stuck into some awkward, physical checks on critical module hook-up piping.

Two and a half hours in and I awoke from a dream filled sleep. Approaching the Marathon Brae Bravo platform, from my seat I could see the hundred metre tall structure, fixed to the earth's surface beneath the giant North Sea. Floating next to the platform was the Swedish support vessel the Safe Britannia and my accommodation for the next fortnight. This would be my home where I was to share a bedroom with three hairy arsed drilling folk and sit next to species of animals in the dining room, who would not give it a second thought to carrying one large plate back to the table filled with steaks, chips, mushy peas, cherry crumble, custard, gravy, toast and marmalade.

The normal stage of events for the choppers was to drop off and collect resources independently, from both platform and vessel. If the first stop off was the lower helideck on the Britannia, the pilot would set down, workers would get off and workers would get on before rising from the surface in a straight vertical line that would bring the chopper alongside the higher, Brae B, helideck. He would then set it down on that helideck and switch out the workers before heading back to Aberdeen.

On this occasion, something different was about to happen that helped me fill a small area of my survival suit. The pilot set down on Brae and everyone alighted from the aircraft. Apart from the two pilots, I was the only one continuing down to the Britannia.

In this specific reversed, but relatively safer, manoeuvre the chopper would rise from the platform helideck, head out to sea in a large banked arc of about a mile radius before returning to the lower helideck of the vessel. As the chopper headed out over open waters, the angle of bank was so steep, I was pleased to be restrained by the seat belt while staring down at the waves. There was one unusual but fairly significant other concern; the side access door of the helicopter had not been closed. I had no means to alert the pilots because passengers were not assigned headsets. If I had released my seatbelt to scramble a few metres through to the pilots I would have tumbled out of the aircraft.

Two minutes later we levelled out, descended and touched down on the Britannia. My heart rate settled and the helideck operations chap had a heart attack when he approached the already open door to see me sitting there on my own with a look of worry on my pale face.

The helideck operations guys on the Brae Bravo platform filled two of the empty seats on the next chopper back to the beach.

# FOREWORD

I have rewritten this book a few times for reasons of a personal nature. Some of the rework had a lot to do with mentioning names of individuals in the book. I had received negative feedback from my second wife to the style in which I had prepared the narrative. She had stated that she simply didn't want her name in the story, even though I had reassured her that most of it was all good.

But what to do for all the other names in the book? Simple. I switched many of the names around.

If a story about Tom was relevant, he would now be called Terry. If a bloke called Terry was in another story, he would now be Gerald. The same approach for surnames. Jones might be James, and so on. Therefore, what you are about to read (if you've gotten this far already) is filled with names who may not be whom they really are. Or whom they were. Or both.

Furthermore, one day, my grandchildren may want to know more about what Grandad actually did for a living. Indeed, they may not give a shit either, but at least they would have been offered an opportunity to read and understand what Grandad was up to for his working life. And this, is the prime reason for my writing it.

# An Introduction

As the title of this book suggests, the oil business has changed throughout the years that has driven its workforce into areas of wealth, while in other times taken away that wealth, replacing it with financial hardship.

The oil and gas engineering sector is struggling to survive. We live in a world that is supported by alternative forms of energy like wind farms, solar panels and electric vehicles.

There are environmental challenges, aboriginal land rights, Greenpeace, organisations protecting wildlife and oceans densely populated with discarded plastic material, some of it sadly consumed by the sea's inhabitants. And we now have Greta.

News items about oil spills from tankers, derailments of gasoline filled railcars and sour gas pipeline ruptures that poison the land with contamination and threaten life.

And we slice our way through community forestry to acquire landscapes rich in fossil fuels, casting aside sparsely clad, ancient civilisations only for the rich and wealthy to depart by helicopter a few months later leaving a devastating mess below.

We extract oil and gas from the crusts and depths of this special planet while we continue to build hydrocarbon facilities for liquefied natural gas (LNG), nuclear installations, offshore production platforms, jack up drilling rigs, coal mines, gas plants, chemical and polypropylene manufacturing plants.

So, why do we still want to spend funds extracting these commodities and building the plants when clearly, they are spoiling our world?

The answer is simple; *we still need oil and we still need gas.*

Global gas supply chain issues can attest to this. Yes, we absolutely need to consider alternative and renewable energies. But the void between ditching the burning of fossil fuels to create energy and being solely reliant on the renewables is huge. We are not there yet and for several years to come oil, gas and renewables must find a place on our planet for attention and development.

Everyone on planet earth still relies upon derivatives of oil and gas. The coronavirus pandemic suspended energy development projects and extraction while employees normally engaged on construction facilities spent time in isolation. Oil corporate executives being paid a fortune conducted emergency board meetings and cut back their staff by thousands as profit margins ceased and serious losses prevailed. For a few moments in the second quarter of 2020, the price of a barrel of Brent crude oil dropped into the negative for the first time in its history. This essentially meant that if you wanted a barrel of oil from Shell, the Dutch company would pay you to come and get it!

Stockpiles of the commodity had spilled over and storage facilities were filled to capacity with few or no users. Vehicles and aircraft operations were suspended and gathered dust, no longer required while the public were binge watching animated movies and another detective series littered with Scottish actors. Then, in 2022 the price of a barrel of crude skyrocketed to more than a hundred bucks and levelled out to the mid-eighties in 2023.

Furthermore, cyber-attacks on pipelines can immediately halt the flow of hydrocarbons and delivery, thereby demanding increased extraction. When a mainstream pipeline in the American panhandle was recently hacked, the price of a gallon of fuel at the local pumps increased from $1.99 to $5.99. This stark rise happened because, quite simply, folk need that gasoline and were willing to part with their hard earned cash to fill their SUV.

The world is changing and I fully accept the fact that we have to change with it. But try to answer each part of this two part question:

    a.    Can you switch off the fuel supply to your home, indefinitely?

    b.    Can you survive without using a mechanically operated mode of vehicle or transportation of any kind?

Did you answer yes to both? *Of course you didn't.*


We have not seen the end of oil and gas extraction and development. Offshore oil and gas exploration has not waned and recent new, significant, discoveries have been made in the North Sea, off the coasts of Malaysia and the Gulf of Mexico, Australia and Brazil. North Sea lease applications, once a thing of the past are now being resurrected and quickly approved by the government. This is raising fresh, aggressive protests by recently commissioned organizations with their representatives dangerously chaining themselves to tall structures and super-gluing their arses to busy road surfaces in an effort to gain attention. And the subject of inland fracking is once again on the table for discussion. While new oil refineries are being built on the African continent and the Americas, grass root LNG and other petrochemical facilities are rising in western Canada and South Korea. In fact, there are dozens of global hydrogen facilities right now going through business case, feasibility and conceptual studies, front end engineering design, procurement, construction and commissioning. Oil and gas feedstocks for these hydrocarbon facilities are increasing each quarter.

Corporations are trying hard to support the global call for climate change and reduce the greenhouse gas emissions by investing sometimes close to a third of the capital costs of a project to capture or re-use the carbon content.

There is also an effort to severely cut back the use of plastics in products and packaging. Some of the plastics are renewable but it is unlikely we shall see a switch from plastic back to paper carrier bags in a supermarket as this change would effectively raise the focus of attention towards deforestation. Supermarkets have the answer; sell more shopping bags designed for permanent usage that cost £5 a shot (or eight quid in Harrods!). And when you forget to bring it into the store, just buy another one. I have forty-seven bags stuffed into the back of my car seats.

There have been many media publications on the development of electric vehicles but over the past forty years the bodywork has migrated away from steel towards the much less dense, carbon fibre panels. These carbon fibre panels support the lighter vehicle and increase fuel savings. Carbon fibre is made from fossil fuels as its name suggests. Should we bring back steel bodywork for electric vehicles and open up the coal mines?

Employed as a piping designer since the 1970s in the energy sector I've worked on many large projects, some of them financed in excess of US$30bn. Educated and trained in the UK the opportunities over fifty years have allowed me to support a reasonably comfortable lifestyle and spend a considerable amount of time in countries that include Canada, USA, South Africa, Venezuela, Kazakhstan, the Ivory Coast, Norway, India and China.

It's been a varied and mixed life trying to survive the many oil and gas

15

downturns the world has seen, while enjoying the good times in between.

Spending days at a time isolated on stormy, North Sea offshore platforms with nothing to see for miles. Carefully checking for scorpions hiding in work boots on hot, desert-like jobsites; walking high up on frigid, steel pipe racks in minus thirty degree Celsius temperatures where your skin will stick to metal, while holding a tape measure and notepad. Entering a large vessel wearing a gas mask and oxygen cylinder to avoid inhaling residue gases.

Navigating several ladders and a vertical ascent of a hundred metre tall vessel when it was raining, only to get to the top and find the entire structure swaying… and the rain had turned to snow with an icy platform to negotiate.

I've had a few deathly silent helicopter rides over dense, fog-saturated areas of the North Sea, on one occasion landing on the wrong platform.

My life has been peppered with some amazing, fortunate experiences in the energy sector and this book will take you through the changing times from the seventies when the extraction and development of fossil fuels moved the world forward to a point where our homes are now littered with useful, and not so useful, plastic objects.

There are plenty of stories as a drawing office piping designer, or *piper* as we are affectionately known. Practical jokes played in the office, the pressures of working overtime sometimes through the night to meet a deadline. I'll talk about the wonderful, social sides of an industry once loved and cherished by those who were fortunate enough to be a part of it.

I've seen the industry as a true testament of achievement and quality where successful projects took as long as they needed to get finished. Then there is the infinite experience of rushing projects only to make a whole lot of costly mistakes along the way, sadly evident and too late after the champagne bottles have been emptied, when the facilities are built and the lawsuits commence.

We see the same struggling oil and gas sector now, but populated with low-paid, poorly qualified resources employed in communicatively challenged engineering offices employed to get projects out in record time often with insufficient respect and a disregard for quality.

These inherent values are sadly, all too often replaced with the all-important demands for low cost and compressed schedules with impossible milestones.

16

Engineering offices of the past where designers with a solid knowledge and background in their craft enjoyed their working day among other trained folk are now replaced with aggressive, inexperienced engineering managers and project engineers who's prime objectives are to get the job done quickly, at the cost of quality.

The energy industry has consumed my working life from the early age of sixteen before I really grew up to the old geezer I am now, in my sixties.

Projects used to be fun. But *fun*, is not the term I would describe energy projects nowadays. A drawing office environment fifty years ago carved out a brotherly, supportive approach to each other in the team which meant great work was turned out and everyone around you reciprocated with respect for one another. Projects these days just do not have that same level of respect within the team as less experienced managers pretend to know what they are talking about, while failing miserably to organise the right team below them because they haven't had that all-important training and grounding.

Open plan engineering drawing offices in the seventies were designed to support communicative environments between fifty pipers on drawing boards that encouraged verbal, open discussion on areas of design. There was just one telephone landline between us.

If young Joe was laying out a compressor area with critical, high pressure gas piping, everyone walking past his board would know how he was going about his design. If mistakes were made, they were right there in your face and soon enough Joe's section leader or *squaddie* would walk past Joe and casually say, *"Okay Joe, so you've done it like that, eh?"*

Then have a quiet word in his ear before Joe spent the next two days almost in tears, erasing huge areas of pencil work, then dust off the sheet with his board brush and start again.

That engineering floor space was tailored to reflect a personable environment. Since then, we've moved in and out of high partitioned cubicles to see a more user friendly engineering office with open plan seating for computer assisted design (CAD) systems used by designers.

The days of high walls between two individuals when each person had a computer, email and their own telephone did not encourage verbal communication and discussion, forging individuals to grow into shy, timid human beings without want or desire to chat about anything.

Over a wall:

*"How was the weekend, Bob?"*
*"Can't chat right now, Mitch... send me an email."*

Practical jokes were always part of the drawing office culture as pipers would wind teammates up on a regular basis, sometimes bringing tears of embarrassment and humiliation to the unfortunate recipient. Nothing harmful and all taken well. I have included stories from moments in the past where I would have tears rolling down my face from laughing at some of the antics going on. Today, any practical joke would be seen as an act of terror and the instigator would be walked out of the building.

I remember one guy letting off a fire extinguisher in the office, covering everyone and everything around him with a filthy liquid foam, spoiling every drawing on a board. He was given a stern talking to by the department manager then got back on with his draughting.

Outsourcing is now a common component on any project and the western world has gotten used to tearing off chunks of a project for the engineering and design to be executed elsewhere, in what is described as a low cost centre. With China and India arguably being the top two nations to support outsourced work, other countries in Europe and South America also contribute to the work process. China even outsource their own outsourced work to Vietnam where more savings are applied to the cause.

These decisions, while supporting a cost-effective approach, will always have a detrimental effect to the numbers of resources living in the city of the home office.

Why is this allowed to happen? Why should educated and qualified residents of their home town struggle to find work when project managers happily accept shifting 90% of a project's engineering, fabrication and construction work overseas? We are cutting our own throats and it is madness. More on this, later.

I wanted to write about the oil and gas industry and its changes over the past fifty years but if I simply scribble stuff down about the Middle East, North Sea development or OPEC's grip on the oil prices it's not going to be any different to a plethora of books already written. Though informative, they are actually boring and most folk will cast them aside in a minute.

Instead, I'm going to write an autobiography of my past, for my grandkids.

This will include projects I've worked on, some great, others terrible. The companies that employed me, the many great guys and the few I care not to cross paths with… ever again. I want to write about the oil and gas engineering cultures while sharing the history of the years I've enjoyed in the business.

This book will take you through my experiences in energy development and its enormous change, as seen from my eyes; first as an apprentice piping designer based in London, England then onto life in the 2020s when I started to go mad.

# 1974 – 1977

I started out as an apprentice piping designer on those green slopy things called drawing boards in smoke filled offices. Oil and gas projects were in abundance all around the world. Arabian and North Sea oil development had just been established with a few dozen offshore platforms already drilling and producing hydrocarbons for the global markets. There were not enough qualified engineers and designers to sit on new, high draughting stools as client based operations were busy studying the next project to increase output and make more money. Everyone was a winner. I was sixteen years old and just getting stuck in to the world of employment after spending five years at Ilford County High Grammar School for Boys. I was slow to grip the work thing and hadn't really grown up even when I received my first paycheque. Back in school I was always talking in the classroom and playing practical jokes. But a three-year piping design apprenticeship with Stone & Webster Engineering in Holborn turned me into an adult (sort of), put me through the grinder, taught me the basics and principles in piping design and allowed me time to catch up and test my levels of intelligence, which didn't take too long.

I have made a lot of friends and still try to stay in touch with many, one way or another. We used to laugh more in the drawing office when we didn't have electronic devices and actually talk to your neighbour instead of sending him an email. Practical jokes were common and pipers got away with a lot of things then.

The petrochemical industry has migrated from mechanically controlled drawing boards to Computer Assisted Design, or CAD with two monitors on each desk, a docking station and the correct lighting above them. There is a mouse pad instead of an ash tray and these days you'd be lucky to find a pencil on anyone's desk.

Luncheon Vouchers, those small white slips of paper your company would hand to you in an envelope every month with a salary slip, could be submitted in any local sandwich bar to buy food. Lunch times started at the

20

same time and finished precisely one hour later.

The typical eight to five working day with an hour for lunch has been traded in for more flexible, family attentive hours where a piper can start at five a.m. and leave at two p.m. His colleague may come in at nine and leave at six.

Women, who were rarely employed in an engineering environment in the sixties and seventies other than in secretarial roles, can now be seen securing positions as piping designers, managers of engineering, project directors and CEOs.

The old-fashioned tea trolley pushed by a sorry looking old dear whose nicotine stained teeth resembled a row of bombed houses, has made way for kitchens fully stocked with hot beverage options and refrigerators. No longer do we have to pay for a cup of coffee.

Smoking in the office over the drawing board was common place as cigarette ash collected on the parallel slide. Smoking in the office has been replaced with exercise tutorials that pop up on your screen every thirty minutes and, to supplement this, your company may offer a subscription to a nearby gym.

Five day working weeks are now a thing of the past as engineering companies allow their workforce to increase the hours they work between a Monday and Thursday, then take Fridays off. Parts of a working week are now offered, working from home.

In any drawing office of the old days, modelling rooms were set up used to build plastic models of a facility at a scale of 1:33 1/3 and kitted out with plastic pipe materials, tools and adhesives while models of the ethylene plant, refinery or offshore platform being engineered in that office location would be hand crafted in the model room before being assembled on one dedicated area of the office floor. So, to put this in perspective, for a constructed operating facility where the true length might be four hundred metres in length by two hundred metres in width, the scaled model of that same installation being assembled on the drawing office floor would be about twelve metres by six, or forty feet by twenty.

Around these office models, design reviews would be conducted with a dozen people and decisions recorded.

Scaled plastic models and drawing boards have long since been replaced with expensive, complex computer model software packages including PDMS, PDS, E3D and SmartPlant, or SP3D. More on this, later.

The result from substantially increased costs to a project with all this new stuff is to ship scopes of work off to low cost engineering houses based in New Delhi, Mumbai and Manila. The term *low cost* the home office prefer these days to be replaced with the words, *high value engineering centres*, or HVEC. Make no mistake, they are essentially, low-cost engineering houses often with a three to one ratio of hourly rate. So, for every chap employed in a London or Houston engineering office, for the same dime you could get three resources overseas instead. Attractive? *You bet it is.*

And the piping designers sitting at the drawing boards once churning out pieces of art called General Arrangements, Plot Plans, Piping Studies and Isometrics are now replaced with multinational and multicultural individuals that know their CAD systems very well indeed. However, due to the changes in industry and the elimination of apprenticeships there have been few resources coming through the training channels. And these folk called 'designers' have little idea and acumen of what design is actually all about with minimal, critical knowledge so acutely required in engineering, design and building a hydrocarbon facility.

Today's engineering office as portrayed above, is a far cry from what we had all those years ago. But the question we like to ask ourselves is this: Are things *really* better now? Are projects any cheaper? Do they get built faster than they used to be? Is the quality of deliverables any better now?

On a project nowadays regarded as a *paperless job* do we really use less paper? In truth, we probably do.

Project managers on today's projects might be in their thirties. They have pages of qualifications but some have never been to a construction jobsite, seen a pipe or understand that a 2 inch, 2500# rated ball valve might need two persons to lift it.

Piping designers were always dressed immaculately in their Farah trousers, Ben Sherman shirts, gold plated cufflinks, Austin Reed ties and oxblood brogues. They owned things called brollies, Mont Blanc fountain pens and briefcases, drank Dom Perignon and bought bottles of thirty-year-old vintage port. Not always to drink, but to lay down for a special event.

They purchased top end appliances from Miele, and drove BMWs, Mercedes, Jags and Porsches.

I used to own two Jaguars, one a white V12, 5.3 litre XJS with an explosive acceleration, while the other one was a rare, 2.8 litre manual XJ6 with an overdrive. Both cars cost me a fortune to maintain.

Suits, ties, cufflinks and waistcoats are now replaced with jeans, baseball caps and training shoes.

I recall a recent project where the manager of a process engineering group sported a smart white shirt and cufflinks. But, he always wore the same pair of beige trousers that sported two frayed holes on his arse and one on the knee. How can a bloke get dressed in the morning, carefully put on his cufflinks and climb into a pair of tattered old trousers.

Just to top this off, below his trousers were a pair of old, worn runners. And he was one of the smarter chaps!

There have been enormous transitions in our industry. The components that turned it away from being a solid business with tremendous quality in the deliverables issued to the client moved towards a less exciting environment of dishevelled, rudderless and poorly executed, low cost international projects managed by unqualified resources where senior experience is supported by a single page resume.

I left a great, grammar school in Ilford County High at the age of sixteen. It was May of 1974 and I wasn't looking forward to the long term future.

But I was happy as a pig in shit. The short-term future looked wonderful, too. It would consist of a scorching summer and there were young girls out there who liked to wear bikinis at Valentine's Park swimming pool, we would sit in the back rows of the Pictures, spend time in The Wimpy Bar or get a boat out on the lake for an hour under a blanket. This was *my* future.


After leaving school, my dad got home from work one evening and asked, *"Well, son, that's it! What are you going to do for a living?"*

It was a good question but one I preferred not to answer right away, though it was admirable that someone cared. I was, most definitely, not ready to go to work just yet. I had spent the last eleven years at school and surely someone would realise I needed this down time! With pocket money from Dad and a Saturday job at a shoe shop, it was now time for some R&R.

Dinners were provided, there was no rent, my undies and shirts were washed every week, the fridge was always stocked and, in truth, life was pretty damn good at home. Not sure why any young lad with half a brain

23

would want to change it and go out looking for a job. I got stuck into the summer, played some football, met a few girls and carried on regardless. Things were peachy.

After three months of this, Dad pulled me aside and asked the question again, *"Son, what the fuck are you going to do for a living?"*

With nothing substantive to tell him, we sat and discussed the options. There were not many.

I had chosen not to stay on at County High's Sixth Form. Well, that's not strictly true, it was the school that made that decision having only acquired the three 'O' Levels to my name; Maths, English Language and Art. I had flunked several 'O' Levels by wasting my time out and about and choosing not to swot up on my studies. Maths I sailed through. I was amazed to get an Art qualification because my drawing skills are not worth diddly squat. You should see my drawings of a cow or a dog. Cave drawings have better definition.

My English Language skills were equally poor at the time but have improved a bit that allowed me to write this story.

Dad was first employed in the late fifties as a piping designer in the petrochemical industry, probably starting off on sheets of papyrus. He would have been thrilled when linen entered the market. It was the seventies and jobs were in abundance, especially now that North Sea oil & gas development was proven to be successful and lucrative for all the lease holding, operating companies.

Becoming a piping designer was not common knowledge to most and recruiting officers who paid useless visits to schools never touched on these things. Banking, accountancy and insurance opportunities were posted but open heart surgery, diamond cutting, movie directing, circumcision assistants and pipers were not generally understood to be sought after jobs.

Of course, the folk who went on to sixth form and later, university, had all these options made available. These guys knuckled down at school and fully deserved to get on the next train.

Dad had suggested I make an effort to get into his industry and, in truth, there were worse alternatives. Trouble was, it all sounded like hard work and likely to interrupt my time at the swimming pool. We discussed the possibility of writing to several oil and gas engineering companies and I nodded with less than an effervescent zeal to it all.

One Sunday afternoon, the old man climbed up on a chair in his bedroom and reached to the back of the cupboard, pulling stuff towards him. Rummaging around in the collective mess, he found a large roll of dusty blue prints which he carefully slid towards him, just as half the contents of the packed cupboard came crashing down on me. The roll of drawings was not the first thing that caught my attention but two copies of *Playboy*! I picked them up and as my eyes were focusing on the best pair of tits I'd ever seen in my life they were soon ripped from my sweaty hands and tossed back into the cupboard. *"Focus, son."* I was.

The roll of drawings was opened up and flattened out on the dining table. Each one was huge and measured almost four feet by three. One particular drawing gave Dad a smile and he sat down on a chair to describe all aspects of the content. I had no idea what it was but was definitely intrigued to know more about it and he went through it in detail.

It was a piping general arrangement drawing (GA) showing six separate plans of something called a Distillation Column, or vertical vessel, and came under the umbrella of *static mechanical equipment*. Essentially, the column, also known as a tower, was a tall, skinny steel cylinder about two hundred feet high with a diameter of around nine feet. Each of the six cuts on the sheet showed what the tower would look like if sliced through the middle at various elevations. A bit like showing two plans of a house; downstairs and upstairs.

There were lots of small circles reflecting plane cuts through the vertical piping and large circles for cuts through the column itself. There were platforms for standing on and getting access to valves and instruments. There were ladders to access these platforms and cages around the ladders to stop people falling to their death two hundred feet above the ground. A good idea, I thought.

There were access holes into the tower called manways along with valves and handwheels, pressure, temperature and level instrumentation. Rectangular shapes on the drawing recognised electrical cables, laydown areas at ground level (known as *grade*) and drop zones were identified, too, providing the operators with a clear vertical space for lowering internal materials from any platform on the column, down to grade.

Next to the shapes were beautifully written, hand printed capitalised notes describing the shapes. Platform elevations and piping line numbers, equipment number and tag numbers of instrumentation. There were things called 'nozzles' that were connected to the tower and each nozzle had its own number like N1 or N2. The piping was shown either dropping down the sides of the tower or heading off in a horizontal direction to and from something called a pipe rack, or a home for lots of pipes.

Around the outside of the drawing were several small, independent three-dimensional sketches showing a number of small piping arrangements. These more detailed sketches were necessary because the scale of the drawing did not show enough clarity around congested areas of piping. In the bottom right hand corner of the drawing was an area known as a 'title block' reflecting the name of the drawing, the equipment it was portraying and the project it was part of.

To the left of the title bock was a 'revision block'. This lined area would show the stages of development, formal issue, any revisions and re-issues and the initials of the persons who were involved in developing and approving the GA: the designer, checker and supervisor. In the top left of the drawing was a North Arrow advising the reader how the drawing fitted into the geography and prevailing wind data to support the piper when designing anything and avoiding hydrocarbon gases drifting towards a naked flare. Even this north arrow had an art of its own.

I was mesmerised by what Dad had showed me and we spoke for a couple of hours as I asked a stack of questions, gradually excited by the sheer complexity of it. The drawing required skillsets in Maths, English and Art! I was made for this.

Dad explained the general subject of oil and gas to me. North Sea exploration, onshore refinery engineering along with projects he'd worked on in the past in England, Canada and Libya. He told me what the piping designer did, the process engineer and civil, structural, electrical and mechanical engineers while simultaneously informing me of what instrumentation is found on a project. He discussed the managers, printers, secretaries and how these drawings get to be issued to third parties for fabrication. I was slowly being hooked and he could sense the enthusiasm from my attention span lasting longer than six minutes.

The following day, he brought home from the office some large, clean sheets of white paper, some pencils, rulers, scale rules, rubbers and draughting tape. He asked me to tape a clean sheet to my bedroom desk and simply copy the contents of the GA we'd been looking at, onto the clean sheet.

I used a compass to draw all the circles and the scale rules to measure and draw straight lines. When the pencils got blunt, I sharpened them. Any errors, I erased and reworked them. My printing was crap to start with then gradually improved as I practised the alphabet over and over again in capital lettering. The text standing straight, then at a slant towards the top right.

I spent two full days and evenings copying this one drawing before the old man took a long hard look, laughed his head off and told me it was good enough to take along to an interview.

I then wrote several letters of applications for employment with companies Dad had suggested, as he knew which ones were taking on young scrotes like me.


A few weeks later and after more printing and draughting practice in the bedroom, in between stealing quick glances at *Playboy*, Stone & Webster Engineering Limited in Holborn, brought me in for an interview as an Apprentice Piping Designer.

The Drawing Office Manager, Mr Hubert, was sitting across the desk from me, puffing on a pipe. We discussed my education and he asked me if I had an example of my drawing abilities from school. Believe it or not, I had not taken Technical Drawing at school, preferring instead to opt for Woodwork. (A fat lot of use that turned out as my handyman skills thereafter have amounted to diddly squat).

*"Yes, sir,"* I said. And from my new, brown briefcase I unfolded a piping general arrangement drawing of a Distillation Column. The drawing covered his entire desk and ash tray and the pipe fell out of his mouth. He was simply overwhelmed by this neat engineering drawing in front of him and was rather expecting to see a drawing of a house or a first and third angle projection of a machine bolt. Mr Hubert asked if it was someone else's and how I had come across the drawing. I told him the full story and it impressed the heck out of him.

One month later a letter arrived in the mail informing me that I had passed the interview and a start date in early September was secured. I remember that moment as a sixteen year old and quite proud of the efforts I had put into the copy job. Dad took a lot of credit by easing me into the cause and I shall always be thankful to him for steering me in that direction.

Come September, I was suited and booted and headed off to work on the Central Line into the West End of London and a position of employment with Stone & Webster.

My first few days as a paid employee were spent in basic training and being introduced to my immediate supervisor, a stern chap called John Butt. I was also expected to spend one day a week attending day school to further increase my currently small library of educational qualifications. A further two evenings a week would also be spent at evening classes on the same course.

I attended the enrolment session at the Romford School of Technology, near Becontree, Essex. It was a bit overwhelming for a sixteen year old with all the different courses being offered but a relatively straightforward responsibility. There were literally dozens of course enrolments that night and the entire college was packed out with newcomers, moving from room to room, signing up their lives.

I settled down at the Stones offices while the course started well enough, too. Around the second or third Monday of the course, the new lads in the class were all of similar age groups and were each asked to introduce themselves and the companies they worked for. Pete, Barry, Terry... Murphy's, Taylor Woodrow and McAlpine. One or two of the lads worked for Wimpey too. The only Wimpy I knew was the one I'd buy a hamburger and chips from on a Friday night.

When my turn came, I told the tutor I worked for a company called Stone & Webster. They looked at each other with bemusement and hadn't heard of the firm. I explained that they were one of the largest petrochemical engineering companies in the world, specialising in the engineering and design of ethylene installations. More blank stares. We continued for a couple more weeks talking about dumpeys, theodolites and soon enough, bricklaying.

*Bricklaying, really?*

I was now starting to get a little anxious after spending an entire month being taught the advantages of an English Bond from a Flemish Bond and where we might use a Queen Closer. In truth, I didn't give a monkey's toss where a Queen Closer would be used and my first thought was that it might be on the structure surrounding a large gate at Buckingham Palace. It didn't sound like something remotely related to a pipe.

There was nothing at all in the course on the subject of Piping

28

Engineering and Design. On a break I looked into this. With abject horror, it was apparent that I had enrolled onto the wrong course. What a frikkin dipstick.

It was close to Christmas and near completion of the first term and I was much too embarrassed to reveal this news to anyone on the course, anyone at work and anyone at home. Instead, I carried on regardless through an entire year without anyone actually knowing about this fundamental cock-up I'd made.

Working life back in Holborn was taking shape and one of the pre-requisites were that I spend eight weeks in each relevant department. One of these was the *Reproduction* department which called for the entire eight weeks being isolated down in the basement of the building. This was known as the *print room*. It was simply an awful place to be and where the manager, a stern chap called Arthur Loblaw, laid into his team with authority, discipline and assertiveness. Arthur was a stickler for schedule and getting things out on time. There were hundreds of work orders and after handling blueprints every hour of every day I went home each evening stinking of ammonia and ready for a shower. It would be less acrid if I had a position of employment gutting fish without tools. Commuters sitting beside me on the train home were asleep in seconds.

Looking back, I learned a lot from this horrible spell. I learned about the virtues of time-keeping and quality in precision when inserting two thousand sheets of A4 size paper into a mechanical hole-punch the wrong way round and only realising this when trying to place them into a ring binder. And just as Arthur walks past with a cup of tea in his hand. *"Mr Jagooooo, what the FUCK are you doing, lad?"*

Another benefit was learning how to fold large drawings. Believe it or not there is a fine art to this. Once folded, if you pick up one corner the drawing should completely unfold and open up on the table in one short flick of a wrist. Of course, in what we call a paperless world today, we still have lots of large drawings in an engineering office, but not that many large sheets. Try asking a young project engineer how to fold an A0 size drawing. He wouldn't have a clue. In fact, printing rooms no longer exist in engineering offices as any necessary copying will be done by a local printing company.

Moving on, the Instrument group were a wonderful bunch of guys. The manager, Cliff Drummond, was an absolute diamond and he gave me a terrific amount of support. White hair and a deep husky voice, he sat me at a drawing board deep within his team of designers who all had a great sense of humour telling the filthiest jokes I have ever heard. It was also pretty clear that a young, mouthy now seventeen year old cockney trainee was going to be set up like a kipper.

I was as green as a cucumber and, on one occasion, couldn't see this coming.

It was a Friday afternoon and I returned to my board from a tea break to hear Cliff and a few other chaps talking about a *one man band*. I had arrived at the back end of the conversation as the guys all agreed that it was just a legend and in fact there was no such thing as a one man band. *"Err, guys,"* I spoke up. *"Of COURSE, there's such a thing as a one man band; I've seen one."*

For the next twenty minutes I tried to describe to my Instrument fellows, the operations of a one man band and how it all worked. They were fascinated.

First, I described the mouth organ by shaking my head from side to side, holding my hands up to my mouth. I then went on to show the guys how this one man band played his accordion or a banjo, while blowing on his mouth organ at the same time. *"Mitch,"* they said, *"you're talking absolute bollocks."* I wasn't, honest.

Then came the drum on his back and how the rapid movement of his elbows would raise and lower the dongers into position and clash with the drum... followed closely by one cymbal attached to the inside of each knee.

Arguing the toss for fifteen minutes I could now be seen running up and down the office looking like a chicken with its head cut off waving arms and elbows around, blowing raspberries and lifting knees up to my chin trying to prove the existence of this one man band.

Then it clicked. I'd been kippered.

It was funny as hell with everyone creasing themselves just before the weekend.

*Who would do this to a young apprentice?*

I then moved onto the Vessels group. A Vessel draughtsman is, sadly, no longer to be seen in the engineering office. These guys were good, developing drawings for heat exchangers, horizontal vessels and vertical distillation columns; like dad's one I had copied!

Heat exchangers consist of a twenty feet long steel shell with hundreds of small tubes less than an inch in diameter running down one length of the inside, turning and running back along the shell. The tubes would have a cooling medium running through them such as cold water while the shell encompassing the tubes would have a hydrocarbon service like a hot gas. The idea is that the cold water piping immersed within the hot gas would bring the temperature of the gas down, and heat the temperature of the water. Consequently, the cross sectional view of a heat exchanger is quite complex. Large scale A0 drawings were necessary to depict each and every one inch tube. Today, vessel drawings are developed by the contractor building the heat exchanger.

I learned that the inside of a distillation column is furnished with dozens of trays at various elevations that contain small openings and bubble caps. The hot oily liquid enters the column near the top and, with simple gravity, drops through the centre of the equipment flooding the trays along the way from the top to the bottom. At specific elevations, the liquids are extracted from the column by positioning piping nozzles and piping to route the liquids away from the equipment towards other areas of the plant.

While the liquids fall, the gases that form part of the fluid, rise. This immersion of dropping liquids and rising gases change the state of the fluid. As a result of this chemical reaction, hydrocarbon gases like butane and propane are captured near the top nozzles, while light liquids like paraffin, gasoline and petroleum are drawn off further down the column with heavies like bitumen extracted closer to the foot of the column. Each extracted product has its own sales interest, of course.

While the instrument chaps taught me to beware of getting set up, the Vessels team taught me how to drink large quantities of strong beer on a Friday afternoon.

This eight week period was one of the most laughable and memorable times of my life as an apprentice. But not always for the right reason. Enter Graham Kneel, a short bearded chap I had a tremendous amount of time for. Graham was a great support for a youngster like me and took me under his wing to offer vessel and materials engineering support and lead me astray down several avenues.

Graham loved his real ale and down at the Pakenham Arms, a pub with history going back as far as the 1850s and just a few minutes from Holborn,

I got to drink a beer called Ram Rod. Now, as you'd expect from a name like this it was not a light ale. Furthermore, in the same pint glass was a half pint of *Young's* Special. The result after two and a half hours of this behaviour without a bite to eat on a Friday was that it didn't end well.

Stumbling back to the office, tacking from one side of the street to another the backdoor fire escape would get us up several floors to the Vessels area with fewer folk watching than if we had all squeezed through the front reception doors of the building and into an elevator, laughing our heads off. I falsely assumed that I might get away with it entirely sometimes and sit at the drawing board trying poorly to appear that I'd been there all day.

One or two chaps would choose not to go back to the office but head straight for the station and a train home. The upside of going straight home was that no-one saw the state you were in from all the Ram Rod. The downside was that a timesheet would have to be corrected the following Monday with four hours removed which essentially resulted in an expensive Friday lunch with the boys.

On one occasion, I was so drunk but went back to the office and straight to the khazi from the pub and sat on the floor for fifteen minutes, chucking up.

A few Fridays like this and struggling home on the tube, my folks got to see me fall on my face as they opened the front door.

Back at the office, it wasn't long before my department manager got to hear about it and threatened me with the sack. As a seventeen year old, this was not news that might help my career so I cut back on the Ram Rod on a Friday afternoon and knuckled down while making a decision to work harder.

Graham also liked to play darts and, if we were being good boys at lunch, we spent the odd evening after work on a Friday, pairing up as a team and giving guys in the local smoky boozer a run for their money. Now darts is an intriguing game as it's not only about trying to hit that spot on the board but knowing what spots to aim for well before you throw the dart. My knowledge of mathematics served me well in a game of darts and toward the end got to know what spots on the board to aim for that would finish on a double.

Darts matches were all the rage in the 1970s with most landlords roping off areas of a pub hosting competitions. There was always a dart board somewhere in the back of the pub. Darts is probably making a bit of a comeback as it remains highly popular on the telly. Bristle boards are used all the time these days but fifty years ago some old pubs in the streets of London continued to use dart boards made from solid elm wood. The sound of a dart hitting an elm board cannot be emulated and each evening after 'last orders' and the folk have all gone home, the publican would remove the metal ring and plunge the dart board into a bucket of cold water to stop it from drying out. Overnight, the tiny collective holes made from several hours of darts would close up, ready for the next event.

Drinking, darts and one more thing Graham introduced me to: Indian food.

London is now chock a block with Indian restaurants but not in the seventies. On any weekday lunchtime back at Stones we might drop into the closest *Standard Tandoori* for some chicken korma, meat madras or a vindaloo for lunch. In those days, the restaurants were not always that clean and occasionally you'd spot a cockroach scampering across a nearby table cloth of a vacant table.

Menus also had the more expensive option; like, for an extra 5p you would get your chicken 'off the bone'. Ever since those days at the office I have loved my Indian food and over the years got to passionately enjoy cooking Indian food, too.

The upshot of working in London in that era was that the social scene was exceptional and, to this day, I am proud to have been a part of it.


As I moved through my training programme I got to enjoy company functions like the Stone & Webster Christmas Dinner and Dance and attend evenings called *stag nights* that involved a club or a bar, a stage, comedians and strippers. As a seventeen year old it's quite an eye opener standing at the front of forty guys listening to effing and blinding and watching women take their clothes off to reveal big white, floppy tits. Just like they were in Dad's *Playboy*!

I had a constant lob on for more than two hours and for some reason, there used to be stag dos almost every second Friday, organised mostly, I recall, by the pipe stress agencies in London.

This idea would soon blossom into *strippagrams* where an unsuspecting piper and a few of his workmates are enjoying a quiet birthday lunch on a Friday, only to be interrupted by some young girl dropping in and tracking down the birthday boy, then removing a fur coat to reveal a gorgeous body and huge breasts. She would then hop onto his bulging lap forcing the poor bloke to lick Devonshire clotted cream from her nipples. *These were rough days, let me tell you.*

As my apprenticeship moved forward, so I got to understand the kind of colleagues I could relate to and, equally, the ones I couldn't. Not everyone in the petrochemical industry is squeaky clean and good sorts, but thankfully, most are.

The ones that stand out might fall into a number of categories:

First, there are the arrogant ones; Pipers who claim to know just about everything there is to know about piping and anything else in between. Some of these guys get right up your nose as they constantly preach how good they are, what they've achieved, why they are on a higher hourly rate than anybody else and are known as the Number One piper in London.

Then there are the good guys. Designers, who will go that extra length to feed some helpful information your way, share snippets of technical stuff from the past, asking questions about their own specific design area and clearly taking an interest in your own personal life while treating you with respect, even if you were a young apprentice. *"Good morning, Mitch. What did you get up to at the weekend, mate?"*

Then there are the tight-fisted chaps who will always be happy to join a group out for a beer or two and accept pint after pint, but when it's their turn to buy a round they're either hiding in the khazi or have slipped out the back and headed off to the station.

*"Oh, I see John's disappeared again."*

These guys can eat an apple through a letterbox and always have an excuse in their back pocket, instead of some folding.

My eight weeks in the Electrical Group was not that memorable, apart from the work I was given, which was memorable for the wrong reasons. *It was shite.*

Thousands of A1 size single line drawings had been developed for an ethylene project in Libya. Each drawing was created in lead pencil on transparent Mylar, or drawing sheets manufactured from plastics. They were all checked then issued for construction and filed away by the document management group in a drawer of a large piece of metal furniture called a *plan chest*.

Two years later, along came another project for the same client that had identical scopes of work as the first job. The site facility was exactly the same, as was the electrical design. Only the project name and coordinates had changed. So, with a few tweaks and modifications, the drawings that had been filed away a couple of years back could be resurrected and re-used as the basis for the new project. Stone & Webster had found some poor, young bastard to help make these modifications.

I was asked to remove from the drawers, large batches of the original drawings and take them down to Arthur's print room. I would need to write on the requisition, *"1 reproducible copy of each original"*.

A 'reproducible' copy, apart from the obvious explanation of it being reproduced from the original is actually another sheet of plastic Mylar. However, where the line work and printing was previously administered with a pencil onto the front of the original drawing sheet, the *repro* as it was known, had the identical information now etched onto the back side of the sheet with a sort of darkish brown ink, therefore making the appearance of the drawing to be a terracotta like colour.

The next stage was to make changes to the new original including the new project name, drawing number, revision status etc. amazingly, using a Wilkinson razor blade.

Holding the blade carefully between forefinger and thumb, by adopting a scraping action, I would remove the dark brown ink work from the back of the new drawing sheet. It was important not to slice off sections of the document or, indeed, my thumb.

The vacant spaces that remained would then see my efforts with the new data, printed onto the *front* side of the drawing. This cookie-cutter approach saved a vast amount of time in the engineering and design. From a project cost saving aspect, this meant buying exactly the same mechanical equipment, piping, structural steel, instrumentation and electrical facilities used for the first project.

Before starting this exciting activity, a paper blueprint copy of each sheet was already marked up by an electrical designer. Each markup had dozens of redline comments to assess and incorporate.

When finished, this would have the lasting effect of creating a brand new drawing for a brand new job, with a brand new drawing number... all from an existing electrical drawing.

Let me tell you now, this had to be the most deplorable and boring job I was ever asked to do in my entire time as an apprentice. No-one in a supervisory position had any inclination to help me understand more about the electrical department or was keen enough to show me around. I sat there, day after day scraping plastic sheets with a razor blade.

The one time I struck up any kind of conversation with anyone in the group was when one guy scampered over to my desk late one day and said, *"Stop that fucking whistling."*

To an apprentice piper the process engineering group proved to be very informative as I got to understand the first stages of chemical related engineering on a project. The process engineer is an extraordinary guy with a bottomless pit of knowledge and expertise. He will establish flow criteria for oil, gas, water or air and specify the size or diameter of the pipe that will carry it.

The process engineer will also identify what isolation is required to shut off a system. He will understand all engineering criteria when considering static mechanical equipment like columns, vessels, drums, tanks and heat exchangers. He'll have in depth knowledge of rotating equipment like pumps, compressors and steam turbines.

The process engineer is no dipshit and also knows what it takes to extract gases from oils, liquids from coal and how to transport liquefied natural gas across the oceans. He'll also know how to correctly dispose of waste hydrocarbon services into the air or recycled through a heat recovery system. I have a huge amount of admiration for a process engineer. The negative aspect of a process engineer is that they haven't a clue how to finish what they're doing and this has a detrimental effect on a schedule.

Lock two process engineers in a room while they engineer a small utility building with air, steam and water services and when you unlock the door nine years later, they'll still be at it and tell you it'll be finished, Friday.

I learned that process engineers are also a law unto themselves, revisiting piping systems again and again and again. Changing line sizes on a high pressure steam line from six inch diameter to eight inch before reversing back to six inch a week later and holding three meetings the following month to determine if the line size should be six or eight inch. After finally making a decision, they settle on ten inch. Two weeks later, the line is deleted anyway but a month after that a new process engineer will have joined the project, taken on the steam system to engineer and what'd ya know, we now have a twelve inch steam line.

During these weeks of indecision, instead of simply waiting it out before the piping designer gets involved, the project manager insists that the piping design does not stop because he wants to see *progress*. So, the piper designs a 6 inch system, erases what he's done and plugs in a larger 8 inch line before changing it once again to a 10 inch. This heavier line size affects structural steel design and suddenly the steel beam supporting the line is increased in size and takes up more real estate, of course so others are involved. When the line is deleted, the original space consumed by that 10 inch steam line is now replaced with a 8 inch gas line. A month later the whole process starts again when the piping designer, now pulling his hair out has to find a space for the steam line when once upon a time... he had it! Half the piping budget has been used up by so many changes.

Process engineers used to have in their area what were called *master* stick files hanging on sturdy, mobile stands. These files are essentially three feet long items made from two aluminium bars with hand-locking nuts. A hanging stick file four feet tall will hold around a hundred paper drawings and will reside on a stand with other similar files.

We're gonna get into the technical weeds a bit, here.

Hundreds of schematic process drawings known as flow sheets, or piping and instrumentation diagrams (P&IDs) collectively represent the entire process, instrumentation and piping scope of a project. The content of these drawings would include mechanical equipment like columns, vessels, heat exchangers, pumps and compressors with their motors and drivers, turbines, drums and storage tanks, fired heaters, reactors, heating and ventilation equipment, air coolers and flare stacks that discharge nasties into the atmosphere.

The idea is that these drawings will show every single pipe connecting each item of equipment. If any equipment does not require a piping system, it will not be shown on a P&ID.

Furthermore, every instrument required on a piping system will be identified on the P&ID monitoring pressure, temperature, level, flow control, metering, pressure and temperature relief, corrosion and emergency shutdown.

Independent line numbers are applied to each piping system on a P&ID. Components of the line number shall reflect types of materials, operating temperatures and pressure, insulation thicknesses to either conserve heat or protect from harsh winters and any heat tracing to provide additional weather protection if the facility is in colder climates and not built in Orlando, Florida.

The P&ID drawings would also show valves, strainers, filters, expansion joints, flanged joints and a plethora of notes from a process engineer to steer the piping designer towards a solid design.

Notes like DO NOT POCKET, MINIMUM DISTANCE FROM CONTROL VALVE and VALVE LOCKED CLOSED would also be shown and are all applicable to the design of any piping system.

Many years later, hanging stick files would be replaced with things called *roller boards*. A roller board is a simple wooden structure about eight feet long by four feet wide (2.5m x 1.2m) and raised slightly at the back end and sloped towards the reader about four feet or 1.2m above the floor.

At each end of the structure is a wooden barrel furnished with a crank-like handle. A few hundred feet of transparent cellophane is wrapped around one barrel and, much like the smaller application of an old camera film, stretched across the eight feet of flat board with the other end of the cellophane taped firmly down to the other barrel. The cellophane is used as a base to tape down every P&ID (and plot plan) on the project. Once they are all in place, the idea is to crank turn a barrel and all the drawings move towards the left or right, so making it easy to look at several drawings in a short space of time, while standing in one place.

This method remained by far, and still is, the best opportunity an engineering team has to monitor the process, piping and control systems or instrumentation development of a project.

Sadly, in our current CAD-driven world the physical presence of roller boards has now been replaced with the electronic roller board (ERB). The idea of this shift is to retain all comments, redlines, markups and changes to the P&IDs electronically on a computer instead of on full sized, hard copy drawings. One concern with the ERB is that it does not encourage conversation. A project manager, process engineer, or piping designer can no longer stand around the roller board and discuss a specific area of the project, so vitally important. Instead, we receive emails of warnings that these drawings have been revised and re-issued. But again, without much valuable conversation. The ERB may serve the purpose of retaining some sort of change management but it simply does not provide the project with the transparencies required to manage one of the most critical, expensive deliverables on a project; the piping.

My eight weeks in the civil, structural and architectural (CSA) group was a solid experience as I got to learn about several key contributions to any project.

For one, the ground or grade level paving throughout a facility protecting underground piping and utilities while supporting the movement of vehicular traffic, cranes and heavy haulers. I was taught about concrete foundations and piling that supported buildings, mechanical and electrical equipment, pipe racks and platform structures. Then, the steel structures themselves that carry the piping and provide above ground elevated access to valves and instrumentation.

A few weeks in the document management group was next and an odd sort of folk they were, too. There was Joe, a huge round bloke who took a liking to me when he invited me to sit next to him at his desk during lunchtimes, eating sandwiches. There was a short, skinny document controller called Maureen who could set someone on fire with a single glance but was a really nice lady. I was to spend a fair amount of time with Bob Weaver who helped me appreciate quality in ones work. A few other forgettable people in DM and then there was the manager. A tall, stocky, assertive and immaculately dressed chap called Alan Yelling with slick, greased hair who wore those elasticated, sleeve garters. Alan had his own office and smoked Rothman's cigarettes. I got on well with these folk and without the introduction of Microsoft products yet, spent most of my time drawing up lined sheets of paper and printing rows and rows of documentation and numbers reflecting drawings that were being formally issued from the project, both internally and externally beyond Stone & Webster.

It was here I learned very quickly to be accurate, smart and quick with the pencil. I developed my own sort of style of printing and the more sheets I printed, the better it got. If I was too hasty and a sheet came out looking like crap, Bob would give it back to me and say, *"Mitch, please do this again, it looks like crap."*

What would turn out to be a most unusual observation was the fact that my printing over time, would look exactly like my dad's printing! How strange.

There was also one awkward situation, I recall, while in the DM Group. Alan had started to ask me to pop downstairs and get him stuff. It would start with a packet of cigarettes and I have never smoked in my life so found this chore rather obnoxious. Then it would be a sandwich, then a sandwich and cigarettes… with a coke.

I was most annoyed about this and one evening told my dad. He told me that the next time this wanker would ask me to get him something, just tell him politely that I wasn't here to do these kind of things but I was here to learn about document management.

Indeed, the following day I once more got Alan's shopping list and plucked up the courage to tell him straight, that I was unhappy about popping out to get him his lunch and fags.

He was quite taken aback, as I was, and for a few seconds we stood there facing each other not really knowing what might come next. Until he replied, *"Okay, Mitch, that's fine."*

Nipped it in the bud. *Good old Dad!*


In any oil and gas engineering organisational structure the piping group consists of a number of independent areas covering the following sub-groups:

Plot Plan Development
Piping Design around Mechanical Equipment
Piping Design between Mechanical Equipment
Materials Engineering
Stress Engineering
Materials Management & Control
P&ID Draughting
Underground Piping
Building and Plumbing Services
Heating, Ventilating & Air Conditioning (HVAC)
Piping Checking
Piping Standard Details
Pipe Support Design
Weight Management & Control
Loss Prevention
Fire Protection

One of the very first considerations when locating a large hydrocarbon treatment or refining facility anywhere in the world is to make sure it sits close to a source of water. While offshore production platforms are furnished with desalination facilities or have fresh water shipped to the installation, many inland fossil fuel reserves are discovered several hundred miles away from a body of water and shall require a camp of a thousand folk to build, operate and maintain the downstream facility. It might then be prudent to run pipelines over the distance and position the camp and production facility near the water source. Even build an airport close by, too.

Touching briefly on safety, fire protection listed above is a label for piping systems that address two kinds of water required: firefighting hydrants and monitors plus a separate system for deluge sprinkler systems.

Fire hydrants are positioned towards the outside, safer areas of a hydrocarbon facility and are what the firemen in a fire department use to hook up to hoses retained on local hose reels, if and when a fire breaks out. Monitors are positioned closer to a potential source of fire like a gas compressor and can be manned, or remotely operated if close to a fire.

Not all hydrocarbon installations have a fire department close by. National codes will normally dictate what is required but some operating companies might choose not to install a firewater protection system but rather, let a facility burn to the ground because it may not be permanently manned.

Back to the apprenticeship and one Monday morning, a new starting point. I had moved so many times in the first twelve months I had not yet acquired my own desk and personal work area.

I was shown to a drawing board and a desk in the piping layout and design team amongst dozens of designers of all ages. At my desk there was a cast iron, mechanical draughting stool that weighed half a ton. Using one or two levers the unit spun around and went up and down. A few drawers in the desk including a wide drawer to hold large drawings. I was introduced to the senior pipers and was very nervous meeting these folk who were to be my neighbours for a while. One or two knew my dad and they all thought very highly of him, too, which helped break the ice. From the comments received, I knew he had set the bar, high.

It was important that I got to know my drawing board. A heavy metal base formed the support for a large rectangular board about five feet left to right, by four feet top to bottom (1.5m x 1.2m). It was an inch thick. The top surface of the board was covered with a malleable, green acrylic sheet about an eighth of an inch thick, glued into a permanent position. At the foot of the base was a long, foot operated bar. Stepping on the bar while holding the board would release the fixture and allow the board to be carefully raised or lowered. A lever on the underside of the drawing board would free up another mechanical arrangement and allow the board to be tilted to a vertical or horizontal position, or somewhere in between.

Using both hands and one foot a drawing board could be positioned to suit the draughtsman's desires on height and angle, whether he or she preferred to sit or stand, while working. An electric lamp might be clamped to one corner of the drawing board.

At each side of the board was a system of pulleys and wire cables attached to a horizontal parallel slide that ran across the entire width of the drawing board. The parallel slide was used to draw perfect horizontal lines and could be adjusted by turning a couple of screws to bring it back into line if it drifted from true horizontal. An adjustable set square resting on the parallel slide helped a designer with the vertical lines, or any lineage running at an angle, like thirty or forty-five degrees.

The chaps in the office were all older than me. My project piping lead, Graham Walley, was a sort of nice bloke but had a sense of humour similar to that of a depressed undertaker, whereas the other chaps on the floor were a laugh a minute and kept out of Graham's way. Most of the guys wore white or light coloured shirts with rounded collars, stacked shoes, wide paisley patterned ties and large, bell bottomed trousers. Lots of moustaches and an ash tray on almost every desk. Music in the seventies was fantastic but the fashion was atrocious. In those days I had shoulder length, permed hair and wore high Cuban heel shoes that made a lad of five foot six look closer to six feet. I tottered around getting the piss taken out of me most of the time while dishing it back. It was all about the comradery, respect, working friendships and the drive to learn from the guys on the boards around you.

In those earlier years, drawing offices were completely open plan with rows of drawing boards, one after the other. No cell phones of course, there was usually just one telephone landline in the middle of the area and the piping lead would be aware of pipers on the phone too much. Every time it would ring, guys would briefly stop work and wondered if the call was for them. *"Mitch, it's the phone again,"* some joker would shout.

That open environment served a young apprentice, well. Every conversation could be heard, every telephone call witnessed and equally important, if there was a discussion around a drawing board, everyone would get to hear the positive or negative comments about that individual's piping general arrangement or study. There was nowhere to hide and years in such an open plan setup undoubtedly helps an individual develop their character and confidence.

Before I started work, Dad and I had gone shopping for a few bits and pieces. Not having done any technical drawing at school I really had nothing. We walked into a shop that catered for the draughtsman.

First into the basket was an adjustable set square. This transparent, perspex drawing instrument would sit on the parallel slide of the drawing board and be free to slide to the left or right. This drawing instrument would allow me to draw lines in the vertical, or lines at other specific angles between vertical and horizontal by turning a small screw that released one section of the set square and rotate it into the desired angle.

Two types of scale rules followed the set square into the basket. These are about a foot in length and have a three-sided triangular cross section containing six different scales on one ruler.

Metric scales including 1:20, 1:50, 1:100, 1:200, 1:500 and 1:33 1/3. Imperial scales of 1 inch to a foot, ½ inch to a foot, 1/8 or 3/8 inch to a foot and one particularly unusual scale of 1:10560 which I soon learned was six inches to one mile and handy for, well, not a lot unless you are designing the next motorway.

We bagged dropleg compasses for drawing average size circles, protractors for measuring angles and a beam compass for larger circles up to three feet, or half a metre in diameter for heat exchanger tube sheets.

Erasers, or 'rubbers', H or B leaded pencils depending on how hard or soft you wanted the line work and printing, 'B' being the softest of all leads that would make the most mess on the drawing. And with these pencils came a small block of disposable sandpaper sheets to apply any desired shape on the tip of the pencil.

There were also propelling pencils, chisel tip pencils and clutch pencils. Each one with spare leads to install when one was used up.

There was also an erasing shield; a small piece of stiff, thin metal the size of a wallet that had holes in it when deleting small sections of a drawing without removing adjacent, important pencil work.

One unusual item that the old man threw into the basket was a small, soft pillow of chalk. This was used to tenderly wipe down drawings and remove any excess lead around the working area that might turn into a real mess after several days of activity. The powdered chalk would also provide a sort of granular buffer protecting the delicate pencil work from any movement from the parallel slide. Pretty ingenious, then. No longer heard of now, of course.

There were also choices of plastic pencil grades for use on a plastic or Mylar sheet, instead of true 'leads'. Designers usually talked about *plastic leads* which is a bit of an oxymoron, but these plastic leads were less intrusive resulting in a cleaner drawing.

Finally, into the basket went a set of French Curves. These are plastic, transparent shapes a designer might use to create an unusual and irregular curve demanding a tight or longer radius. If you write music, the symbol of a *treble clef* might be a good example of an irregular shape. If you don't write music, like me, you won't have a clue what I'm talking about!

Drawings were created in either pencil or ink. If pencil work was not appropriate for the project, black ink might be used on drawing sheets.

Now, there is a very different culture between ink-based and pencil-based draughting. Ink is always used in conjunction with stencils for applying shapes or writing text.

Pick up any normal twelve inch (30mm) ruler and you'll note that one side is flat, while the other is slightly curved, or *bevelled*. Flat side down for pencils, bevelled side down when using ink.

If you were to draw a line across the sheet using ink and the flat side was down on the drawing sheet, once you started to move the straight edge there was an inherent risk of dragging the ink along with it creating a large black smudge on the surface of your drawing and rendering it completely useless and a bin job.

This would quickly be followed with a DCM message from the squaddie (don't come Monday). Other than a short spell of stencilling in ink, thankfully I always worked with lead and plastic pencils.

In the late 1980s, after enjoying several years of bar work overseas, an acquaintance of mine, Jules, was looking for a position of employment. After pouring pints and taking care of English and German pissheads throwing up in the roads of Arenal, Majorca, she wanted desperately to get a career under her belt. And having spent my last fifteen years in piping, she looked to me for a bit of support.

I had an idea and called an agent called Mike Swindle who I knew well and explained the situation to him. There were stacks of opportunities for project work around at the time and I asked him if he might have something for Jules? I told him that she had received basic training in draughting but had moved away from it for a while. Bullshit of course.

Mike got her fixed up for an interview with the London Underground and when I told Jules, she was delighted and asked if it was checking passenger's tickets or operating the doors of a train?

London Underground was busy in their engineering department probably designing new extensions to the Jubilee Line and developing drawings for the air, water and electrical cable utilities that go with it.

Jules went along to the interview and the guy who was meant to conduct the interview had been off sick that day so his deputy sat down with Jules. He asked just a few basic questions and when she might be able to start. It was that simple and what d'you know, she was offered the position!

I gave Jules a few crash courses in design and draughting while stocking her up with pencils, straight edges, scale rules and anything else she might need on the first day of her new career with the London Underground. Looking forward to a new start, that first Monday, Jules headed off into the West End.

Her boss to be was now fit and back at work. He showed Jules to her drawing board and desk before introducing her to all the other folk in the drawing office.

Then he gave her a job to do and left her alone to get on with it. A busy, existing detailed drawing several years old that needed modifying to the redline comments already marked up on a paper copy, or checkprint. The original drawing, very dense with lineage and printing had to be revised by the end of the week.

After a close look at the drawing she did not have a clue where to start. After retrieving her drawing instruments from her briefcase and placing them on the parallel slide, it was important to change the position of the

45

drawing board that was presently just below eye level and much too high for a girl just under five feet tall. She fumbled around trying to guess how to operate the board and found the foot pedal. After stepping on it without firmly holding the board with her two hands, the board shot up into a vertical orientation nearly knocking her out and distributing her drawing instruments around the office.

Gathering herself and smiling at her colleagues she sorted the board out and taped the original drawing sheet into place using some masking tape.

It was about now that, just as she was about to start transferring the comments onto the drawing, her close neighbour stepped up and stopped her from using her pencil. *"Sorry to interrupt, Jules, but this drawing is in ink."*

Of course, she wasn't prepared for this and hadn't discussed a solitary thing with me about drawing with ink. Here was Jules, hoping to strike a new career with London Underground and was not getting off to a great start.

Instead of quickly telling her supervisor that she in fact had no experience working with ink, she chose to give it a go, borrowed an ink set and stencils from her colleagues and made some effort to make the changes.

It was all going very well as she placed text and lineage onto the original drawing using the stencils and bevelled rulers. Then, as she stepped back in admiration, an accidental adjustment of the parallel slide turned her artwork into a black splodge across the drawing.

Holy shit!

Her wide mouthed supervisor was hopping mad as a tearful Jules was dismissed with immediate effect.


The senior piping designers at Stone & Webster knew a lot about their craft and were gracious enough to help me along with anything I needed help with. And this was just about everything, including work, personal stuff and even relationships.

I got to draw things called isometrics, or *isos*. These are fabrication drawings of a piping system, broken out into manageable sections of pipe for a fabrication contractor to build. The drawing sheets are class A3, eleven inches by seventeen inches in size (300mm x 450mm) and made of translucent plastic *Mylar*. The beauty of using all plastic-based drawing sheets were that they would not tear, by accident. Torn drawing sheets occurred on occasion, when caught up in a large printer, or crumpled at the rear of a drawer in a plan chest. If the sheet was A0 size and made of paper, it could mean losing an original drawing where a few hundred hours of thought and design were now lost.

The isometric is essentially a 3D view of a piping system with the plant north of the drawing pointing away towards the top left. Therefore, east would be towards the top right while west, down towards the left and south bottom right. Vertical sections of any piping system would be simply straight up, or straight down.

The body of each isometric original sheet was furnished with faint, parallel lineage about a quarter of an inch apart from bottom left to top right and top left to bottom right where the angle between these two sets of lines was about 35° and to this day have no idea what governs this figure.

Once a piping GA has been prepared, the attention is then turned towards preparing an isometric. In a piping team, there would normally be one or two *isometricians.* Or younger, piping designers who could draw several isometrics a day.

The isometrician would use the information against a specific line number on the plan view of the GA, to route a section of the line on the iso sheet. The drawing is not to scale and might include the straight lengths of piping, valves, elbows, tees, branch connections like weldolets or sockolets, flanges, welds, dimensions in three planes, and a complete list of materials including reference to any piping special items and pipe supports.

The issued isometric would allow a couple of activities to start; a) the already purchased piping materials can be updated and, b) the pipe fabrication contractor can start cutting and welding the piping materials together.

Over the course of several months, thousands of isos are churned out of the piping design team on any large project. And, over time, it is these fabricated sections of piping, once erected in place on a module or at site, that forms the backbone of any petrochemical installation.

Well, I was crashing out these isos about one an hour and very much enjoyed what I was doing. The piping checker would take a print of each isometric and using a set of coloured pencils cover all parts of each drawing.

Yellow would mean it was correct, blue would mean incorrect so needed modifying or removing, red comments would indicate something to

47

be added, while green would be a simple reference note to the isometrician like, 'leave as is' or 'use larger text height'.

I might've been turning the isos out in record time but they were coming back to me from the checker just as fast without much yellow on them!

You see, although I was drawing isos quickly I was not attentive enough to the right detailed information. Remember, the fabrication contractor would be cutting pipe to my drawings and if mistakes were evident, they would be costly.

Engineering manhours amount to about 10% of the total installed costs (TIC) of a project after all construction work.

Embarrassed and frustrated I would have to backtrack, revisit the original piping GA and correct the information I'd put on each isometric before submitting the isos once again, back to the same checker for what we call a 'backcheck'.

Let me tell you, a few days of this rework taught me a huge lesson in why a piping designer must be on the ball. While the schedule is important, there's no point in hitting the dates if the quality of the deliverable is crap!

One thing I'm always telling my piping group is that if you rush and get a drawing out on time and it's crap, the client will always remember it's crap but never remember it went out on time. Wait a day or two... or even a week, and get the drawing out right, the client will always remember it being right but he will likely not remember it went out late.

Apart from isometric drawings I also got involved with setting up spreadsheets in binders. Talk about a boring job. No Microsoft Excel of course in those days and I would create a master sheet with dozens of horizontal and vertical lines. Xerox machines had just made an appearance in drawing offices and carbon copies were slowly disappearing out the window. After creating dozens of these original sheets, I would print off several copies and place these copies in a binder.

Because I had established half decent printing and line work from so much practice in the document management group, I was *always* getting stuck with this work. This, of course, interrupted my design of piping systems and creating isometrics or GAs.

In truth, I put up with a lot of crap in my three years as an apprentice but it also helped me prepare for tougher times ahead when it would be prudent to chill, nod your head and accept what was asked of me instead of throwing someone out of a nineteenth floor window.

On occasion, the project would need to develop a plot plan. A plot plan is a drawing of any given plot space, of any size, and would normally show all the pertinent structures on an area of real estate including roads, mechanical equipment safely segregated, electrical buildings, fence lines, gate access, firefighting equipment, flare stacks, storage tanks, battery limit isolation valve platforms and other large structures.

There would also be heating, ventilation and air conditioning or HVAC equipment, access and operating platforms for valve stations and a main pipe rack.

There would also be banks of heat exchangers, air coolers on top of the pipe rack and a control room referred to as the heart of the process unit where operations personnel would be permanently based, monitoring coloured screens of critical data that reflected how the unit was operating at any given time.

Drawn to a scale of maybe 1:500, 1:1000 or larger, a site plan would also be required for a project. The site plan is a look at real estate associated with the proposed facility but taken from a much higher elevation and covering a footprint of maybe a dozen square miles or kilometres. The drawing would show all the applicable operating plants, unit plot plans side by side, offsite tank farms, access railway lines in and out of the facility, nearby highways, bridges, road connectivity, ponds, lakes, rivers, oceans with any boat and offloading jetties.

Piping Studies and General Arrangements were my favourite type of drawing to get stuck into. Before taping a brand new drawing sheet to the drawing board, a few things need to be known by the piping designer before the pencil touches the drawing sheet.

First, the actual scale of the drawing needed must be understood. If the project was being executed using Metric dimensioning like millimetres, centimetres and metres, piping studies and GAs were usually developed to a scale of 1:33 1/3. A similar scale used for a GA on an Imperial project dictated by inches, fractions of an inch, feet and yards, the scale of 3/8" to one foot would be used (which is 1:32 in metric conversion and close enough to 1:33 1/3). In simple terms, for every thirty-three feet of real construction, the same item would need just one foot on the drawing. Large scale site plans can often be up around two miles by two miles, or 3.2km square.

If the drawing sheet you are using has one metre of true available space to project the site, based on a 3.2km sized facility, the scale of the overall site plan would be 1:3,200. Got it? *Good.*

Before the age of CAD, piping designers in the seventies were categorized as a D1 or D2. A D1 piper would be a Senior designer with at least fifteen years' experience while a D2, or Intermediate, had much less. A young fella-me-lad like myself drawing isometrics and a new kid on the block would be called a D3 isometrician.

I remember John Kerry at Worley Engineering in North Finchley, a great piping designer who had a unique, dry sense of humour referring to me as a D37.

Nowadays, a resume for a Senior Piping Designer might reflect just four or five years of experience. The bulk of this short length of time would be experience in computer design and most definitely not, the length of experience found in piping layout and design.

Throughout my apprenticeship I was immersed among contract senior pipers who had worked at different companies in London and some had started acquiring positions in continental Europe like, Germany, Holland and Belgium. I was getting to hear whispers of serious money I hadn't even thought about before in the past.

However, I was engaged in an apprenticeship and soon enough my training in the office was to come to an end as Stone & Webster bought me a ticket and a bunk bed on a sleeper car up to the northeast of England where I was to spend the last six months of my time, working on an actual petrochemical installation.

I learned something before I'd even arrived. My top bunk sleeper on the train I shared with a chain-smoker and at eighteen years old I hadn't smoked at all, being repulsed by the entire culture throughout my childhood.

I also learned from that choking night on the train, never to let someone else make my travel plans.

I checked in at The King's Head Hotel in Redcar-by-the-Sea and they gave me a single room the size of a mouse's earhole.

During the working day, I got to spend time on the No.6 Olefines Plant at ICI, Wilton in Teesside, just a short taxi ride from Redcar. No.6 Olefines had been up and running a couple of years so a live operating unit. All the piping, valves and fittings I had been putting down on paper I could now see for real and large as life as I started to gain experience on the construction side of the fence. I met stacks of good folk and also tried to date one or two of the office gals. Not the tea lady, though.

After interesting times out at the site each day, I would get home and most evenings, shower, shave and after spending twenty minutes drying my hair… get out on the town.

Trying to meet a girl in London was like nailing jelly to a wall. At any given night club in the West End or local places like the Epping Forest Country Club, Tiffany's or Room At The Top in Ilford, time after time I would get the cold shoulder and blanked when asking for a dance.

But NOT up here in Teesside!

I had never seen so many girls in pubs and clubs ready for a natter, a drink, a dance, a dinner out, or a leg over. Or sometimes, all of the above.

The Geordies love a darts match and on occasion I'd walk into a pub by accident when a darts match was starting. I might be asked to step into a team when someone hadn't turned up, or at the very least offered some sandwiches while I read the paper sipping a pint.

Of course, the fashions in Redcar were very different to Ilford and London in 1976. With my long, curly permed hair I would wear tight brush velvet jeans, Lurex V-neck sweaters and pointed spats on my feet. This of course, was out of left field in Teesside where flared trousers were still all the go, along with parted, brylcreamed hair and rounded collar shirts covered in *Homepride* men.

Back at the jobsite I was soon boosting knowledge of my piping skillsets by seeing operating piping arrangements in place. I got to appreciate how some busy areas, if not considered properly for correct access and maintenance in the design phase, would be a nightmare on a daily basis when Operations folk have to squeeze through tight spots to get to a valve handwheel, duck under an exposed steel beam, lay down on an oily floor to gain access to a drain valve or cautiously lean across a handrail a hundred feet above ground to record the reading on a pressure gauge.

I discovered that it is these negative and essentially unsafe things observed at site that help a piping designer when designing the piping systems on the drawing board or a 3D CAD system.

The trouble all piping designers face today is this; When in Model Design Reviews and the designer is trying hard to make a small change and bring that valve handwheel or pressure gauge closer to the platform, the effects are that the model would have to be changed thereby offering up discussion on whether there is sufficient time to make the change. These days I get absolutely fed up with these comments and project engineers telling the attendees, *"If it's safe, meets code and works: leave it alone."* Sorry, but it's bollocks.

I had plenty to do on site and one day was asked by the field engineer to wander over to the materials warehouse and a bloke called Ray Simmons for a *long weight*. I found Ray, nice bloke, and he told me to take a seat. Of course, I hadn't a clue what a Long Weight actually was but sitting in that same chair an hour and a half later, I did.

Bastards. *Set up, again!*

I had opportunities to look closely at some of the more complex mechanical equipment and vessels. A compressor building is a frightening place to be if you have no hearing protection. You walk into the building with three large, high temperature gas compressors moving sour gas around under pressure and the detected energy levels are enormous. (Sour gas is correctly described as a fluid with more than six parts to a million of the deadly, hydrogen sulphide.) Even after slipping in a couple of ear plugs the acoustic levels are up around ninety decibels and right on the industrial limits. You can't hear yourself think.

Gas compressors are volatile items of hydrocarbon equipment that increase the operating pressure and therefore push gas fair distances around a facility. Without compression, it's not gonna move that far. Walking around at grade beneath the compressor access platforms and machines you have this feeling that you want to just get out of the building and as far away as possible.

After completing the six months practical up in County Cleveland and chalking up more than three years of my piping apprenticeship, I returned to the offices in Holborn to continue my career with Stone & Webster Engineering Limited as a now, fully fledged, piping designer. I'd also had six months away from my continued education and after eventually registering for the correct course was close to securing some qualifications.

But things weren't going that well in the office as I was being asked to do menial tasks like writing up spreadsheets and making changes to the rear side of reproducible drawings. The chaps around me continued to be a tower of strength offering ideas and suggestions.

But they could see I was still being treated as *the boy* and pulled me into a pub one day after work. Most of them agreed that, for me to move on in my life after being an apprentice, I would now have to leave Stone & Webster and take a contract position in the piping market. *My heart was racing...*

I was given telephone numbers of three agencies and, in quiet moments, nipped out of the office to make a few calls from a telephone box across the road and was positively surprised at the responses when talking to each agent.

There were a number of positions up for grabs and soon enough I had secured an interview at a small company called Black, Sivells and Bryson way across the south and west side of town from my home in Gants Hill, Essex where I lived with Mum, Dad and my sisters.

The interview went well and I was offered the position as a D3 piping designer. But also had to reassure the company that I would be starting work in just two weeks' time!

This was not going to be easy because I was on one month's notice with Stone & Webster. I chewed on it over the weekend.

My current salary was £1,980 a year, or a little under £1 an hour. The hourly rate for this new contract was to be £3.90 an hour, four times what I was on at Stones! After letting the other piping workmates know, I was hooked and made the decision to move.

So, on the Monday, I called Mike Pembroke at the agency and agreed to start at BS&B. Giving notice to Graham Walley and only giving two weeks' notice, he was not a happy camper. Being a long time company man, Graham reminded me how much Stone & Webster had invested in me. I reminded Graham of the crappy types of work he was still giving me and that was the reason for my departure. He nodded and tried to accept it.

I was excited and nervous, heading out into the world of contract piping! I was just nineteen years old.

Not one hour after handing in my notice the office telephone rang. *"Phone again, Mitch."*

It was Mike Pembroke and he had a proposition; Mike had offered me *another* position at a small company for just one week, starting the next day! No interview, but £4.50 an hour, with unlimited hours. The job was mine if I wanted it. Blimey.

After tapping out some numbers on my new, white Commodore calculator (the 'in' thing replacing my logarithm tables and slide rule), an 80 hour week would give me £360! This was two months of my salary with Stone & Webster earned in just a week!

Another huddle around the drawing boards, the piping colleagues said go for it!

I went sick for the rest of the week and got paid for it from Stones while I clocked up around eighty-five hours working the rest of the week and following Saturday, too.

I spent my last week at Stone & Webster Engineering Limited before having a leaving do on the Friday where I spent nearly all my previous week's earnings down the Pakenham Arms, treating my S&W friends I'd made over the last three years.

Now, I'm not sure why I took the plunge and chose to move on from, what was then, one of the best engineering companies in the world. Looking back, if I had stayed I probably would've retired early with a very nice pension. But I wasn't going to fight every time I wanted something interesting to do at work. I would go out and find it for myself, trading a company driven working life for a contract, project driven working life and to this day, have never looked back.

# 1978

The first few months at BS&B went well and I made a real effort turning out the piping drawings. I was working a lot of overtime, doing a great job for the company and each weekly paycheque was around two hundred quid. In two months I had made as much as I had done the entire previous year at Stone & Webster.

I was living back at home after renting a room for a while in a shared house. Dad was not happy with me for a few reasons; first, for taking a week off sick and getting paid for it while I was plugging in a timesheet for a second job. Second, I was earning more money than him and although he would never show his emotions or jealousy, I could see it was a hard nut to swallow. I was nineteen and he was forty-eight.

And third, he didn't like it when I called a taxi one stormy Friday night, to go pick up a Chinese takeaway I'd ordered.

I started to enjoy the sense of having money around me. I took my mum and dad out for dinner at a fancy restaurant and treated us all to a night out in Drury Lane to see Jack Jones at Christmas. I bought my sister, Deb, a new stereo system for her room and paid £50 for silk shirts at Christian Dior. I was out and about with my best friend Gary, treating us to nights out at pubs and clubs around London while he focused on Art College.

I was soon shocked when the contract at BS&B came to an end and I found myself serving one week's notice. This was something I hadn't considered and the fact that, while the contracts may have been lucrative, they may also be short.

A few positions for a week or two here and there, before I joined a company west of the city just below the A4 flyover. Alpha Laval was about a two hour drive for me around the North Circular Road and, after parking up each morning, emotionally it felt like I'd already put in a day's work. Good bunch of guys and a bit more responsibility for me. Saturday overtime, one of the chaps would bring into the office an entire hi-fi stereo system. Nice thought it was too as we all began dancing next to our drawing boards while crashing out isometrics.

At lunchtime I used to walk to a sandwich bar, pick up a ham and tomato sarnie, collect the *Evening Standard* and read it back at my desk. The Engineering section of the newspaper was always full of piping jobs, some with the shortest text:

*Pip des long cont rate neg.* Or, piping designers wanted, long contracts available and the hourly rate is negotiable meaning… up there.

One day I spotted a simple ad that read, *"Piping Designers Central Africa"*.

A war had only just broken out in Zaire but I was intrigued and gave the agent a call.

Terry at the agency advised me that the ad had been misunderstood in dictation and it was actually West Africa. I was even more intrigued and asked a few questions. The gist of it was that a sugar refinery in the Ivory Coast owned by Tate & Lyle had a few piping designers out at site working for a Canadian company called Redpath Sugar Industries.

One of the contract pipers currently back in the UK on leave had not called in at an agreed stipulated time. The agreement was such that, if he didn't call back in two days, his position would be replaced. Terry asked me if I might be interested in heading out to West Africa. In that single moment, I said, *"Yes!"*

Well, a couple of days later I was advised that I was now approved for the position after which we met up at a pub in Brentwood, Essex, to discuss the contract. I was twenty years old but my resume stated, twenty-four.

You see, I had already come unstuck with one interview for a position based in Iran where I was rejected because I was not twenty-one years old, the minimum age for obtaining a working visa in the Middle East. From that moment I had made a decision to boost the age on my resume by four years. I was twenty but my ressie showed me as twenty-four. Trouble was… I looked just fifteen.

Wednesday came and I was hanging around the office telephone. It rang and my heart skipped a few beats. After a few words with Terry I was officially assigned the position in the Cote d'Ivoire. My heart then missed the next two beats as I was told I would need to be on an 8.00am flight to Abidjan that coming Saturday! Once again, here I was giving less than desired notice period. However, in this case my piping section leader was good as gold and I departed Alpha Laval that same day I gave notice, without any hard feelings.

I spent Thursday and Friday faxing paperwork, getting a few inoculations sorted, buying tropical clothing and hugging my dear Mum who was a basket case. Her only son was heading off to Africa.

After a brief stopover for a flight change in Bamaku, Mali, I came down the stairs from the 737 and sprinted across the tarmac. I thought my arse was on fire as I struggled to handle the 120°F heat, rushing past a line of African travellers as I gasped for oxygen.

I arrived in Abidjan and was met by a short, local lad in flip flops who drove me across town to the Golf International Hotel. After unpacking my bags, down at the pool I took a look around and, to my wonderful astonishment, saw women everywhere. Not just local lasses, but slim, gorgeous English girls. At the poolside bar I was informed by three of these beauties, that there was a British Airways worldwide convention for this long weekend and what do you know, I had checked in the same day. It's a rough life but someone has to do it.

Getting to know a few of the lasses I was advised of a party the following evening, upstairs at one of the rooftop lounges and did I want to go?

*"Well, let me think about it for a minute."*

The party was a treat and I hit the sack late. Enjoying the Holiday Monday round the pool, popping headache pills every fifteen minutes, I started to take in the African culture, gleamed at the opulent foods displayed on buffet tables and listened to most folk nattering away in French. I was excited at staying here for my assignment and life couldn't be better.

The following morning, a nice girl approached me in the restaurant as I finished breakfast and introduced herself as an HR representative. She asked me if I had checked out yet?

*"Err, run that by me, again, please?"*

Apparently, we were off to catch another flight and misreading my contract it was apparent I wouldn't be seeing the flight attendants at the Golf International Hotel any more. I rushed up to the room and rapidly packed my bags.

The twin engine Cessna took us over bush and game landscapes and banked in sharply to land at the airstrip supporting the town of Korhogo while herds of antelope scattered. As we left the airport in a taxi I realised, a little late in fact, that this part of the country was a much better place to build a sugar refinery, compared to, say, the inner city of the nation's capital, Abidjan.

On the first floor of a large site-based trailer I soon hooked up with my supervisor, a lovely Louisianan called Tom Tyler who put me to work.

My job was to take Flowsheet markups covered with changes, and draw isometrics straight from the Flowsheet. No piping general arrangement, no studies. I chewed this over for more than a day before coming to appreciate that I had absolutely no idea how to do this. I then spent another day and a sleepless night secretly freaking out about the assignment I'd taken and made a bold decision to go see Tom and confess I was out of my depth.

He explained the entire concept to me and how I would need to interpret the P&ID markups by checking the actual site areas of equipment and existing pipework out at the refinery. Then, sketch and measure up the required fabrication of spools to fit the new piping onto the existing piping. Finally, back at the trailer I would need to draw up the isometrics on a drawing board. No GAs.

He then closed the door and we both had a heart to heart. Tom asked me how much experience I had in sugar refinery piping design. I said not much experience in really anything and just fresh out of a piping apprenticeship with Stone & Webster. Furthermore, I was not twenty-four years old, but just twenty in fact but felt I needed to bump my age up if I was really going to get a position in the business as a piping designer and hold down a responsible position, overseas.

Tom smiled and told me that the agent had advised Redpath that I was twenty-eight years old and had verified that I was more than equipped with the experience to do the work, make quick decisions and head up a small team of pipe fabricators.

I was shaking, unsettled and was sure I was about to get the elbow and the next flight out… I'd be on it.

Tom then put his hands in his pocket and asked me if I was related to a man called Dick Jago, because he'd worked with this great guy in Nigeria. *Dick was my uncle!*

Now, the entire balance of the conversation turned for the better and with a hand on my shoulder he said to me, *"Mitch Jago, y'all gonna get through this and let's keep this age issue just between the two of us, okay?"*

I almost burst into tears and wanted to give him a big hug. What a genuine, smashing gentleman.

I got stuck in and learned more in the next six months than I had done in the last three years. I took the redline markups out with me to areas of the refinery and, with a roll of plot plans tracked down the actual area where the new piping was to be installed.

Walking down the existing piping I established where the cuts should be, the routing of the new piping and where on this new scope the valves should be located for ease of accessibility. On the spot out in the field, I drew up rough and ready sketches before taking the packages back to my desk where I prepared good, legible isometrics, each with a detailed Bill of Material (BOM).

The drawings were signed off and moved to the pipe fabricator's yard, a kilometre up the road. I would hop onto a *mobilette*, a sort of small engine motorcycle, and travel backwards and forwards between the drawing office and fabrication shop. Now, all this stuff was right at the coal face and my previous work in London had come nothing close to the experience I was getting out here in West Africa.

Tom Tyler was also a happy man because I think my efforts and base training had helped confirm back to him that, sometimes, you just gotta give a young lad a chance. He indeed did and I shall always be grateful to him for persevering with me.

After returning from my spell out in the Ivory Coast, I joined a company called Worley Engineering. Based up in North Finchley, Worley were a growing force on the offshore engineering scene in London and owned by an American, Steve Worley. Mobil Oil had awarded the detailed design contract for Beryl Alpha to Worley, a large North Sea offshore oil development.

Worley were also one of the few engineering firms offering premium rate overtime. This essentially meant that your contracted hourly rate would be good for the standard, forty hour week. However, overtime above eight hours between Mondays and Fridays would be at 'time and a third', Saturdays at 'time and a half' while any overtime on Sundays would be paid out at double time, or as we called it, *Double Bubble*.

I had made some dosh from my assignment in the Ivory Coast and purchased a large, white, Jaguar XJ6. With walnut trim and that old, lovely smelling, worn Prussian blue leather upholstery it was indeed a rare car because it also had a relatively small 2.8 litre engine, and a manual gearbox with a switch for an overdrive facility. The two petrol tanks at the rear held so many gallons of fuel, it cost me a week's wages to fill it up.

My Dad… again… wasn't happy. *"You're wasting your money, son."*

Worley Engineering had more jokers and pipers with a sense of humour under one roof, than probably all the other companies in London, put together. Practical jokes were never ending and every project at Worley had folk who were game for a giggle.

I was assigned to a project and reported to a Polish section leader Jan Konkorski in a satellite office, a few miles up the road from North Finchley. On my first Friday morning it was timesheet day and I had to fill out a single sheet that identified the hours I'd worked that week. Of course, I hadn't worked any overtime so put down a straight forty hours or five, eight hour days. A chap called Roger Blinks walked up to me and asked me how many hours I was recording on the sheet, so I told him. He told me to change it and add two hours to each day except the Friday.

I thought this was a bit cheeky and told him I didn't really want to do that because in truth, I'd only worked the forty hours and not forty-eight. Furthermore, I did not want to entertain a possibility of getting sacked in my first week on the job!

Roger insisted I change it because the pipers were concerned that if we all didn't show overtime on each time sheet, the client would take away the opportunity and privilege and cancel the OT. I was nervous and didn't wish to upset anyone. I didn't even know what position Roger held down on the project and, in truth, many pipers relied upon a certain amount of overtime each week.

Reluctantly under pressure, I modified the sheet to show forty-eight hours and submitted it for approval. About an hour later I hear the piping lead at the front of the office calling my name.

*Oh fuck, you're kidding me.*

A sickly feeling rose up in my throat as I slowly walked down between the drawing boards towards the Polish squaddie.

He asked me why I'd booked overtime when I'd worked no overtime at all. I told him it was an error because on the last project I'd booked dozens of continuous forty-eight hour weeks on the trot and made a simple mistake.

I apologised, retrieved the timesheet and removed the eight hours of overtime. Roger was laughing his head off but I was angry and pissed off. I could've been walked out and it was a practical joke I was not happy about. Amazingly enough, Roger and I were to both enjoy a wonderful friendship over the next forty years.

I spent the next few months on a project development in Western Australia for the client, Woodside Petroleum. The North Rankin 'A' offshore platform front end engineering design (FEED) was to be executed in London with detailed design moving to Perth, a year later.

It was the first time I had been involved in offshore platform work and enjoyed the work I had been given by my lead, John Kerry. I was studying piping design around several Christmas Trees which involved high pressure ANSI piping and transitions from a higher ten thousand API pressure and pipe specifications. A Christmas tree is a large, complex piping material component that sits on an operating deck directly above a wellhead. The main function of a Christmas tree is to manage the high pressures and flowrates of oil or gas rushing from the reservoir, buried deep below the ocean floor and up through to the platform. The tree consists of piping, casings, valves and well kill facilities; a chemically supplemented substance called, 'mud'. But not the mud you and I see in waterlogged grassland or on a soggy building site. This is a chemically composed type of mud.

On our piping floor was also a model shop.

One Monday morning, Barry walked into the office after enjoying a two week holiday at a European ski resort. One leg was in plaster and he was making an effort to walk with the aid of two crutches. The washrooms were just a few steps away from his desk so when duty called he would leave his wooden crutches resting against his desk and hop across to the toilet.

On the Tuesday morning, as Barry skipped to the loo, one of the modellers grabbed his wooden crutches and rushed into the model shop. He removed the rubber stoppers from the bottom of each crutch and using a saw, removed about one quarter of an inch, or a few millimetres from the bottom of each crutch before replacing the stoppers. He then quickly put the crutches back next to Barry's desk.

Wednesday morning, the act was played out, then again on Wednesday afternoon. By now, the chaps were all in on the laugh.

This went on for a full week and come five p.m. on the Friday, we said goodnight to Barry and bid him a good weekend as the smiling faces on the chaps in the drawing office watched him hobble away to the elevators, seriously bent over his doctored crutches.

The following Monday, Barry arrived at the office with the same crutches pegged in the same position he'd left work with on the Friday. More trimming Monday and Tuesday and by Wednesday, someone just had to say something. *"Hey Barry,"* he called out as he left work for the day. *"How's the leg?"*

*"Okay, thanks. Plaster comes off in three weeks but I've been having terrible backaches, lately."* Poor bloke. It was a good few weeks before he knew.

Overtime was always in demand at Worley, as previously stated. Extra hours were made available to all in an effort to maintain the schedule. Whoever worked the most overtime in one week was awarded the 'Yellow Jersey' and a desk mounted model of a *Tour de France* cyclist's top. More overtime meant higher paycheques and higher paycheques led to more toys. Guys were buying Jaguars, BMWs (or Bob Marleys as we called them, as in *Bob Marley and the Wailers*).

Then there were nice washing machines, quality hi-fi music centres, handmade shirts and shoes and large, Sony Trinitron televisions that then, weighed a ton. Work was in abundance in London and hourly rates were rising all the time and the dosh just kept on rolling in.

Pipers were booking lavish holidays in Thailand, South Africa and Disneyworld while taking on huge mortgages for family homes in smart, sought after areas further away from the city. Properties that would give a family that extra space in the garage, expensive farmhouse kitchen or two extra bedrooms and an English country garden. Some guys were so far away from the office that their journeys by British Rail and the London Underground would take two and a half hours to get into work and the same time to get home. This commuting was all in addition to working the overtime, of course. Leaving home at four a.m. and getting back after nine was not out of the ordinary.

Pressure mounted in the office, but equally at home by the desire to increase the working hours and attain more of life's material goodies. Sadly, families suffered as the father and husband were at home less and less, while striving to work more hours to pay for the extra costs their lifestyle demanded. It was all a highly charged environment, made all the easier by a long Friday lunch and several sherbets.

On the Phillips' Maureen offshore project in Worley's Wood Green offices, sixty hours a week were being booked by most folk and suddenly one Friday, word got around that all overtime was to cease, effective immediately. The guy sitting next to me, Don Bowen, was absolutely furious about this decision and, in an angry state of mind, rushed over to the piping lead, Ron Greenland. An argument broke out which then turned ugly when Don picked up one of the heavy, draughting stools and with arms at full stretch tossed it at Ron who just managed to duck out of the way before it came crashing down onto his desk. It was an amazing spectacle to watch as security were quickly deployed to the scene. Don was packed up and escorted out of the building in fifteen minutes, never to be heard of again except in several bars over time when the story of *Bowen the Chair* would be recited.

The execution of projects in the late seventies was enormously different to how they are now delivered, fifty years on. As eluded to earlier, open plan drawing office configurations invited conversation, communication and a true sense of a 'team' environment.

Piping engineers were qualified with degrees and experienced in what they were doing because they had been trained in a specific field. Designers like myself had come from an engineering background, but without the degree. Project managers had respect for designers and piping engineers, although the leadership of a piping group would, normally, not be assigned to a degreed engineer. Strange observation, but the piper with the design background would tend to know more about the operations and running of a piping group, than the true engineer normally focused on a blinkered, engineering environment.

Project planners were always up to speed with milestones and achievements. If you missed a deadline and a plot plan did not get issued on June fifth, on June sixth before you'd grabbed a coffee the planner would be at your desk asking for reasons why the drawing didn't go out yesterday.

This kept you on your toes and encouraged effort to actually get things issued and out of the door on time. This is all assuming, of course, that the schedule in the first place had been accepted by the lead piper and equally important was achievable… at the time of sanction.

Today's planning is very different. No-one would approach me with a baseball bat asking if a plot plan had been issued on June fifth. Instead, I wouldn't hear anything until August nineteenth when a new schedule would be published that showed schedule 'creep' to the right. A new issue date of September sixth for the plot plan would be plugged into the schedule by a twenty-two year old planner whom would not first ask the piping lead for his opinion on the new date, before publishing it.

Pipe stress engineers are an integral part of an oil and gas engineering project. They address critical flexibility in a piping system where high temperatures and pressures are a factor in design. Years ago, a stress engineer would walk up to a piping designer's drawing board with a coffee and discuss it with the designer. No emails, no letter of intent, no interoffice memorandum, just good old fashioned talking and a flow of ideas.

The piper would then take the comments, rub a few lines out here and there, then draw up a stress sketch and forward it onto the stress engineer. When received, the engineer would log the sketch and was already up to speed with the design so may be able to return it, approved, the same day.

Today's environment is, strangely, different. Some stress engineers take forever to assess a piping system and isometric issue dates are constantly missed while any small change to a piping system would require a completely new stress sketch and analysis to reflect the change. Many stress engineers today have no idea where any piping designer sits in the office and are reluctant to open up conversation should it turn towards the possibility of the stress guy making a verbal decision. Everything has to be in writing and a stress analysis conducted using the recognised Caesar II or AutoPipe stress analysis programs. Furthermore, every single piece of piping needs a stress engineer to sign off the fabrication isometric. Even an open ended one inch line from a pump casing drain! It is what it is.

An increase in the sheer size of projects over the past twenty years have seen an influx of new, international and multicultural, young stress engineers. They are terrific on the keyboard buttons but, regretfully, know very little about the craft of piping design. This shortfall has a serious impact on how long it actually takes for stress activities to be completed for any given area and contributes to missed target dates. So, when the piping lead tries to hold his stress team's hands to the fire on delivery of completed stress systems, the stress engineers feel pressure in releasing a product too early. When it comes time for the stress engineer to sign off the isometrics… we sometimes see stress engineers giving notice to leave the project before signing over their systems and possibly be held liable should any life-threatening catastrophe occur on an installation.

Worley Engineering had many characters working in the Piping Group and were fun to be around.

Practical jokes were continuously on the go and our poor old Technical Clerk, Bill Eaton, was usually a target.

Bill was responsible for moving drawings upstairs to the document control group. He always had a pile of documents on his desk but was seldom there and was often seen just riding up and down in the elevators. A real lazy bastard.

One day he brought in a new packet of Rich Tea biscuits and stood the packet upright on his desk. Graham would take a razor blade from the model shop and, without moving the packet, slice the wrapping close to the bottom, but all the way round the circumference. The biscuits sat piled up, within their wrapping. Bill would return from the elevators and make himself a cup of tea. Stirring his tea he made a lunge for the packet and lifted it up into the air only to see thirty biscuits quickly distributed around the office. Everyone, except Bill, cried with laughter.

Graham is also a fisherman and on another day, had his fishing rod in the office to take down to a shop to be repaired. When Bill was out and about in the elevators, Graham opened up Bill's Tupperware sandwich box and discreetly removed a smoked mackerel his wife had packed for his lunch.

When Bill settled down at noon to eat his lunch, he reached for his container. Sitting there with his feet up on a stool, staring into his box you could see the anguish on his face while he tried to remember if he'd packed the fish.

Behind Bill's desk, Graham slowly lowered down in front of Bill's face, the striped mackerel till it appeared in front of Bill's sad face. You couldn't make it up.

One warm, summer Friday evening the Mobil Beryl Alpha project squad had been invited out to a function at The *Old Caledonian* ship, moored at

Victoria Embankment on the Thames. A smart, private room had been organised and paid for by the Mobil senior executive. Canapés, hors d'oeuvres and a complimentary bar all supported by debonair servers dressed in waistcoats and bow ties. This was a posh event and nearly all the Worley pipers tagged along.

The event commenced at eight p.m. At four o'clock the pipers left the office and went straight into a pub in North Finchley before grabbing underground trains into London's West End.

When we all arrived, it was fair to say that about half of the forty folk in attendance should really have been home in their beds and not attending a private project function room in the cellar deck of an historic venue and world heritage site.

Jim had asked for a pint but the cocky male server behind one of the small bars where the buffet table was positioned told Jim he'd had enough and, besides, they were only offering wine or port. Things got heated up and quite unexpectedly, in seconds the place erupted with a food fight.

Sausage rolls were spun across the room. Fish sauce covered prawn vol-au-vents were collected up and followed the sausage rolls through the air while the recipients lobbed chicken drumsticks and cheese sticks in the opposite direction.

The cocky barman was then targeted by everyone in the room as food throwing changed direction and the barman realised he was isolated behind the bar. With food flung towards him at a rate of knots, and a look of sheer panic and fear in his eyes, he pulled down the steel shutters and dived onto the floor.

Up on the main deck, now populated with various members of the paying public totally unaware of the catastrophe that was unfolding downstairs, I was frog marched to a mobile linen basket on wheels. Thrown inside and with linen tossed on top of me, I was then catapulted down the varnished, wooden deck of the Old Caledonian. With families diving off to the side every few feet this was a nerve racking experience and as I gathered speed the tub hit the bump on the deck above the prop shaft and I shot through the air, landing on my arse in front of a small family, out for a pleasant evening.

While this was going on, back in the dining area, the barman had not surfaced and the food chucking had turned to liquids. One original oil painting had a pint of London Pride thrown onto its canvas and Charles the

1$^{st}$ had tears rolling down his cheeks.

It was an amazing night that ended with the Worley pipers running away from the ship and playing knock down ginger on the second floor of the Waldorf Hotel before the evening finished with several of us being thrown out of a night club called The Global Village. Even as a twenty year old, this was an incredible night out!

Back in the office Monday morning, the enquiries began. The administration department of The Old Caledonian had written to the senior Executive of Mobil Oil and wanted to know what happened that Friday evening? Verbal and written complaints poured in and the Worley Beryl Alpha project team spent most of the day asking every person formally invited what folk were to blame for the disruptions.

But, strange as it seemed, no-one asked me that morning so I kept my mouth shut. This was essentially because I was not working on the project at the time and, thankfully, was not on any list of attendees. Everyone else who was approached said they knew nothing about the disruptions. A week later all was forgotten and the Old Caledonian bill for damages was paid. I heard it was up in the thousands.

A couple of years later, fire engulfed the vessel and it ceased to be considered any longer for public events. Especially to oil and gas projects.

# 1979

Bob Fyfe was the Piping Manager at Worley and hadn't a clue how to handle his piping team. On one occasion he would send Bill Eaton down to the pub at three p.m. on a Friday to get the pipers back to the office. They told Bill to bugger off.

One Friday afternoon two piping workmates spotted overalls and hard hats in some obscure room under a staircase, along with a toolbox. In an impromptu moment of hilarity they slipped on the overalls and hats, grabbed heavy tape measures and a clipboard then walked straight out into the middle of the three lane Finchley Road at Tally Ho corner. As the slow moving traffic ground to a halt while several other shoppers looked on, each guy wandered to one side of the road and held the tape measure between them. Horns and honking, the two pipers were unperturbed, sipped coffee and scratched down information on their clipboards.

The driver of a bus full of passengers asked, *"What the heck is going on?"* He was told that a new motorway was being planned for the area and some preliminary information was required to close out the feasibility study. *"You're kidding,"* he said. *"I live just round the corner!"*

The following week a local newspaper reported a bogus team had held up the Finchley Road traffic.

After a spell on the Phillips Maureen platform project, I felt a bit restless. Calgary, Alberta in western Canada was picking up work at an alarming rate of knots and there was a severe shortage of piping designers over there. Born in Canada I had already secured a Canadian passport on the strength of my birth certificate and, without the necessity of a working visa, smiled at the opportunity to see that part of the world.

And so it was in the springtime of that year I bought the guys a few leaving beers and secured a twelve-month return trip ticket on a Wardair flight out to Calgary.

A recognised agent in the business, Ron Hinchcliff met me at the airport in a yellow, 1965 E-type Jaguar. Ron was the owner of a growing agency that supplied petrochemical resources but also the owner of the

68

largest company in Canada supplying plastic model parts to engineering firms. Ron was a character and knew my old man. We got along well, even after interviewing me in the car from the airport to a hotel:

*"What's the radius of a six inch elbow, Mitch?"*

*"Is that a short or long radius, Ron?"*

I guess a twenty-one [twenty-five] year old trying his luck overseas would have raised a few alarm bells. We laughed.

After a short space of time settling in, Ron fixed me up with a position of employment without an interview. A company based in smart offices downtown run by a bloke known as *The Italian Stallion*, Tony Palma.

Tony was a smashing, tall fella with immaculate dress sense and had asked me to study a piping arrangement for a new area on a local Alberta plant. Not much equipment or piping but a smallish area in which to fit all the facilities and materials. I had P&IDs and a plot plan and that was it. No field trip, no piping general arrangements, no isometrics. I was flummoxed and hadn't a clue how to even start going about this without a field trip.

You see, Ron had sold this twenty-something chap as a singing, dancing, golden bollocks D1 senior piping designer. My rate was $18 an hour and I can only assume that Ron's cut was maybe five bucks which equated to Tony paying Ron $23 an hour.

After several weeks of struggling to pull it all together, Tony came into my office and invited me out to lunch. Over a filet mignon, he suggested that I needed a larger company to glean experience from. A fair comment. I explained the difficulties I was having in supporting the exercises being asked of me. Tony then put forward an idea. He said he would be happy to retain my services, keep me on and pay me $18 an hour but only if I ditched the agent. Well, I thought… this is no problem and nodded my head in appreciation and approval.

Back at the office I picked up the phone and dialled up Ron Hinchcliff. I essentially advised him that, sadly, I could no longer retain his services and from Monday, would be working directly for Tony Palma.

I can tell you straight, that this news did not go down too well. In fact, there was nothing short of an eruption on the other end of the line.

*"Oh, is that right, Mitch? We'll see about that."*

Approximately three and a half minutes later, Tony left his office and the building shook as *The Stallion* waltzed up to my drawing board.

*"You screwed up on me, Mitch!"*

69

Indeed, I had. What an idiot I was.

After the dust settled I moved on and joined a large engineering company called MHG International where, under the wing of a piping manager called Reg Foller, I was once again immersed among a number of senior pipers who steered me in the right direction, from which I learned a heck of a lot.

I had leased a downtown apartment in a block called Central Towers, just walking distance from MHG's plush offices at the foot of the six hundred foot tall, Calgary Tower. I adored the lifestyle of an Essex boy, in Calgary. My workmates were good folk and I made many friends. Restaurants were amazing, the skiing and Rocky Mountains exhilarating and, generally, the quality of life was exceptional.

But after several months in Canada, personal reasons outside my control dictated that I made a decision to move back to England.

# 1980

Back in London, I secured a contract with Davy Power Gas on a Chinese Alcohols Plant. There was an inordinate amount of overtime and I found myself working six days a week with the odd Sunday thrown in. Ken Thrust was the squad leader on that project and there were a few characters in the piping team.

Ken had made an agreement with management that we could also take work home with us too, if we were up for it. This would get us an extra two hours an evening OT, on top of the two we were working after five p.m.

Around three in the afternoon, rolls of isometric originals and check prints would be handed out to the pipers who agreed to the extra hours and work from home. We would take the drawings home on the train with us and make the changes on the kitchen table. But we could only take this work home after we had completed the two specified overtime hours in the office. This little arrangement was affectionately known as *The Chinese Takeaways*.

Ken would occasionally leave early and after saying ta ta to the group, could be seen through the glass windows walking towards the elevators heading down to the ground floor. As soon as the elevator doors closed, there was a frantic rush to open up the rolls of isos and start crashing through the takeaway work before we would leave the office. This, of course, would put a huge dent in the efforts required to finish the work at home bringing the twelve drawings sometimes down to three or four or even none… and allow us to enjoy a short time at home with the family instead of working on draughting stuff.

On one occasion, there must've been fifteen or sixteen pipers crashing through the homework twenty minutes after Ken had gone home when suddenly, the elevator doors opened and Ken started to walk towards us.

*"Holy shit,"* someone would shout… *"It's Ken, quick, he's coming back to the office!"*

In Davy's offices there was a vending machine on the piping floor that dispensed a variety of bread rolls filled with a variety of stuff like ham and tomato, beef and mustard, or grated cheddar and pickle, cucumber or onion. For a slightly cheaper price there was the option of having a plain buttered roll without a filling. I began to notice that at three p.m. each day one of the structural designers would head up to the machine and buy a buttered roll. As he retrieved it from the bottom shelf, I would see him quickly scoop up all those bits of grated cheese and onion that had slipped out of the rolls over the course of a day before patting them into the middle of his buttered roll and returning to his desk. A truly horrible, miserly act.

One afternoon, just after lunchtime, into the bottom shelf dispenser of the vending machine I sprinkled a modest handful of eraser shavings collected from the parallel slide of a few drawing boards and watched our colleague go get himself a nice cheese roll.

*Hey, don't have a go at me… I had been set up enough times over the years!*

The Chinese project was infamous for a brave decision by a lead piping supervisor I have yet to see again in the industry. Quality and the right supporting information is such a critically important component of our industry. Project disciplines are forced to work against less than perfect or incomplete data. Examples are piping designers working to an entire scope of process flow sheets where many drawings are either incomplete, not yet started or fraught with numerous markups. The project schedules dictate when the process engineering group must publish issued for design (IFD) quality documentation with all drawings finished, checked, approved, signed off and formally issued to the rest of the project.

The process team had not actually issued flow sheets and had missed deadline after deadline. Line sizes were being changed, then changed back again. Valves were in and out while instrumentation tag numbering was being revised on a constant basis.

Over several weeks the piping group had expanded the designs in anticipation of these IFD flow sheets. Piping engineering and design hours had been carefully estimated months earlier and were now already in jeopardy of running dangerously low. With a less than strong project engineering team that should've been more assertive with the process group something simply had to be done to force the issue.

The overall lead piping engineer was a bloke called Dave Dare, or *Dan*

*Dare* as he was affectionately referred to from the *Eagle*, comic hero.

Now, Dave was a strong force in the project team and didn't take any crap. One Friday afternoon of a long weekend just after lunch he asked all the piping designers who were still in the office and actually back from the pub, to go home early with the assurance that they would get paid up to five o'clock, or the normal clocking out time, and all approved timesheets would not have to be modified. We all went home for a long weekend.

After his team had all left the building, Dave then invited all senior project management folk to stop by at his office for an emergency meeting. They appeared and all had noticed an empty piping office. Dave told his gathering that he had instructed all the pipers to go home. The project director asked Dave, *"Why on earth would you do that?"*

Dave responded by telling him that, unless the pipers had received *issued* process drawings to work with, they were not going to spin their wheels, waste hours and recycle work so early on in a project where the entire piping budget might be eaten up six months early.

A heck of a lot of overtime had already been worked over the weeks and everyone was used to seeing a full squad of pipers at their desks each day.

The project director immediately acknowledged what Dave had done and with his project engineering puppet entourage close behind, rushed up the stairs to the next floor where the process engineering team were getting their coats on ready for a nice long weekend.

The process team was pulled aside and each one had been instructed to take off their coats and work till nine o'clock that Friday evening. Furthermore, if each process engineer did not work at least twenty hours over the weekend and every drawing prepared and made ready for an IFD issue Tuesday morning, they would all be sacked.

When the pipers all arrived back in the office on the Tuesday morning, every one of the hundred or so flow sheets had been signed and copies sitting on Dave's desk.

While Dave's approach worked well for that particular project in London, today's project ethos is a very different animal. It demands a strong piping lead to resist the temptation to expand a piping team and publish design information before all the ducks are in a row but sadly, today's piping lead doesn't get that support from his PM who'll tell him to increase his team even if it's too early. This helps the client believe that the project is

73

advancing when it really isn't.

But when the shit hits the fan later and the hours are exhausted, that same PM will question his lead piper why he manned up far too soon?

That's one reason why it's important to have a strong piping lead who generally knows what he's doing.

Flow sheets and plot plans must be at a good level of quality before a design team grows. It's no good working with scraps of paper and hand drawn flow diagrams of the project's process intentions. For a piping deliverable to be high in quality, the process definition must also be recognized as being of high quality, too.

Plastic model review dates might be set by management without a clear understanding of what should be in the model to be able to conduct a meaningful design review with the client. So many times, the design has not reached a level of quality to conduct the review but the review goes ahead, regardless.

Changes requested on projects executed in the seventies could only be implemented if the project manager signed a carbon copy of an internal memorandum, or a letter. With the introduction of computer aided design (CAD) platforms, it is much too easy to make changes. If Joe on the drawing board wanted to modify a heat exchanger arrangement and move the equipment a bit to the north, there would be serious erasing and replacement of pencil work on the original drawing so endorsing the change would be a well-considered decision.

These days a CAD designer has that hidden luxury of spending a few days on his design without anyone noticing. He simply creates a study model somewhere in space and, when finished, drops it into the real model thereby replacing the current design. It all goes unnoticed without so much of a peep out of the piping lead who is often far too busy addressing paperwork, manhours and schedules. On that note, it is absolutely critical for a lead piping engineer to assign some of his second row to audit and oversight. Especially, when HVECs are introduced to the project.

Changes to flow sheets are the nemesis for any piping designer and create havoc in the schedule. What might start out as a harmless change by modifying the line size of a steam supply system from twelve inch to eighteen inch, this would have extraordinary consequences.

First of all, the real estate taken up by the steam header on the unit pipe

74

rack will need to be increased which, in turn, will have a knock on effect for all the adjacent piping. This adjacent piping will have to be shuffled along and moved to different positions on that level of the pipe rack. These changes to a busy pipe rack may then deem it necessary to relocate several lines from that level to another level to be able to fit the larger steam line onto that desired level of the pipe rack. So, here we have several lines that have moved, along with all the branch connections and take offs. But the branch connections and take-offs will likely be expected to change sizing, too. What was originally expected to be a four inch branch take off from that twelve inch header may now be an eight inch line supplying steam to a user.

With a line size change comes changes to the pipe support types, too and the insulation thicknesses change. The valve sizes will also change and we find ourselves going back to the procurement contracts of suppliers of valves purchased, the clauses regarding changes closely examined and how the project manages modifications to valves already in fabrication.

Then, the structural engineers must reconsider the additional loads now apparent from the heavier piping materials. Larger sized steel beams might be required to support the 18 inch steam line.

As piping designers prepare for model reviews, behind the scenes process engineers are making changes to their work that the pipers may not get to officially hear about for several weeks.

Then, just when things are settling down and changes slowing down, the lead process engineer resigns and is replaced by a new fellow who has the right to do things differently;

And yes, the steam supply header changes to 10 inch!

# 1981

At Bechtel's offices in Hammersmith, London under the piping section leadership of Mike Morrison, I worked on an Indonesian refinery project to be built in an area called Balikpapan, for the national client, Pertamina. I had been assigned a fairly straightforward design area consisting of several pumps and large diameter piping. I studied the positions of equipment, piping, pipe supports and material requirements. The smaller scale, piping studies were looking good and I was ready to turn them into fully fledged, piping general arrangement drawings.

The internal design review with my Bechtel peers did not go well. With days of effort applied to my work I had *not* considered the minimum, client specified access and maintenance requirements around these large pumps. It was evident from the review that there was inadequate access resulting in the spacing between each pump footprint, increasing substantially. These simple changes had the disastrous impact of throwing the entire layout in the bin and starting again.

More hours would be required to fix the problems that Bechtel would *not* be able to claim back from the client, simply because one of their pipers had screwed up and made a catastrophic mistake in his judgement. Mike was sympathetic, but this was a lesson I learned the hard way and since then, have remembered that situation when considerations like access and maintenance must be deemed, important.

Having been back in Blighty for eighteen months I was missing Canada and made a decision to head back overseas. Handing Bechtel my notice, I was soon back on a Wardair flight across the pond. Calgary was going through an unprecedented period of serious investment in oil and gas development as the process of synthetic crude was being established from the surface mining of oil sands or *tar sands*.

I found a downtown apartment to rent and bought an immaculate, five year old, cream coloured Chrysler *Le Baron* coupe, complete with cream coloured upholstery and an eight-track stereo system. Eight-tracks were disappearing around the early eighties making way for the smaller, Dolby cassette tapes. In music stores, I could buy an eight-track cassette for fifty cents. Boney M were not that popular any more.

I secured an interview with the Montreal Engineering Corporation, or MONENCO as they were known. My rate of CAD$18 in 1979 had long been surpassed and I was now hearing of rates up in the thirties.

Ray Holland interviewed me. Nice, short, old school kind of chap with a dark jacket and tie, white fisherman's beard and a withered hand he kept hidden in his jacket pocket. Ray offered me a position as a contract piping designer and the hourly rate was $35, just about twice the rate I was being paid eighteen months earlier!

The Keephills Power Plant located west of Edmonton and owned by Calgary Power had awarded a multi-million dollar detailed design contract to MONENCO. A sizeable team of pipers had been consolidated to execute the three years of engineering work.

There was little doubt I was going to retire before I was thirty.

On the surface things couldn't be better, except they were just about to get *much* better.

In the northwest of the ever-expanding Calgary was another new community breaking ground called *Ranchlands*. A new detached, four-level split house had been built on Ranch Glen Drive and I made a move towards buying the property. There were so many properties being built and all developers were desperate for your money.

After normal negotiations, the purchase price was set at $120,000. I had not acquired much of a credit rating since arriving in Calgary so was cautious in trying to borrow funds. I had saved up $15,000 as a down payment but needed the $105,000 balance to tie up the deal. After a few telephone calls and meetings with potential lenders it was evident I would be able to borrow the funds to get me into the house.

$88,000 came from one mortgage lender but with interest rates around the country, extraordinarily high. I secured the loan at a whopping interest rate of 21%!

The $12,000 top up mortgage from a separate lender was secured at… 25%!

The remaining five grand could not be found from a lender and I thought the deal was going to get away from me. However, the builder was an independent entity and to save the purchase he stepped forward with the extra $5,000 that I agreed to pay back over twelve months at $550 a month. So, we were sorted. The mortgage payments were $1,729 a month and with the builder's loan it all added up to a whopping $2,279!

At the ripe old age of twenty-three years old I was right in the financial deep end with a brand new house in a booming city. I had a great, long term position with a handsome hourly rate that would bring in more than six grand a month. No trouble, whatsoever keeping up the payments.

*What could possibly go wrong?*

The flooring of the new home was laid with a beautiful pale green, deep pile carpet emitting a wonderful smell. I had bought living room furniture, a television, dining suite and a new, state of the art, electrically heated waterbed.

Waterbeds were all the rage in the 1980s and there was a waterbed store on every street corner. Forty Winks Waterbeds, Waterbed Warehouse and Sleepy Head Waterbeds to name a few.

On the day of taking possession of the new home, it was critical to fill the bed with warm water. Cold water would be okay but it would need seventy-two hours to heat the water. Conventional spring filled mattresses warm a person up in seconds after hopping under the sheets, but unheated waterbeds would be inherently dangerous to sleep in during the night as the immense volume of cold water depleted the body heat from the individual. Hypothermia would set in, undetected, while the poor, inebriated fella snored away to his inevitable demise.

It was November and Calgary's freezing cold weather had arrived. I had assembled the waterbed structure and unfolding the large, silicon like bladder prepared to fill the bed.

Just, one thing missing… a hose.

It was not easy to find a garden hose in November but driving around the city I managed to get my hands on one hosepipe remaining on a shelf at Kmart. Dashing home I unravelled the hose and removed all the kinks by running the hundred foot length around the base of the walls on two levels of the house.

From the source of water at the ensuite bathroom sink taps, the hose ran everywhere; through the lounge, into the kitchen, up and down the stairs before plugging the other end into the filling point of the mattress bladder.

With the kinks out, I checked each connection and turned on both hot and cold taps.

I could see the water flowing freely from the tap but after waiting a few seconds for the hundred feet of hose to be filled before moving over to the bed, strange, but I could see no water coming through the other end. Re-checking the connections I decided to take a look at the rest of the hosepipe and thought there might still be a kink in the hose.

As I looked at the lounge my heart missed two full beats. The hundred feet of kink-free hosing was distributing tall, fountains of water directly onto freshly painted walls and a brand new carpet. I sprinted back to the bathroom and, breathing intermittently, immediately shut off the water supply.

*FFS, I had purchased a sprinkler hose!*

If I had taken the time to read the packaging on the hosepipe in Kmart, I would have seen this. There were small, hidden nicks every two feet along the entire length and I was gutted by not simply paying enough attention.

I slept on the couch.


Eight hours' drive north but still in the province of Alberta, surrounding an insignificant town of Fort McMurray, lies an area the size of Scotland that has its own secrets.

Buried in the surface of a vast, uninhabited landscape is a conglomeration of low grasses, water, sand, mud, clay, rocks and more importantly… an oil-based fossil fuel called *bitumen.* A family of native Indians first discovered these bitumen deposits almost three hundred years ago, when taking the kids out for a picnic. These folk would use this sludge like substance as fuel for fires, and to patch up holes in the canoes before heating it and providing a more permanent binding on their simple, wooden vessels.

Just about the same time I had learned to ride a bicycle, a company known as Great Canadian Oil Sands (GCOS) were investing serious wonga on a leased area of land near Fort McMurray. Struggling to find the funding GCOS needed to complete the project, the Sun Oil Corporation stepped in and gave them a leg up. So, it was that in 1967, the Suncor Plant went into operation after total installed costs of a quarter of a billion dollars, more than twice the original estimate, were spent.

For many reasons, large, global projects always come in much, much higher than estimated. Yet projects have legions of estimators throughout the entire development. So, what on earth are these estimators doing right?

And, even more amusing is, what might an estimator's resume look like when all the listed projects are known to come in way over the top?

*"I see here you worked on the Channel Tunnel, Mr Gobbit."*

"Indeed."

*"Very good. And are you aware that the project came in nearly four times the original estimate, sir, and seventeen years late?"*

"Yes."

*"Of course. And may I ask then, Mr Gobbit, why we should hire you to estimate the cost and schedule for this new project called 'The Parting of The Red Sea'?"*

With no deep mining, or expensive, conventional vertical drilling requirements to extract the bitumen from its earthy enclosures, the land is excavated by operating large, often monstrous, items of mobile mechanical equipment called draglines and bucket wheels.

The excavated materials are dumped into the back of huge, six-wheel heavy haulers that carry the deposits to conveyers that consequently shift it onto bitumen extraction, production and refining facilities.

Check out the movie *North Country*. Apart from drooling over Charlize Theron, it'll give you an insight into what this life was all about up in these parts, years ago.

After separating the solids from the liquids and gases, the hydrocarbon contents are sold off to investors and the fluids delivered to a destination using rail cars. Or, the service is diluted with water and moved through a series of pipelines that meander across Canada, serving its investors and customers.

In the twenty-first century Canada has a huge national problem concerning the distribution of hazardous goods across the country. There are several arguments raised in government offices and the courts.

A hundred plus cars on freight trains, snake across the country delivering, in the most part, wheat products and hydrocarbon liquids. One train sometimes pulls more than one hundred petroleum filled railcars. This method of transportation does not move the stuff as fast as it should to supply the demand and, while relatively slow compared to overseas passenger trains that can travel in excess of 400km/h, until more recently, these railcars are deemed fairly safe.

But a horrific incident a few years back in the small town of *Lac Megantique*, Quebec, saw dozens of liquid petroleum gas (LPG) filled rail cars speed out of control before derailing onto a packed bar restaurant one

Friday night. The ensuing explosion killed 47 from the instant fireball.

Consequently, there are many folk who are not in favour of moving hazardous goods by railcar.

So, pipelines are used all around the world to expedite the movement of liquids and gases in much larger volumes and under much higher pressures than railcars. A product like bitumen is heated and diluted to give it better flow characteristics and make it less sticky, or *viscous*.

And just in case you didn't know, pipelines do not transport wheat, corn or electricity.

This method of transportation for hydrocarbons is not squeaky clean, either. Pipeline ruptures, while uncommon, do happen. If it's an above ground water line, the fault will get diagnosed and sorted while no-one gets to hear about it. However, if a thirty inch diameter section of an underground pipeline carrying high pressure natural gas springs a leak, it will be detected pretty quickly and the negative press will be all over it like a bad fitting suit.

Products flowing through a pipeline also require a boost of pressure now and again, especially when travelling hundreds of kilometres across rising and falling landscape. Compressor stations are installed in strategic locations to boost the pressure of gaseous fluids like air and natural gas. Turbines will boost the pressures of steam filled pipelines while pumps will boost the operating pressures of liquids.

Along with the United States of America, Canada has a unique argument regarding native Canadians or *First Nation* folk. These indigenous peoples are vehemently campaigning to support the last bastions of land ownership and preservation of culture afforded to them. They demand to be heard and have respect and representation in governmental politics.

Like it or not, oil and gas is here to stay for a while. The world does not have in place, yet, a market of mass produced, competitively priced vehicles powered by electricity or other forms of non-fossil fuels. California, a US state leading the way in alternative energy is selling electricity to its residents but with an enormous price tag. And, by the way, to make electricity a fossil fuel like natural gas is burned. And contrary to some daft newspaper reporting, electricity cannot be stored, either, unless in battery format.

# 1982

Alberta was now going through a huge transition as the oilsands market was saturated with a glut of oil. Canada's economy had peaked and interest rates were still at an all-time high. Inflation was more than 12% a year and unheard of.

I came into work one Monday morning to be advised that the Keephills project work had been severely reduced in scope and MONENCO would only require the resources to complete all current workfronts, but no more. Effective immediately, all contractors were given one week's notice. This was just about the worst news I could have hoped for.

There were about ten piping contractors in the office and I was one of the last in, so the first out.

I contacted Fluor Canada in the south of the city, fixed up an interview and before I'd left MONENCO on that following Friday, had secured a position as a Principal Piping Designer with Fluor Canada.

However, my $4,000 a month gross salary was much less than the $6,000 I had been enjoying. Furthermore, once the deductions had been removed from my salary, I was actually receiving about $2,500 net a month. The $2,279 loan payments alone consumed almost my entire pay before I bought a sandwich.

No more than twelve months after arriving back in Canada, things were starting to go pear shaped in Calgary on the scale of a really large pear.

In the previous two years Alberta based engineering companies had sent over to the UK, battalions of HR folk interviewing a plethora of engineering resources in the UK. The successful applicants of engineers, designers and managers were now selling up in England and moving their families to Calgary and Edmonton on work visas.

Then, from legal representation and advice within these Canadian engineering companies, extraordinary decisions were being made at a high level by corporate executives to make an attempt to stop these new recruits from getting on a plane in England and avoid them entering Canada. Even with a secure permanent staff contract in place.

At the relief of the corporate executives some Britons said yes and stayed in the UK. But, for many others, it was too late and families had already sold their homes and, having already purchased air tickets from instructions issued by their new company, were just days away from travelling.

It was a desperate situation for everyone concerned. Companies trying to get out of a hole, and families in need of desperate legal support for their relocation west, across the pond.

There were also stories of company representatives who were advised by lawyers not to turn up at the airport to greet their new recruits, as it might compromise the legal standing of the firm.

An absolute shit show as Brits felt the impact both in the UK and Canada.

I sold the Chrysler, threw in three hundred and fifty eight-track cassettes with the deal and for $500 bought a pale blue, 1966 Chevrolet *Belair* in half decent condition. It really looked like shit, too. The front left, adjustable quarter light window glass had been broken and was replaced with a triangular piece of wood.

Fluor were busy but, with no new projects being signed, the only work in their Calgary offices was finishing off existing projects. This might take eighteen months at most. All levels of staffing were acutely aware of the situation.

Oil companies had made decisions not to proceed with further oilsands investment because the federal government had agreed not to supplement the growing costs with compromised, tax concessions. As a result, a game of poker was being played between the Canadian government, desperately needing the fossil fuels, and the independent oil companies, desperately seeking the revenue.

At 1.00p.m. Mountain Standard Time on a day in November 1982, the entire petrochemical industry stood close to a radio and listened to the momentous decision from Canada's government to reject all subsidies that would keep the national oilsand development, live. That same day, dozens of companies suspended or cancelled huge *mega projects* as they were collectively known. Effectively, at that moment, everyone working in the energy sector in Alberta was put on notice.

# 1983

I knew my time was coming, Fluor were already letting go hundreds of resources.

After trying to sell the house, or indeed rent it out, it was equally important that I planned the right move. As my Suncor project at Fluor wound down, I made a decision to leave Canada and head back to England. In truth, it was the only wise choice left.

For the previous three months the Alberta conservative government had supported folk in my position by supplementing mortgage payments which was something that provided a glimmer of hope. While that helped me out for a few months it was not something to plan a future on. It was time, once again, to leave Calgary for a second time and head back to England.

I sold as much stuff as I could and I tendered my resignation at Fluor. The company then tried to retain my services by setting up a twelve-month assignment in their Haarlem office in The Netherlands, but this did not materialise. They understood the situation, of course, and accepted the status quo and my desire to move back to England.

I was late on just about every monthly payment and with letters being forced upon me by my lenders the financial situation I was in was nothing short of heart breaking. While I was embarrassed at fleeing a terrible financial dilemma, the survival instinct kicked in and I desperately wanted to get the heck out of Calgary.

I knew there was work back in the UK. The North Sea program was in a very buoyant state with new, grass root projects being assigned and executed in London, while brown field revamp projects were being given the green light up in Aberdeen. The prospects looked positive.

As if things couldn't get much worse during this period, there was another awkward situation bubbling over. Since moving to Calgary and providing continuous, positive feedback on the Calgary *boomtown* scene, there was sufficient interest from my mum, dad and two younger sisters to emigrate to Canada. As a Canadian citizen it was possible for me to sponsor them all as my immediate family and I had initiated the paperwork. The unusual component of all this was the fact that my mum and dad had separated a couple of years before. The family sponsorship project was simply no longer tenable.

While they were awaiting news from the Canadian government and the status of their application, I broke the devastating news to them all.

I told Dad, first. He was more than understanding and already knew the score from conversations we'd had and from his piping workmates who also were up to speed with the rise and fall of work in Alberta, so he had been expecting the call.

But at hearing the news, my mum and sisters were upset and would have to make alternative plans for their future. Unfortunately, my mum, now living in Colchester, Essex, had unwittingly and prematurely found a buyer for her house and a date had been set for the completion of the sale. She had made a decision to buy a bar in Majorca! *FFS, Mum.*

Meanwhile, I had just about sold anything and everything in the Ranchlands house and moved in with a friend for ten days.

Before flying out of Calgary, I had sold the Chevy with the wooden window and now needed a run around for a few days. I rented a car from a place called *Rent-a-Wreck* with an office on the Crowchild Trail. This innovative car rental company offered folk an opportunity to rent second hand vehicles at a fraction of the cost of a new car that could be rented in the Avis or Hertz type markets.

Terry, a Liverpudlian, was the manager and we discussed the state of the energy crisis in the city along with my reasons for leaving Calgary. I had told Terry that I couldn't sell or even rent my house and at the coming weekend was returning to London. Terry then told me he was actually looking for a place to live and could he take a look.

With all the furore from the previous weeks I was exhausted, but could see some light on the financial horizon. Terry was a charming bloke and had captured my interests.

I showed him the house.

He fell in love with it and wanted to rent it straight away. I told him I had tried asking for $1,200 a month but had no luck due to the declining rental rates over the months and residents leaving the city. Over a coffee, giving the entire idea some sustenance and with no written contract, I agreed to proceed with the idea and we settled on a rent of $750 a month.

I wanted some sort of promise and honesty to what we were agreeing to, so Terry gave me about $200 in cash and five, post-dated cheques each for $750 and we shook hands.

He asked for the keys to the house and with a pause and high level of scepticism, I gave them to him. It was Thursday and my flight out of Canada was Saturday afternoon.

The first cheque was payable the following day, a Friday. After half an hour with the bank teller, she confirmed my worst fears. Indeed, the cheque had bounced with insufficient funds in the account. I was sad, embarrassed and beside myself with fury.

I called Terry from a public call box at a bowling alley. He was apologetic and told me he was on his way down to see me with the $750 in cash. I waited. He never showed. I called him a couple of hours later; *"Sorry, Mitch,"* he apologised, *"I got caught with customers but will be there shortly."*

I waited, but nothing. I called several more times, but no answer. It was late, Friday afternoon and I was flying out less than twenty-four hours later.

By now, I realised I had been set up and made to look like a fool. I called again and Terry actually picked up. I gave him crap over the phone and his words were, *"Hey, Mitch, don't give me that shit! I've given you cash and what do you care anyway? You're moving back to England."*

Stunned, I sat alone in the back corner of a coffee shop balling my eyes out. How could I be such an idiot?

Taking a deep breath I recovered my composure. I flagged down a taxi and headed to the rental office. It was closed, of course. I then redirected the cabbie to the nearest hardware store where I bought two new sets of door keys and a couple of screwdrivers. He then took me to my house in Ranchlands. Slipping him a few extra notes than he was expecting, I asked him to park fifty metres up the road but wait for me.

What my new found friend, Terry, had overlooked was that I still had my own set of keys to the house.

I opened up the front door and stepped inside. Terry had already started to move in. There in the middle of the lounge was just about everything he owned. Rugs, furniture, clothes, stereo system, ski gear, golf clubs, tables, chairs, kitchenware, boxes, vinyl LPs, a mattress and linen. He must've spent that entire Thursday night shuttling stuff back and forth.

Moving at a fast pace and starting with the rugs I quickly moved everything from inside the house, to the front garden which was covered in two feet of snow. With the rugs down first I piled up his belongings on the sofa, armchairs and tables. I wondered what neighbours might be thinking if they were looking out of the windows. It was Friday afternoon with most folk at work.

It was about minus ten degrees outside but I was sweating buckets and no more than one and a half hours later the garden was full of Terry's belongings.

I then turned my attention to the locks and switched out the front and back doors. I legged it back up the road to the taxi driver who probably had lots of questions but after giving him a bit more dosh, he chose not to ask.

From a call box on the way back to my friend's house I made one last call to *Rent-a-Wreck*. The phone rang and Terry picked up.

*"Good afternoon, this is Rent-a-Wreck, how can I help?"*

*"Hello, Terry,"* I said. *"It's Mitch. Are you sure you don't want to reconsider our arrangement?"*

*"No, Mitch,"* he retorted. *"I'm waiting for a customer so please fuck off and good luck in England."*

I thought about putting the phone down, but stayed on the line.

*"Okay, Terry. Though, I think you ought to know that right now your entire belongings you spent all night moving into my home, are all sitting in deep snow out in the front garden."*

After what seemed like a full minute's pause in the conversation, Terry replied. *"Listen, Mitch, let's talk about this. I'll get you the money."*

*"I don't think so,"* I calmly replied.

*"Fuck off."*

As the Boeing 747 lifted me into the frigid, Alberta sky, I had a tear in my eye and vowed never to return to Calgary.

Back living with my dad for a while, it was only a couple of weeks before I was taken back on at Worley Engineering to work on an offshore British Gas platform project called *Rough*. The project offices were in Tottenham, north London. It had been four years since leaving Worley to head out to Calgary for the first time. I was now back at the company on a premium rate and was looking forward to the fresh opportunity after the more challenging, frustrating last few months.

I soon purchased a first floor, two bedroom maisonette in Woodford Green and furnished the unit with the essentials that did not include a waterbed.

The project was in a sorry state and British Gas were desperate to finish the engineering phase having assembled a large construction team in Scottish and French fabrication yards. Late changes hindered progress and without drawings to put all the pieces of the jigsaw together there was a huge expensive delay to completing the installation of piping materials.

The project was great to be part of with numerous characters in the piping team.

One guy used to travel from and to Hastings each day spending a total of five hours commuting. There was a bakery near his local station and before climbing onto the early morning non-stopper he would hand over his list and pick up warm, fresh Chelsea buns, jam doughnuts and Eccles cakes and we welcomed him with open arms when he walked into work each day.

Piping office culture was, once again, not without its stories.

One evening after working overtime, Ken Harefield hopped into his yellow Mini and headed back home to Brentwood, Essex. At a set of traffic lights he pulled ahead of a cyclist, Jack who was also employed on the project as an Instrumentation Designer. Jack immediately takes offence to this swift manoeuvre and screams abuse at Ken who shouts it back. This barrage of abuse goes on for half a minute before the cyclist smashes his pump onto the roof of Ken's car.

The following morning, Ken approached the cyclist back in the office and asked him to cough up the dosh to fix the dent in his car roof. Jack declined.

A couple of weeks later and one evening around six o'clock when folk are starting to drift home, Ken calls a few of us over to the second floor window overlooking the bike racks. Jack appears in his yellow and green cycling wear, jumps on his bike and starts pedalling. But he doesn't get too far. The tires on both wheels had been shredded beyond repair with pieces of rubber dropping off all over the place.

As the rider dismounted and glanced around for clues we all pulled back from the windows and grinned. Not very nice, but I guess you don't mess with Ken and his Mini.

Everyone on the project was working Saturdays and Sundays and getting paid a handsome sum each week. As the Easter long weekend approached, we were all burned out and looking forward to the break with the families as no overtime was scheduled. The client was worried about this slowdown and so had communicated an idea to the Worley project management; British Gas wanted to know what it would take to have the piping group come in over the Easter long weekend in an effort to finish the project?

We were all given wind of this and, before any of us were hauled into a room, began to discuss it between ourselves in pockets of amusement around the drawing boards. The question put to each of us would be this: What do you want to be paid if asked to work all four days of this upcoming Easter weekend; this meant Good Friday, Easter Saturday, Easter Sunday and Easter Monday… eight hours each day? There was no choice on the number of days.

No rest for the wicked.

It was clear to us all that there was a small fortune to be had and we all knew it, especially with the project winding down. Current premium rate overtime meant that the pipers were getting time and a third for all overtime hours on a normal Monday to Friday. Time and a half for Saturdays and Double time for Sundays and public holidays. The invoice for this long weekend would be a monster.

British Gas would be asking each one of us independently what it would take, gather up all the responses, and make one common, collective decision.

Pockets of conversations were evident around the drawing office as we all started arguing amongst ourselves. Some folk believed we should ask for double time for three of the days, but triple time for Easter Sunday! Others thought that a more modest time and a half for each day was fair because we were getting to work all four days, anyway.

A few didn't want to work at all supporting the fact that we had all worked plenty of overtime over the last twelve months and were looking forward to a break and time off with the family.

One by one we were each brought into a meeting room with one representative from the client present and the piping lead supervisor. I had plumped for the normal pay structure: Double time for Friday (a statutory holiday), time and a half for Saturday, double time for Sunday and time and a half for the Monday (even though it was a holiday).

By late afternoon we had all tabled our requests and British Gas went away to make a decision.

The following morning, the decision had been made. The British Gas client management were shocked at the demands originating from some of the pipers and so, decided to terminate the engineering in the London offices and move the entire remaining piping work to an office in Scotland, close to a fabricator!

As such, every contractor in the London office was given one week's notice to leave the project the day before Good Friday. We were to get to spend Easter with the family, after all! This was a lesson to us all how greed can steer folk in the wrong direction. Looking back on all this, the project was driven by weak Worley management. They should have really steered the piping group towards the correct decision and discussed it with British Gas before the client made that decision that would put fifty pipers out on the street.

Looking for alternative work, the industry was struggling a bit and I decided to get out of the Piping game. This was not a simple decision on my behalf either, but work was just not available.

I looked at all the newspapers. I never realised that the UK had no less than twelve daily newspapers! I checked the ads and listened to the radio. I went to the library and sat there reading newspapers for hours on end. Nearly everything took me back to one common denominator: Sales.

In truth, I do not have much of a problem with selling anything. If I was going to leave the petrochemical engineering sector after just nine years, it was evident to me I was going to have to sell insurance and pension funds to the general public.

Providence Capitol Life Assurance Limited interviewed me and accepted my application as a *financial adviser*. They put me through a training program where homework consumed my days, nights and weekends. After several weeks learning the ropes of the industry I had been saturated with legislation on finances, regulatory guidelines and policy descriptions. I passed one examination after the next and enjoying the change of craft, immensely, began to throw everything I had into my new found occupation.

Mr Shlomo Fellus was my area supervisor and we both hit it off well. A tall Jewish chap with an immaculate sense of dress ethos, he drove to the office in a new red Ferrari 308 and parked it well away from my twenty-year-old Ford Escort.

Half expecting to start cold calling, Shlomo handed me a tall pile of pink cards, each about eight inches square. On each pink card was typed the information pertaining to all Providence Capitol's existing clients. Names, addresses, ages, family details and existing policies. Schlomo asked me to look at the pack, make the calls and provide a service to each client by offering the latest information available and how these customers might benefit from updating their investments. I started calling the folk in pink.

In any telephone calls the secret was not to divulge too much information over the telephone but to arrange a meeting at a mutually convenient time.

At first, it was not easy to make the call. I was nervous and the other salesmen were always close by and ear wigging on every word. I soon found a patter and started to enjoy my new found environment, establishing a level of confidence with every call.

I would suit up with a tie and get out and about driving all over London, while listening to the Electric Light Orchestra on cassette tapes.

Some folk would buy a policy, many would not. Prior to our cell phone era, on occasion, I would drive more than one hour to a house after confirming the appointment from the office by landline telephone, only to find the client out or ignoring the knock on the front door. The hits were plentiful.

I discovered Indian nationals *love* life insurance. I probably did more business with Sikh and Hindu folk than anyone else and although they took care of their children with policies I do not recall one Indian buying insurance for his wife. It always had to be a blood relative. Sitting in the lounge discussing the policies, I would be offered a cup of tea and got to prefer a cup of Darjeeling or Assam tea, to a PG Tips.

One day I picked up a pink card and noted that the client was a chauffeur by the name of Archibald Graham McDonald. I called him up, had a nice, warm opening conversation and discovered that Mr McDonald was interested in increasing insurance coverage for his only child, Chris who was twelve years old.

I arranged to see him at his home in Ealing, west London. It took me two and a half hours to get there before parking up in a dodgy housing estate and ringing the doorbell. There was no answer. After a couple more rings

91

and knocks I was starting to get pissed off. A young lad called Chris answered the door and we introduced ourselves. We skipped up the stairs and walked into the living room.

The scene that greeted me I had not been trained to expect.

The television was on and some cartoon was playing out. On one chair was a man, who introduced himself to me as Archie, Chris' Father. On the couch was Archie's wife Joan, flat out and snoring. On the carpet close to her head were about seven, large half litre empty cans of Carlsberg Special Brew.

One of the first things I was taught in any sales process is to first ask that all diversions are eliminated before talking business. This included polite requests that any television and radio be switched off.

This request was ignored, so I struggled on. Chris sat on the carpet in front of the telly and, at my request, was happy to turn the volume down. I got stuck into the proceedings by offering Archie a good, ten-year program that would provide him with an investment plan for a further £100 a month, to supplement the £100 plan he presently had. The pay out at retirement could be as much as thirty thousand pounds. Twenty minutes went by and Archie was convinced in moving forward with the plan. I pulled out the application forms, filling out relevant carbon-copied sheets on my lap. As I was about to complete the paperwork and get Archie to sign on the dotted line and hand over a void cheque, his wife woke up and in her own words, said; *"Archibald, who the fuck is that?"*

*"Will ye shut the fuck up, woman,"* he said. *"Young Mutch is with Providence Cupitol and he's here ta help increase our investment in young Chris' future."*

His wife started to sit up straight and opened up another can, gulping down half the contents.

*"I told you…"* Joan said to her husband, *"I want to cancel all insurance for that kid."*

*"Shut up, woman, it's been sorted."*

With that, Joan hauled herself from the couch, walked towards me and as I cowered back into the depths of the armchair she reached down, picked up the application form and tore it into shreds right in front of me, dropping the bits of paper onto the floor, before crashing back onto the couch.

Things were not really going as I had hoped and while all this was going on, young Chris didn't do much but continued watching the cartoons.

He also cranked up the volume. Poor kid.

Archie was incredibly polite and apologised for his tyrant queen's handling of the situation. I had started packing up. I don't give up that easily but on this particular occasion thought it best that I get the hell out of there as fast as I could.

I shook hands with Archie and said goodbye to Chris, who turned his head and smiled. The wife had moved to the bathroom, a place where she was likely to be for a while.

Then Archie pulled a five pound note from his wallet and handed it to me as a sort of compensation for the petrol. I thanked him for the offer but quickly rejected the fiver. He stuffed it into my jacket pocket and I gave it back to him. He then insisted I take it and I insisted I wouldn't.

He then pulled out a cigarette lighter from his pocket and right in front of me, held up the note and lit the corner. It smouldered in his hand and fell onto the linoleum. I quickly hopped around in a state of mild panic trying to put out the flame. I picked up the half burned note and scurried back down the stairs, out the front door and over to the car.

Things could only get better.


One colleague, George, at Providence Capitol had been to see a potential client and when George returned to the office he was not a happy camper. He had spent two hours with a chap who was clearly undecided before he told George he wasn't ready to take the plunge and showed George to the door.

The following morning the chap called the office around noon and asked George if he was still okay at selling him the £75 a month policy. George thought about this and asked the client to hold on for a minute. George calmly sat there for six or seven minutes with the phone laying on his desk before picking it up and joining the conversation where they had left off.

George informed his client that the company had just that morning sold the last £75 policy, but after checking with the finance department could confirm that there were several £100 policies left. Would he be interested in grabbing one of these? The chap signed up that afternoon and George had gotten away with murder.


With the insurance stuff rolling along it also occurred to me to get into some sort of catering business, too. The sales stuff was fine but I was finding that the evenings were the time to do the business, not during the day. Enjoying the subject of food stuff and cooking, I thought about the sandwich sector. Maybe there was a market to be tapped?

I drove around Ilford looking for office blocks. After calling in on one or two I found the perfect building near Gants Hill. A number of companies had their administration offices in the block but there was no sign of any cafeteria facilities. The old dear at the reception confirmed there were none in the building. After chatting with representatives from the companies it was clear there was a gap in the sandwich service and, with no kitchen in the office tower, employees were having to bring in their own lunches with few options of anywhere local to buy anything.

I signed up to deliver hand prepared rolls and sarnies, coke and juice to the workforce covering six floors. Each company manager had promised to advise their staff I would be there on Monday.

I planned the lunches, checked out local pricing, and bought large portions of cheeses, hams, butter, tomatoes, cucumber and pickles. The previous day I had popped into an old fashioned hardware store near Stratford and found a three level, stainless steel trolley. It was full of nuts and bolts and the owner of the store emptied the stuff out and took a twenty for the trolley.

To save me lugging it backwards and forwards I was also given permission to lock up the trolley in a storage room at the tower.

The alarm clock went off at four a.m. that Monday and I stepped into action and headed out in the car to a bakery where one hundred and fifty warm, mixed rolls were waiting for collection. Back home on the dining room table I sorted each filling and filled each roll with ham and tomato, cheese and cucumber, ham and pickle, cheese and ham. It took me a while to get the lunches ready and by the time eleven a.m. arrived I had populated three large trays with rolls and cans of drink.

Laying the trays carefully down above each other on the back seat of the Escort I had only a ten minute drive to the building. I pulled away from the kerb and headed towards the end of the street. About to pull out onto the Eastern Avenue, a cyclist came out of nowhere and I jammed on the brakes to avoid a collision.

Three trays of freshly prepared rolls that took hours to prepare, tumbled off the back seat and landed on a very dirty floor of the car. I almost threw up.

Working frantically to dust off each roll and remove bits of fluff, debris and dust it took me an hour before reconfiguring the trays and arriving at the building.

As I rolled my trolley out onto the first floor shouting *ROOOLLLLLS*, two men and a woman approached me as if I had stepped from the elevator wielding an AK47.

Unfortunately, notice of my arrival had not been transmitted to the workforce and would you believe it, everyone had brought their own lunch with them to work!

That first day I sold twenty-five rolls and took a hundred and twenty-five home with me, stuffing them all in the freezer.

The following day was a bit better; I prepared just a hundred and twenty-five and sold forty. Sales gradually improved and after a few weeks the numbers were proving to be much better and up around two hundred.


I continued running the catering business while selling insurance policies for close to a year. It helped pay a lot of bills. I was also fortunate enough to set up insurance policies for several friends and relatives. *They all got plenty of rolls, too.*

The catering and insurance projects were paying a good chunk of the bills, but not all of them. I had not kept in touch with the Piping game for several months and one Monday morning I received a call from an agent asking me if I was interested in a position up in Dundee, Scotland.

I had invested a heck of a lot of time, funds and effort into the two business ventures so was caught between a rock and a hard place.

But piping jobs do pay well when things are on the up and I soon found myself accepting the position with a shipyard company called Kestrel Marine.

Kestrel had been commissioned to build a couple of heavy, offshore modules for Kellogg Brown & Root and I was to get involved in providing drawing support in the trailer offices. I chose to work up in Scotland and travel back down south every second weekend.

After a seven hour train journey and local public transport, I found a room in a B&B overlooking the River Tay and not too far from the jobsite. The place was run by a nice man who was also on call for the Royal National Lifeboat Association. He did prepare a stunning, healthy breakfast each morning: Eggs, bacon, square sausage, fried tomatoes, baked beans, black pudding, white pudding and a slice of bread, fried in the remaining fat. Plus, a plate of toast and marmalade and a pot of tea. I had to put my alarm on an hour earlier to get through this and was clearly destined to lose a few pounds while up here. Not.

Looking out at the vast expanse of water, hundreds of offshore production platforms are scattered around the North Sea, several visible. From the UK coastline, east to continental Europe the land mass that these drilling rigs and production platforms rest on is owned by seven European nations; Belgium, which lease the least amount of real estate, then France, Germany, Denmark, The Netherlands, Norway and the nation that owns the largest area of real estate, the United Kingdom.

The land beneath these waters is segregated into areas called 'quadrants' that will form the basis for issuing licences for exploration. Each quadrant is not measured by its metric or imperial dimensional values, but are sized at 1° of latitude by 1° of longitude. Not to belittle your knowledge regarding how the earth's surface is segregated, but here are a few snippets of information.

A longitude is a vertical line that runs from one pole to the other. There are three hundred and sixty lines of true longitude, each line spaced one degree apart its origin at a pole and destination at the other pole. As one line runs from one pole to the other, the distance to its adjacent line of longitude increases as they move away from a pole till they cross the equator where they remain the furthest distance apart. If you've ever had a Terry's chocolate orange, you'll know what I mean, with the thickest part of the segment in the middle. Our planet Earth has three hundred and sixty segments to go around.

A line of latitude has entirely different values from a line of longitude. A latitude is a true, horizontal line encircling the earth's surface but always equidistant from its adjacent line of latitude, 1° off. Breaking down a degree, there are also sixty minutes in each degree and sixty seconds in a minute.

So, up in the northern hemisphere where the North Sea is positioned, each licensing quadrant will appear in plan, geometrically like a rectangle with the northern horizontal line slightly shorter than the lower horizontal line of the rectangle, due to its position in the northern hemisphere.

Each quadrant is broken into thirty 'blocks'; Six blocks, ten minutes apart in the horizontal and five blocks in the vertical, twelve minutes apart. Each of the thirty blocks is assigned a tracking number that might be for example, 18/27. This equates to Quadrant 18, Block 27. A block may also be broken out into an 'a', 'b', 'c' etc. when more than one drilling platform might be required to extract the hydrocarbons. Therefore, an offshore development that might not have yet been assigned a name like 'Cormorant', 'Rough' or 'Piper' would be assigned a number like 18/27C.

The final position of any production platform in the North Sea is dependent on what quadrant and block the oil or gas has been discovered. Thousands of feet below the seabed are large pockets of hydrocarbons called *reservoirs*. The positions of these reservoirs are found by investing incredibly large sums of money to pay ocean going vessels to drift from one end of the leased blocks to the other, fully geared up with a crew and plethora of rollneck-wearing geophysicists drinking coffee, eating cod and studying the monitors.

Offshore facilities have several purposes. Each free standing structure may be there to provide drilling facilities, production facilities, gas compression facilities, or accommodation and helicopter facilities. Two or more of these structures may be linked by a steel bridge allowing pedestrian access, piping utilities and electrical cables.

Once a production platform is installed and operating and the reservoir fluid has been brought to the surface, the service may go through some stringent treatment programs before being delivered via one or a series of pipelines that sit on the sea bed and run for hundreds of kilometres, connecting other offshore production facilities, or back to a dedicated terminal facility back on the mainland. Examples of a few of these huge terminals on the UK's east coast are *Bacton* (Norfolk), *Theddlethorpe* (Lincolnshire) and *St Fergus* (Aberdeenshire).

Once the oil company executives that commission the search for oil are confident that the hydrocarbons established in the reservoir are of sufficient *quantity and quality* and know precisely where the treasure is, the positive decision is made to take the project to the next level.

A jack up drilling rig is a sea going, barge type vessel that can be mobilised to any part of the globe's oceans and retained in that area to drill wells down into a specified reservoir containing the riches. The main unit engages a crew consisting of pilots and engineers to manage, control and maintain the rig.

The term 'jack up' refers to the vessel's three, tall steel legs, spaced at equal intervals around the rig that tower above the vessel while it is in transit. Once directly over the precise position intended for the test wells to be drilled down into the reservoir, the drilling rig must be secured to the seabed.

The body of the rig remains above the surface of the sea but its legs are 'jacked' down until each leg has been moved to a position where most of the legs are below the water and touching the seabed. The jacking process continues until the steel legs are tethered to the seabed.

Fixed into position, drilling pipes are erected and connected to the sea bed before test drilling commences. The extraordinarily high pressure fluids rising up the drill pipes will be received and handled by the mechanical items of equipment that are a constant part of the drilling rig.

A better definition of the data related to the *quality* of the hydrocarbons in the reservoir will then be apparent that will influence another executive decision on when to decommission the expensive, drilling rig. The oil company will then suspend all further exploration pending comprehensive, feasibility and conceptual studies, based on the data established from the drilling exercise. Removing the rig from its location demands a reverse approach and the legs are jacked up until well above the waters before engines are fired up on the rig and another position on the North Sea determines its next destination.

If these studies prove a business case is worthwhile pursuing, a pre-front end engineering design (PRE-FEED) study will be planned, followed by a FEED, followed by an engineering, procurement and construction phase (EPC) to design the offshore production platform(s).

There are many different types of structures that support offshore production platforms. These range from heavy, dense concrete gravity base structures (GBS) and Condeeps, to steel jackets and tension leg platforms (TLP).

A TLP essentially satisfies two requirements; drilling and production facilities. The platform's operating facilities, positioned close to sea level, is connected to the seabed by twelve pipes, three at each corner of the platform and all around nine to twelve inches in diameter with three inch thick stainless steel walls. The advantage of a TLP is that it can be untethered and the topside drilling and production facilities relocated to other positions of the ocean where other reservoirs may need to be tapped.

But it does sway from side to side in inclement weather, often putting off an offshore worker where seasickness might be an issue.

The most common type of offshore production platforms sit on steel structures known as *jackets*. The jacket is fixed to the seabed and extends above the surface waters high enough to provide support for the topside's production facility.

A steel jacket would be prefabricated at a purpose built yard close to tidal waters, then floated out on large, ballast and air filled pontoons to the site where the jacket is de-ballasted, orientated correctly and lowered into its position on the sea floor.

The facilities that sit on top of the jacket topsides are normally part of a multi-modular construction. There may be as many as ten or twelve, two thousand to five thousand tonne modules hooked together on any offshore production platform. These modules consist of a structural steel framework in which many facilities are included. Oil and gas related mechanical equipment, piping, pipe supports, instrumentation, electrical equipment, cranes, compressors, generators, buildings, drilling derricks, flare and blowdown facilities and means for emergency escape.

Escaping an offshore platform is no simple exercise and I have been involved in more than one hairy incident. Depending on the type and urgency of any emergency there are several opportunities by which to remove one's self from the offshore installation.

The obvious first choice is to climb aboard a helicopter. But helicopters aren't often just idling away on a helideck, waiting for an emergency situation to arise. If the emergency is not urgent, the onshore rescue facilities may dispatch one or more out to the platform and begin a lengthy procedure to remove all personnel. Such examples of this type of emergency could be the weather forecast and a particularly nasty storm approaching. Or, the platform operating facilities have been shut down due to an operational issue, a fire or an unforeseen, extended platform shutdown.

The next less urgent option for alighting an offshore platform is to transfer oil workers to a local shipping or 'standby' vessel nearby which can accommodate extra resources. This has its risks, too, as the mobility of the vessel bobbing up and down in a high sea state creates a dangerous environment when a few dozen folk are trying to be moved from the fixed and immobile platform by crane and basket. Especially in a hurry.

All sea bound structures like boats or platforms, whether mobile or fixed, accommodate lifeboats. Global marine safety regulations demand that the total seating of all lifeboats add up to one and a half times the maximum number of workers expected on the structure at any one time. There are several types of lifeboat. The most common type is the lifeboat that is retained in its horizontal position by supporting structures and when filled with workers abandoning the facility, lowered onto the surface of the waters. The diesel engine would be started and off it goes.

The risks involved in this type of escape are such that, once the lifeboat touches the water and is disconnected from its moorings, strong winds may try to shift the direction of the lifeboat back towards the supporting structure and any hazard making it almost impossible for the designated pilot to correctly manoeuvre out into less hazardous waters.

To assist the correct deployment of this type of lifeboat, the platform may be outfitted with apparatus called a preferred orientation and displacement system (PRODS). One for each lifeboat, these PRODS consist of steel, circular cross sectional long bars fixed to the platform topsides. One end is fixed permanently to the topside structure while the sea bound end is connected to the lifeboat with steel cables. This system stops the lifeboat drifting back towards the platform structure after it's on the water. Once the engine kicks in and the lifeboat moves away from the source of hazard the cables are automatically stretched and quickly disconnected allowing the lifeboat to get away.

Lifeboat stations are normally located on two sides of an offshore production platform. The primary station that may have as many as ten lifeboats is always located on the side of the platform where the least amount of hazards reside including accommodation and sleeping quarters. Another, smaller, secondary lifeboat station that may have two or three craft would be positioned the opposite side of the platform from the primary lifeboat station. This alternate location may be beneath the steel structure of the flare boom and would only be used if the primary lifeboat station cannot be used due to its redundancy caused from the position of an accident on the platform.

Another type of lifeboat is what is known as a free fall system. This is indeed a frightening scenario. Each lifeboat is positioned on the topsides structure but instead of being in a horizontal configuration the lifeboat sits on the back end of a launching chute orientated at around forty-five degrees.

This will allow the lifeboat to point bow first, down towards the sea. Rather like a rollercoaster ride at Disney World but with fewer costs involved, the folk in the lifeboat are fixed firmly into their seat by a belt and harness that will keep the individual's body *and head* fixed tight. A person will not be allowed to move. The force on one of these things hitting the water is quite substantial. The advantage of a free fall lifeboat is that, when it is launched into the ocean and is naturally submerged, its rise to the surface will continue to be in the direction away from the platform, even before the diesel engine has kicked in.

Now, if you ever find yourself out in the middle of the ocean on a burning platform and you need to get off please make sure you *don't* have to choose one of the other options available.

There are a few and stepping forward into any one of them will risk your life in other ways.

Take a life raft, for example. You're on a burning deck two hundred feet above a stormy ocean and next to you is a plastic cylindrical box on a supporting stand. Tipping it off its fixture, the unit drops into the ocean and on the way down, the life raft is deployed and lands in the dark waters. You then have to leap off the deck you are standing on and into the waters below.

So, with your arse on fire and wearing a buoyancy control device (BCD) or life jacket, you jump two hundred feet blindly into the sea with other folk who plan on taking up a position in the raft alongside you. If you haven't died from a heart attack on the way down, you gather speed and at close to one hundred and eighty kilometres an hour, you enter the water like a bullet. The impact will likely kill you, too. Especially if you land awkwardly, like on your back or head, or on someone else.

If, by now, you've bobbed to the surface and established that you are not immersed amongst burning fuels on the surface waters you look around in the dark for the life raft. Good luck with this, because on its way down the winds may have caught it and your life raft is now a full kilometre closer to Aberdeen.

You scramble around for a couple of minutes and remember the training; especially one of the notes advising you that North Sea water temperatures fluctuate between one and three degrees Celsius all year round and once immersed without wearing a proper survival suit, you have about five minutes before hypothermia sets in.

Then you spot the life raft! It's over there, close to some steel shrapnel but the bloody thing is upside down. More scrambling to find the cords, more time. Your hands are numb with the cold and you hear screaming and shouting around you. Tracking the cords, you sling them across the width of the life raft and move around its circumference to grab the ends. Then, with a similar action of walking up a vertical wall while gripping the cords, you try hard to bring your feet up and onto the edge of the life raft and start your climb, one hand crossing the other hand until your body weight on one end acts as a lever and the far edge of the life raft starts to rise up above the water. You keep climbing until the life raft has flipped over onto its correct side.

But, by now, you are completely knackered. Trying to heave yourself the couple of feet up and over into the relative safety of the life raft demands extraordinary strength and stamina.

Get through all this and you are a champion of survival technique.

But, incredible as it is, a life raft is not the harshest means of evacuation from an offshore platform. There is a thing called a Seascape.

This is where you put on a survival suit and leap into a tight, vertical chute that drops two hundred feet before shallowing out to an angled approach that will take you down and into the ocean. Rather like a slide in a water park but without the laughter. These forms of evacuation are common last resort escape thoughts on arctic installations where pack ice around the structure will inhibit the use of lifeboats or life rafts.

Accommodation facilities on a platform include elevators, sleeping quarters, dining rooms, washrooms and entertainment areas like cinemas, TV and pool rooms. Depending on the catering contractor, some offshore platforms have the finest dining facilities, too. Alcohol is never permitted on an offshore platform, with one exception I can recall when the Executive Chef acquired permission to put sherry in a Christmas cake, a week before Christmas. *That slice of cake was one of the best I ever had.*

Above the accommodation module is one more, fairly significant area that is always ready for use; the helicopter landing area, or *helideck*.

Helicopters come and go all the time, bringing miserable workers out to the platforms while returning excited ones back to the beach on the next flight.

When designing helidecks a number of pertinent things are considered. First, the location of a production platform has to be confirmed due to where the actual reservoirs of fluid are established. It's no good fixing a platform jacket to the seabed five miles away from where the new-found fuels are!

The position of the helideck to the rest of the platform is critically important. Once the location of the production platform is understood, eyes turn towards orientating the platform correctly. The helideck will perch on top and astride, the accommodation or LQ. With prevailing wind directions considered, the platform is then orientated such that the chopper approaches and leaves the helideck over open seas without having to fly over the actual operating platform. In aviation, most accidents and disasters occur during take-off or landing. No-one wants a crippled helicopter dropping onto a live production platform with high pressure hydrocarbons flowing through piping and mechanical equipment. Better that the pilot ditches into the waters, however frightening that may also appear. Included in the platform orientation exercises, wave and sea current data are also examined to support safety considerations when helicopters may not be readily available and platform abandonment needs to be by lifeboat.

With the perpendicular sides of the installation considered in a north-south, east-west or in other words a sort of geographically square position above the drilled wells, the accommodation module would likely be positioned to the north side of the platform with its helideck located directly over the northeast corner.

This configuration would satisfy the centre of approach path being to the northeast, directly opposite the prevailing wind direction.

One other small tidbit of information Grandma may want to know is that the landing area on a helideck is marked with a large diameter circle and a yellow painted letter 'H' placed in the centre. The letter 'H' is orientated such that the bar of the 'H' bisects the 240° approach path established outside the boundaries of the platform and associated structures. The 'H' is four metres high, by three metres wide and 750mm thick. Another piece of useless information you now have.

The depth of the waters change dramatically between the southern and northern waters of the North Sea. In the south, close to the English Channel where gas recoveries are more prominent than oil, offshore platforms may sit in just twenty metres (sixty-five feet) of water. The farther north you go and seawater depths can reach two hundred and fifty metres (seven hundred and eighty feet).

I think that's enough techie stuff for now.

103

After my first two days at Kestrel I was on a right downer and regretted my decision to head up to Dundee. The work I was being given was absolute crap, the drawing board hadn't been used in months and was covered in dust. No-one had considered cleaning it.

I had never left a position after such a short time but this was a contract I wasn't sure I'd see out. To make matters worse, the other chaps in the office were not exactly a bundle of laughs with the Scottish/English thing clearly setting things on edge with an English bloke clearly taking a Scottish position.

All of them were whinging about this and that, including how folk working for Kellogg Brown and Root on the other side of the module yard were getting lots of overtime and the Kestrel team pipers were on a flat, forty hour week. Pretty crappy deal if there's no overtime, when someone's working away from home.

Then I heard the telephone ring. It was an office phone and I was the closest person to pick up the call. Besides, no-one was rushing forward.

*"Kestrel Piping Group,"* I said.

*"Hello, can I speak with Gerald, please,"* came the reply.

A short pause as I recognised the voice.

*"Graham, is that you?"* I asked.

*"Yes, this is Graham,"* was his reply.

*"Wow, it's Mitch!"*

We both couldn't believe it.

Graham, my old mucker from Worley, had been up in Dundee for six months working for KBR, which in this case were the client, as Kestrel were the module construction and assembly contractor. Graham and I had not communicated much since I'd moved back to England from Calgary, several months earlier.

After a brief chat I quietly explained my situation to Graham over the phone, telling him I was emotionally hanging on by a thread, almost in tears and very likely, might be on my way south tomorrow.

*Graham had an idea and asked me to wait a couple of hours…*

Early afternoon, the telephone rang in a closed office belonging to the Drawing Office Supervisor and a right wanker. My ears pricked up but couldn't hear the call. The supervisor looked out of his office window at me while speaking on the phone.

Sure enough, the DOS came out of his office and in a loud voice delivered a message in my direction.

*"Mr Jago, you've been seconded to the client."*

He informed me that my name had specifically been asked for, by a KBR engineer, and that I was immediately to be seconded to KBR for an indefinite length of time.

Holy guacamole, I couldn't believe my fortune.

Within the hour I was settling down in another office and, equally important, with more challenging work and much better company with Graham around, too.

Two large, offshore modules were being assembled at the Kestrel site and I spent time wandering out onto the modules checking erected piping systems against construction drawings. It was a good assignment and there was plenty of overtime and I often found myself out on the structures well into the evening. No need to rush back to the digs.

After several weeks on the project, something out of the ordinary happened.

There were about three hundred people working on site each day and one cafeteria to support the hungry needs of the construction workforce. The old battle axe who ran the onsite catering business and café had gone on vacation for three weeks without telling a soul and, as such, access to the kitchen facilities were locked off. She had made no friends by doing this and the KBR management was having a cadenza trying to find a solution to a problem made all the worse by workers downing tools and leaving the site each morning, lunchtime and afternoon to drive into town to grab a bite to eat. In support of union regulations, they were entitled to do this because the lunch facilities, buried in the contractual literature, had ceased to exist for three weeks.

When this happened, I was not that busy with the piping checks and Steve Granger, Graham's supervisor, had asked me if I wanted to put my catering skills to the test by running the cafeteria for the three weeks.

I jumped at the opportunity and was given the services of two secretaries to help me out, along with a budget.

I first gained unfettered access to the kitchen through a small window that had been left half open. Then the three of us got stuck into the task at hand.

Recognised favourites like pies, stews and soups were prepared plus a few new ones I took a shot at, too, including a red hot *Mulligatawny*. Not too many Punjabi construction workers up in Dundee but the soup went down a bundle.

As a result of this new focus of attention, the busy construction task force were fed each day. The entire experience was a blast before I got back to the piping stuff. We even made lunches for a couple of executive lunches. After that debacle, a more professional catering company were brought in and upon her return Old Mother Riley got the Spanish Archer *(El-Bow)*.

Back at home one weekend, I received a call from an agency saying my name had been submitted for a piping design position in Oslo, Norway. I had no idea who had put forward the recommendation but it was a bolt out of the blue.

The Norwegian oil company Statoil were developing a field called *Gulfaks* in their own nation's waters and the detailed engineering for the first of three platforms, *Gulfaks 'A'*, was getting underway up in Scandinavia.

Back in Dundee I talked to Graham and Steve who were both cool with the switch. I worked one more week with KBR and bypassed Kestrel before flying out to Oslo.

I remember the flight very well with Scandinavian Airlines for two reasons. One, the quality of flight attendants was right up there, even the women looked pretty good. Two, SAS served up warmed rolls and butter. A small but rather significant observation.

Oil and gas projects were still a bit thin on the ground in London and this particular project had my attention. The Norwegian contract was for six months on a nine days on and five days off rotation. The pipers were working nine consecutive days of twelve hours and flying back to London every second weekend. This equated to the equivalent of a constant fifty-four hour week and a decent arrangement.

There were plenty of characters on this *Gulfaks* project and many of the older geezers had worked in the country on the Staatfjord projects a few years earlier.

The restaurants and pubs of Norway's capital city had a completely different feel to the watering holes back home. First of all, Norway was not a cheap place to enjoy a beer. My very first Friday evening and a few of us ended up in a local pub. I bought a round and it damn near cost me a week's wages.

I also discovered that the Norwegians, or Noggies as they were affectionately known, were a crafty bunch. If you went to the washroom, you'd come back to discover that your pint had disappeared. The Brits got into the habit of having a beer watch rotation when duty called. Once or twice, a punch up would ensue after catching one of them trying to secrete a pint under his rollneck.

Night clubs were an experience, once you actually got in. Line-ups were common place in Oslo as club venues restricted the number of visitors. Sometimes, it would be snowing while you waited in line freezing your arse off. But, once inside, it was all worth it as places like *Josephine's* kicked off and challengers for Miss World would ask you up for a dance.

*"No thanks, I'm talking to my piping friend."*

Practical jokes continued in the piping office and now and again as usual, some crossed the line.

While Norwegians held down the project management positions, the engineering teams were mostly saturated with British expats throughout the team. The Human Resources group, however, were staffed with local women and one particular HR employee, Kjersti, was not the friendliest woman on the project. We could all tell she was xenophobic and acutely resented the Brits being out there taking Norwegian jobs.

One Geordie, Frank, had a falling out with Kjersti. She had screwed up his flight itinerary back to Teesside for one weekend and had refused to apologise, so he decided to get his own back.

Frank had gone shopping and bought a large, fat smoked, pig's head, complete with ears, nose and a mean look on its face. One morning he stuffed a granny smith into the mouth and lodged the pig's head into one of the ladies two toilet bowls, face up. Then pulled down the seat cover.

Frank had told the other pipers what he had done and we were all at our boards, waiting for Kjersti to go for a leak. Two hours must've gone by before she slipped away from her office and into the washroom. You could've heard a pin drop but a few seconds later we all leapt off the ground a few inches as this ear shattering scream filled the drawing office. Kjersti ran back to her desk in tears.

No-one ever let on who the culprit was, even though we were all questioned about the incident. Sidebar conversations on the subject went on for weeks.

One thing about working so many hours on an overseas assignment is that you don't get much opportunity to see the country you're living in. Nine days on the trot at the office then straight to the airport. The only places I got to see were establishments open at night like pubs, clubs and eighty or ninety restaurants. One Sunday I did, however, take myself on a train up country to an international Olympic ski resort for the day called, *Holmenkollen*. Lugging my camera bag and lenses up the hundred and twenty metre high ski jump the views across the fjord were spectacular. Looking directly down the jump, I recall thinking that the landing area appeared like a tiny target that could easily be missed by someone like Eddie the Eagle with the poor bloke landing in row Q of the expensive seating area.

Flights home every second week would be great as guys looked forward to being back home and getting away from open sandwiches and lumpy yogurt. Lots of pipers on the aircraft and after a couple of hours at the airport's bar, the atmosphere on the plane was highly charged, but in the nicest possible way.

I remember sitting next to Ron Grazer on one flight back to London. As the aircraft accelerated down the runway and the nose tipped up towards the setting sun, Ron reached up and hit the flight attendant call button. Thinking there was an emergency, the girl struggled along the tilted aisle and when she got to the seat she asked in an urgent manner what the problem was?

*"Miss, we'll have a large gin and tonic, vodka and orange and two beers, please."*

But without a doubt, the best thing that happened in 1983 was witnessing the birth of my wonderful son, Ryan.

# 1984

The Statoil contract came to an end and I found myself back in London calling agents once again.

At Humphrey's & Glasgow near Victoria Station I worked on a diverse project and a large modification to a British Nuclear Fuels (BNFL) Windscale installation at Sellafield, Cumbria. I was engaged on an area where valve stations in hazardous service were sealed in units with thick glass windows and two and a half feet (750mm) thick concrete walls. Hand holes and heavy duty gloves would be used to access and operate valves.

The piping lead was a tall, eccentric gentleman by the name of Cliff Burner. For more than two hours he travelled into London every day from Poole in Dorset.

He wore a jacket and tie supplemented with a bright red silk handkerchief flapping from his top pocket as he strolled into the office each morning with a cigarette in his hand. Every word Cliff uttered was for effect as he sought that desperately needed audience. I liked Cliff and we got on well.

While at H&G's I decided to treat myself to some fine dining ware. Harrods in Knightsbridge have two sales a year, one in the summer, the other after Christmas and New Year's.

I had found the perfect dinner service and a fifty-four-piece set of Minton bone China with the *Ancestral* pattern was looking good in display on the third floor of the store. To ensure it was not relocated to another part of the store leading up to the sales event, I visited that floor every lunchtime for a full week just prior to the start of the sale which was to be a bitterly cold last Friday of January.

On the evening before the event, just after getting home from the office, I had noted on TV that folk had already started lining up outside the store. This news did not sit well with me because I had originally intended to rise at the crack of dawn and get the first tube trains into town arriving at the store about six a.m., three and a half hours before the nine thirty opening time. That would've been perfect but this news now meant I had to get my arse up there *right now* if I was to have any chance of snagging this dinner service.

Dressing for a winter's evening outside and carrying a folding camp chair, several cheese and pickle sandwiches and a flask of hot coffee with a few splashes of Kahlua, I arrived at the store at seven thirty p.m., exactly fourteen hours before the doors were to open.

During my lunchtime investigations I discovered that there are no less than eleven entrances around the Harrods property. Some large, many small. Over the last week I had sussed out the door that would give me the fastest access to my basket of Minton China.

I settled down on my lawn chair with my Canadian sheepskin overcoat in the confines of a small doorway on the southeast corner of the store. Sipping from the flask; it had begun to snow. I tried to keep warm by eating and drinking. By midnight I'd had enough of cheese and pickle sarnies and settled down to a book, while occasionally nodding off into the relative warmth of my cashmere scarf.

As time drew on quite extraordinarily, I was interviewed by the BBC around four a.m. The short interview was televised later in the morning. I was tired but hanging in there.

The hours rolled by slowly and the next person to arrive at my entrance showed up at seven thirty a.m. I had been sitting there for twelve full hours on my tod!

As the volume of folk increased around Harrods and its surrounding areas, two policemen were assigned to each entrance to keep the peace and limit the amount of bloodshed when all doors opened. These cops were good sorts and offered to stay with my gear while I headed upstairs. A nice gesture.

Nine thirty approached and I prepared for the rush. There were about two hundred shoppers behind me and I couldn't help worrying that a hundred and ninety-eight of them wanted my Minton dinner service.

With perfectly choreographed, walkie-talkie communication and all television stations seizing the moment all doors opened at nine thirty on the dot. As the two doors to my entrance swung wide open and with two hundred folk behind me I sprinted up the first flight of stairs. This did not go well and with a moment of sudden reality both calf muscles in my legs collapsed from spending the night in frigid conditions of the cold. I crashed onto the stairs shrieking with acute pain as men and women clambered over me to get up to the China.

It was as if an earthquake had struck Knightsbridge and having the right China mattered more than life itself. People clearly didn't give a shit as they leaped over the poor bastard lying flat out on the cold concrete.

I recovered enough to hobble up to the third floor with by now, fifty people ahead of me to discover the Minton still resting there, awaiting its new owner. I grabbed the dinner service, paid for it and headed back down to my stuff at the doorway. Thanking the coppers, I headed off to the office in a taxi absolutely knackered.

Kellogg Brown & Root took me on as a piping designer for what was then a nice rate of £8.10 an hour in their offices, based in Wimbledon. I was involved in a project expansion to the huge existing, Bacton Gas Terminal on the Norfolk county coast. Within the overall Bacton site are a number of land based plots owned by different operators. Each operated area receives gas from southern and central North Sea platforms, via a complex network of subsea pipelines criss-crossing one another along the sea bed before rising above ground, across a few deck chairs and into their relevant separators. The work process separates the gases from liquid hydrocarbons, condensates and water.

Terminals like Bacton constantly go through change and expansion to handle the increased reception of fluids from new offshore platforms being commissioned all the time. There are a few gas terminals dotted around the eastern British Isles including St Fergus in Scotland and another, then owned by Conoco situated at Theddlethorpe, in east Lincolnshire.

I was asked at KBR to develop a new plot plan for the expansion and enjoyed the work fronts that included studying the routing of these pipelines by utilising existing North Sea marine charts that identify all pertinent materials and potential obstructions above the surface of the sea and below, down to the seabed. Wrecks, wind turbines, pipelines, platforms, shipping lanes to note a few.

My dad had recently taken on a cracking position with Conoco. He was recruited from the Matthew Hall Murchison offshore project by a long term workmate at Conoco who liked the old man's working ethics and had encouraged him to move across to the client side.

The new platform, called Hutton, was to be a tension leg platform design. Dad's rate was a very nice £16.40 an hour and more than twice his son's! It was a peachy job for him and he ended up staying with Conoco as a contractor for many more years.

I was beavering away one day on my piping studies at the KBR office and my phone rang. Drawing offices had progressed since Stone & Webster and I actually had my own telephone.

It was the old man with a bit of an update.

Conoco were about to start a feasibility study on a brand new North Sea offshore platform complex called Viking 'C', or *Charlie*. Hugh Frayne, Dad's supervisor had asked if he knew of anyone, like him, who would be able to take on the work and create plot studies and piping layouts on the board.

Dad thought I might be able to fit the bill and asked if I would be interested?

This phone call out of the blue had captivated my attention and of course, I said YES!

He went away and threw my hat into the ring. Not an hour later and a call from Conoco's HR department, I was on for the interview with Mr Frayne.

Champing at the bit and wearing my new brogues I made my way to Park Street and was briefed on the new project; a southern North Sea offshore gas complex consisting of four bridge-linked platforms sitting on steel jackets in shallow waters of the southern sector. The project was in its infancy and had not even established a business objective. It was not yet in a position to be awarded to a FEED contractor.

My position as the sole piper would be to provide plot layout and piping design support on the drawing board while working closely with Conoco's engineers representing drilling, civil, structural, process, mechanical and electrical departments. All went well and, as the interview wrapped up, Mr Frayne identified the need to move quickly and there and then offered the position to me. I smiled, nodded and verbally accepted the offer while suggesting a written contract be prepared, of course.

The words that tumbled out of Mr Frayne's mouth were:

*"Okay, Mitch, all good. Shall we make it simple and duplicate the same contract that your dad has?"*

FFS. I nearly fell over but found my footing and a professional response imitated by Sean Connery in *Goldfinger* when, after that round of golf (filmed at Hadley Wood Golf Club) Gert Frobe was writing out a

112

cheque to cash:

*"Yes, Mr Frayne, that would be perfectly acceptable."*

On the way back to Wimbledon on the tube I realised that my income had immediately doubled.

My dad laughed his socks off and we went out for a beer and a bite to celebrate before he handed me the bill.

I gave notice at KBR and dragged the boys down to the pub. One guy working next to me, Bob Underwood, was a terrific fella. But he was also a cigar smoker and for several months I had to put up with the smoke around me and his filthy ash trays which I was always whinging about.

Preparing for my new position on Sunday evening, I opened up my burgundy briefcase to prepare for my new job only to find the entire contents of Bob's ash tray. Wonderful.

I started work in Conoco's offices in Park Street, just off Oxford Circus, at £16.40 an hour and immediately loved the work I was getting involved in. Each engineer I was working with had a wealth of knowledge behind him along with a degree. I had a certificate for knowing what a *Flemish Bond* was on bricklaying.

I studied a number of alternative platform concepts that included unmanned structures with a helideck positioned directly above the drilling facilities, manned accommodation and helideck, compression platforms with independent flare boom, electrical generation, drilling and lifeboat stations. There were always a stack of options and no sooner had I initiated one study, than another clean drawing sheet was on the board and a new one was underway. These guys loved making changes and changes meant rework and rework meant challenges to the schedules which in turn, meant overtime and overtime meant larger cheques! I was working about fifty-five hours a week and bringing in a grand a week!

One particular week, five of the project team hooked up at Conoco's gas terminal at Theddlethorpe, Lincolnshire. The reason for the visit was to charter a helicopter out to the existing Viking 'B' platform complex located in quadrant 49 in the central waters of the North Sea. The idea was to take a look at the equipment arrangement out there and slide some thought provoking ideas onto this new 'Charlie' project.

There are a number of things I have learned when taking helicopter flights over the years. First, flying on helicopters is not for the faint hearted.

There's not a lot of smiling when reading up on the aerodynamic features of a helicopter. If a fixed wing aircraft has trouble with its engine, there is usually another engine that would help get the aircraft down to the ground. Even if a single engine aircraft failed, the aerodynamics of the wings would help a gentle glide attitude that would bring the aircraft down to the ground safely, allowing the pilot time to choose a landing spot, albeit quite quickly.

However, if that single engine on a helicopter craps out you may as well bend over and kiss your arse goodbye cause you ain't gonna be coming out of it alive. The aircraft would enter into a spin and plummet to the ground with no aerodynamics.

There are few options on how to get out to an offshore platform; you get there by helicopter and you get there by crossing lots of deep water. There's only one thing worse than going straight down to the ground in a helicopter dying instantly from the trauma and that's going straight down into the sea, then drowning in a pool of burning fuel.

The offshore workforce who regularly travel out to the platforms do so in the most uncomfortable and, often, embarrassing conditions. After checking in and a short, ninety second, video instruction on safety that should probably be three and a half days, the passenger is provided with an offshore survival suit to step into.

Once you have removed your site boots, you step into the sealed legs of the Gore-Tex survival suit and bring the rest of it up and around you. The arms of the suit are also closed and the idea is that once fully zipped up there is no opportunity for frigid waters to get into the suit, except through the top.

After zipping up the front, it's now about protecting the head. The end of the zipper finishes about two inches from the top of your head. It's important then that the Gore-Tex is pulled right up to its highest point around the face. Then, using both hands, the suit is stretched and pulled back down and under the chin.

Believe me, it's a tight fit, but you can see and hear and are adequately prepared for an incident. Boots are then replaced before you are seated on the chopper with a book or newspaper.

There are no washrooms on a helicopter and some of the flights from Aberdeen out to a distant oil field are nearly four hours long. As these choppers are filled with inebriated offshore workers it is common for several chaps to release their ablutionary discharges straight into their

114

survival suit, heading straight for the khazi upon landing. Lovely.

The flight from Theddlethorpe to Viking B is forty-five minutes and we were the only persons on board. As the helicopter descended slowly onto the helideck the five of us prepared to step out. Across the windy deck and down the staircase I followed the others who had not visited this area of the North Sea before, either.

One clear but strange observation was that there was no-one to greet us, either on the helideck or below. In fact there was no-one around at all. We looked for personnel and found none.

Moving through to a dining area, still no-one. It was like being on the *Mary Celeste*.

It then became clear that we had been dropped off at the Viking 'A' platform complex and not in fact the 'B'. Racing back up to the helideck, we could see the chopper lifting off and hovering as eye contact was made with the pilot before coming back down to collect us.

We all clambered aboard and ninety seconds later were dropped off at the correct offshore platform a few miles away where someone actually appeared to welcome us, surprised at the news we had already visited one platform this morning.

Not a great start to the day but we soon settled into our activities and a checklist of what we were there to look at: essentially plot space and footprint sizes of critical mechanical equipment.

Offshore production platform plot plan development has changed dramatically over the years. On July sixth 1988, the oil company Occidental's Piper 'Alpha' platform exploded one night and in the ensuing catastrophe, a hundred and sixty-seven men lost their lives or are still missing. This is the highest number of lives lost from any one single accident, on an offshore production platform.

The platform was designed in the early seventies and began producing oil in 1976 before later being converted to a gas gathering platform. The term 'gathering' effectively means that the Piper Alpha platform was designed to receive gas from other local platforms via a network of subsea pipelines rising up to a collection manifold on Piper Alpha.

At ten p.m. on that black July night, several hours after an incorrect installation of a piping valve and materials, the first of a series of explosions occurred in the hazardous compression area.

The accommodation platform, five minutes' walk away from compression was populated with workers, mostly asleep. With the explosion came automated loud speaker alarms and audible warnings. The first was a *prepare to abandon* audible warning that essentially instructed everyone on the platform to grab a lifejacket and in a controlled, safe manner move towards the designated muster area to await further instructions over the speaker system.

This warning is issued by the operators from their seated positions in the radio room and workers must follow these instructions and most definitely not take things into their own hands where panic in the darkness may prevail.

However, due to the platform plot design configuration of Piper Alpha, the non-hazardous radio room was positioned adjacent to the hazardous compression area where the first explosion had occurred. The radio room was wiped out completely and no further instructions were issued, verbal or otherwise.

Deep in the sleeping levels within the accommodation platform, many of the guys stood there awaiting further instructions and some who had thought it a false alarm went back to bed. Others who perished were prepared for the evacuation and standing next to their bunks with a life jacket in hand. As the fire raged outside, the steel structure supporting the accommodation quarters began to fail and, after a short while, the entire structure came away from the offshore platform and dropped into the ocean, quickly sinking to the sea bed as a tomb with close to a hundred souls.

These days, as specifications improve all the time, insurance coverage on plot development will not allow such close proximity between an explosive item of equipment and a control or radio room. On platforms, blast walls are introduced to the plot or better segregation between equipment.

So, once on the correct Viking platform, investigative discussion opened up with a couple of key operators and by the end of the day we had all gleaned enough information that would help me with my plot studies back in the office.

With the extra wonga I bought a three bedroom, pre-second World War terraced property in Barnet, upgraded a few things in the house and treated myself to a five year old white, Jaguar XJS. The V12 5.3 litre engine and my arse six inches above the ground, this cat purred and sprinted.

I was one contractor among dozens of permanent staff engineers and these guys were smart cookies in their own fields. I learned a lot from studying plot layouts for several different kinds of offshore production platforms as I acquainted myself with more marine charts of the ocean floors.

# 1985

As my platform designs gathered momentum and the company started focusing on choosing one of the options to run with, Conoco started looking for an engineering, procurement, construction and management contractor to work on a FEED study. I was excited at the possibility of moving into the offices of the chosen EPC, representing the client.

Unfortunately, the same positive motions that found the position I was enjoying proved also to be its demise. As Conoco's North Sea Hutton project started to wind down, Dad's work was running out and they moved him back into London from a temporary, module yard posting in Scotland. There was only going to be room for one piping guy and I was released. My old man felt bad about it but in truth this was no big deal, I had enjoyed the contract, immensely. Especially the wonga.

But in truth, I had been working in isolation of others. The senior engineers had hard offices and around me was no-one except an open plan draughting area, my board and I. No other pipers to natter to or go for a beer with. Just me, myself and I.

Back down to earth, I found a good position at Matthew Hall Engineering in Tottenham Court Road as a piping designer on the detailed design phase of the Marathon Brae 'B', or *Bravo*, platform. Matthew Hall were a huge, international engineering company competing with companies like Bechtel, Kellogg Brown & Root, Fluor, McDermott, Davy's, Foster Wheeler and Stone & Webster for the big global, mega projects.

Occasionally, projects demand that supplementary piping deliverables above the norm are provided by the engineering contractor. Matthew Hall were expected to develop drawings called system isometrics. Where smaller, more defined isometrics would support the fabrication and construction cycle using A3 size (11" x 17") drawing sheets, system isometrics were created on much larger A1 size (22" x 34") sheets.

A few words on system isos…

There are numerous oil, gas, water, air and other piping systems on any given petrochemical project and these are broken out into two categories of service: Process piping systems and Utility piping systems. Process piping systems cover all hydrocarbon related services for the project. These might be called, heavy gas oil, light gas oil, process liquids, process gases, diluted bitumen, crude oil, light and heavy diesel, naphtha, propane, butane, paraffin, natural gas, liquefied natural gas, light petroleum gas, aviation fuel and a plethora of other descriptions depending on what type of facility being built. Chemical and gas plants, refineries and upgraders, all have their own unique piping systems and services.

Utility systems, of which there are also many, are required to support the refining and production of the primary process systems. These utilities include instrument air, plant air, drinking (potable) water, steam, condensate, blowdown, utility water, high pressure flare, low pressure flare, firewater, firewater deluge and sprinklers, underground sewage, rainwater collection, cooling water supply and return, oily water sewer, etc. They do not have hydrocarbon particles in the fluids so have ultimately different approaches and specifications in their independent piping designs.

The system isometrics, drawn without a scale, would provide the construction and site hook up team with valuable documents that showed on one sheet, an entire piping system like say, a flare system. The flare system could effectively snake through hundreds of metres of an onshore plant or offshore production platform collecting unwanted gases that are either deposited into the atmosphere or collected for further usage as a carbon capture element of the project.

When studying the drawing an operator on the engineering team or at site assigned to oversee the flare system would read the system isometric and immediately be able to quickly understand where the users are located geographically, that would distribute the discarded gases into the system from mechanical equipment and the correct order in which they must be positioned on the collection header.

In other systems where isolation, control and pressure release valves are prevalent the system isometric would also identify such valves in their location on the system and any associated instrumentation like pressure transmitters, thermowell (temperature) connection, flow monitoring devices and remotely operated valves that control the flow of service. The positions of these valves would be instantly recognisable on the system isometric and would take an operations engineer just a few minutes to locate on the platform. Furthermore, these drawings could also be used to reflect hydrostatic test demarcations and pressures between sections of the piping arrangement.

Once out on site after construction is complete and starting at any point on the plant, with the drawing in his hand, the operator would be able to follow the system east, west, north and south throughout the operating facility. Along the pipe racks, up and down vertical vessels, in and out of buildings. One drawing could cover the entire system on a facility that took all day to walk.


The team I was working with were a superb bunch of chaps and a laugh a minute. John Webster, Dave Sulliman, John Lawrence, Peter Bairns and Ian Purdy. Not to forget Eldridge.
I also worked with a nice lad, Steve, who went on to marry one of Dame Shirley Bassey's daughters.

*The pipers always have class.*

I was invited to the wedding near Henley-on-Thames. The church was packed to the rafters as thirty reporters gathered outside, hoping for a natter with Shirl. With a hat large enough to cover several pews, Ms Bassey professionally pulled them all aside to a quiet position up the road and away from her daughter's event for ten minutes, before politely telling them to bugger off. Which they did.

The wedding reception for sixty or so people took place, not at the Ritz on Piccadilly, but Sonning Cricket Club in Surrey. Guests included Soraya Khashoggi, the wife of Adnan Khashoggi the Iranian entrepreneurial businessman whom, in the seventies, was synonymous with arms dealing. It was a lovely reception for Steve and his new wife but everyone was secretly hoping that our Shirl would get up and away from her family, to drop a few songs on us. But it appeared that this was not to be while everyone continued dancing to the sounds from a DJ.

Then, all of a sudden, the electricity in the building completely cut out. Lights and sound disappeared as folk looked at each other in quiet disbelief. Out of nowhere and with succinct timing candles were lit for each table and we all soon realised that this was no accident.

In just perfect, serene surroundings our Shirley slowly stood up from the table next to us and without any electrical support from a musical accompaniment and amongst a congregation you could've heard a pin drop, started singing the Perry Como song *And I Love You So*.

It was indeed an emotional moment and with a hot dog on the way back to the hotel, was a wonderful end to a great day.

Which reminds me of a story…

I was working at Matthew Hall in Tottenham Court Road, west London, high up in an office block above Maples furniture store and right opposite Warren Street underground station. The Marathon Brae Bravo project was just getting into gear and I was part of a good team working on the production of these System Isometrics.

One of the pipers, Dave, had just bought himself a brand spanking new yellow, Ford Capri. He drove to the office every day and parked in a small outdoor car park at the foot of our building. Very proud of his new motor was Dave, and every hour or two he would wander across to the window of our twenty-fourth floor and take a look down below.

Yes, the car was still there.

One Friday afternoon after a lunchtime laugh and a giggle down at the local pub, Mike found a large black bin liner and, making a few scissor cuts, added several curved edges to the sheet.

Nipping down to the car park he dampened and draped the sheet across the hood of Dave's new Capri.

Dashing back up in the elevator and walking slowly back to his desk, Mike prepared us for the practical joke to come and we continued working a few minutes. The scene down below looked convincing.

I casually mentioned to anyone listening, that there was a paint truck down in the car park. Not much reaction from anyone.

A few minutes later one of the other chaps shouted to Dave and told him to quickly come take a look, *"Is that your yellow Capri down there, Dave?"*

Well, the entire team ran over to the windows and the building tilted to one side as we all craned our necks and glued our faces to the cool glass. Way down below were rows of neatly parked cars and a new, yellow Ford Capri in the middle of them all, with a sickly look to its yellow bonnet. Dave paused for a moment before he suddenly twigged and shouted, *"Oh FUCK"*, and sprinted towards the elevators.

It was a good two minutes before we watched him appear from the building and walk across to his car to take a closer look at the offending mess on his hood.

The laughter in our office could be heard over in Green Park as Dave looked up and gave us all the two fingers.

System isos were screaming off the production line and I was enjoying the work. Offshore modules constructed overseas in several alternative locations are moved by seagoing vessels to their final destination, where the offshore platform is to be positioned. They are then lifted from the vessel and into position above the steel jacket on the level known as the module support frame or *MSF*. These offshore modules can weigh up to six thousand tonnes each and contribute to some of the heaviest lifts in the world.

Once these cube shaped modules are lifted into place, they need to be welded out and secured. Part of this work process requires that the piping systems within any given module be connected to their sister piping systems in the adjacent modules. These short, final pieces of the piping jigsaw that sit between two modules are known as *hookup* spools.

The Marathon Brae Bravo project had just over one thousand hook up spool isometrics in the scope. Some of the piping was as small as three quarter inch in diameter and 500mm in length making them easy to install while other hookup spools of systems like seawater cooling supply and return lines were as large as thirty-six inch diameter often including an awkward ninety degree elbow as part of the spool. These sizeable spools made it very difficult to install offshore between the two modules and the piping designer must consider where important field welds would be positioned. The design of each spool is critical to support the constructability and allow the spool to be installed in an efficient manner while avoiding clashes with structural steel and module piping.

Friday lunchtimes were a hoot as the guys set off towards any one of a number of pubs in the area. The Valiant Trooper was a favourite and watches tended to be ignored as the atmosphere in the west end of London on a Friday was always excellent.

If strippagrams were not around, eating competitions were huge. Two chaps set off to try and better the other by trying to eat as many bananas as they could in one hour. It was a tie as both managed fourteen bananas. Not the small ones, either but ones that had a foot of straight run on them.

Kirk Bartlett was a nice, tall piping lad with a life's goal of attending all ninety-two English league football stadiums. This was a tall order because at the age of twenty-five he'd been to seven.

He also reckoned he could eat twelve Big Macs on the trot and within the hour so we cut a deal suggesting we buy them but if he didn't make it, he'd have to pay us back.

Agreeing to the challenge on a lunchtime and to save a few bob we brought back twelve happy meals including twelve Big Macs, twelve bags of fries and twelve large cokes. Now, while this may appear to be a fairly simple thing to do to some of you big eaters out there, it's worth noting that in twelve Big Macs are eighteen baps (three slices in one unit), twenty-four patties, about four pickled gherkins and a pint of relish.

The game was on and Kirk started off well, whooping down the first four in about fifteen minutes. He took sips of a coke to ease the effort and it was clear to us all with all those buckets around him he wasn't going to go short of a drink.

After about half an hour, Kirk was halfway to his target. But as the ninth Big Mac disappeared, a pale look came over him and he just sat there, silent. One bite from the tenth and he was off to the khazi, not to be seen for two hours.


Alan, a quiet piping checker worked also at Matthew Hall. It was the mid-eighties and a busy time in London. Alan's wife was having a few difficult health times and Alan was emotionally aware of this while at the office. There was one telephone serving the entire piping group and Alan kept an eye on the phone throughout the day.

Brian, another but much louder piper working fairly close to Alan, chose to spend most of the day on the phone talking to friends, wife, girlfriend and others. In fact, Brian hardly did any piping stuff because there was simply not enough time in the day.

Each time Brian put the phone down, Alan would approach it to make a call only for it to ring. Someone would answer the phone and, yes, the call would be for Brian.

This was driving Alan bananas. So, one Monday morning, Alan came into the office with a huge, brand new expensive portable mobile phone and probably only the eighth person in the world to own one. He bought it to maintain communication with his poorly wife.

One of the chaps managed to find out the telephone number of Alan's

123

new phone.

The phone sat there on Alan's desk that first Monday and it didn't ring once. Alan never made a call because the costs were astronomical. The phone was there to receive a call, should it be necessary, from Alan's wife.

On the Tuesday afternoon, everyone stopped work as the large, white mobile started ringing. Alan was halfway back to his desk before the fourth ring, and he answered the call.

A male voice on the other end said, *"Can I speak to Brian, please?"*

# 1986

More than a year into the project I had an awkward decision to make. Graham, my old mucker from the past, had moved back to the London area from Dundee and was working for a small company called Howe Baker in Elstree, Hertfordshire, just about fifteen minutes from home. He had asked me if I was interested in working alongside him in this country estate home converted into an engineering office. I probably had just a few weeks left on the Marathon project but chose to give notice and join the small team at Howe Baker.

The team was, once again, a cracking bunch of chaps with Graham, Brian Nolan, Derek Cleverley and Phil Captain working under the watchful eye of an old school chap called Lew Cloaks, the lead piping supervisor. Lew was one of two guys in the piping business who wore a wig. He did not take kindly to any adverse comments about his syrup but continued to wear it every day even when daytime temperatures were up in the thirties.

Lew was also a golfer and we had both attended many organised 'society' days playing thirty-six holes at some smart golf club in the prettier areas of England. After thirty-six holes out on a course it was most refreshing to climb into a nice shower, take a shave and dress smartly in a jacket and tie before sitting down to a formal dinner with speeches and prizes. These are great events, let me tell you. But on most occasions Lew attended and because he did not want to take off his wig, he always chose not to shower but instead slip out of his damp, sweaty shirt and into a clean shirt and tie.

After a few months at Howe Baker it was clear that the project was winding down and I was released. It was also apparent that the Marathon Brae Bravo hook up work was still far from being completed but there was no position for me back on that team.

This was a hard lesson I was to take with me onto other projects; don't jump too soon; projects have a habit of going on and on and on!

Christmas in the piping group was always a hoot. Plenty of organised piss-ups, long lunches and the occasional long evening in great London pubs.

I set up a lunch at a smart restaurant in Goodge Street and made the awful mistake of not collecting any money up front. When thirty of us laughed and joked our way through four hours of steak, beer, wine, port, cheese and brandy it took two girls to carry the bill to the table. Only four of us remained and it was time to pay up. Unfortunately, after we all chipped into the kitty the bill was still up around several hundred pounds and I had to cough up the dosh. The following morning I tried to recover some funds from the other guys who were at the restaurant but that's when the excuses came out. Many of the attendees paid a bit but some only confessed to have had one beer, or just drunk coke, left early and had just one glass of wine, etc. etc.

I was left with over a hundred quid coming out of my own pocket. Another one of life's lessons and, since then, I love to organise project events but always take a good deposit before the event.

Christmas time back in the office was just as much fun. The pipers would all go out and buy a gift-wrapped pressie for a fiver to put into a large box for the 'Lucky Dip' prize giving just before we broke up for the holidays. The large cardboard box full of goodies would then be stuffed full of straw and Pat would take it round to all the girls. Brenda was one of the project secretaries and always up for a spot of giggles. She would occasionally grab the arse of a piping designer, sometimes me, as other chaps would throw a suggestive remark about her rather large breasts back at her. It was always fun and nothing ever got too awkward. It was the eighties.

Now, Pat was a chap who was not light in the trouser department. We all knew this because he had a habit of bringing his todger out into the relative security of a group of chaps standing near the bar. He looked like Yul Brynner in a roll neck.

So, Pat had cut a large hole in the bottom side of the cardboard Christmas box and holding it close to him, approached Brenda's desk. *"Ooooh Pat,"* she said, *"is it my turn to pick something?"*

Brenda had plunged her arm into the straw and rummaged around, when Pat leaned over and whispered in her ear, *"The best ones are at the bottom."* With that news, Brenda leaned forward and wandered deeper into the box. The immediate shriek and look on her face suggested she had clearly discovered the largest gift in the box.

The London piping scene was quiet again but work fronts up in Aberdeen were increasing in abundance. I found a six month contract up there, again with Foster Wheeler Wood Group who I'd worked with in Norway a few years earlier.

After driving ten hours on a Sunday and checking into a guest house close to the downtown area, I started work in their offices the following day.

Piping design activities in Aberdeen were a different animal than what I'd been used to in London, Oslo and Calgary. While new offshore production platforms were still being commissioned, existing platforms were going through phases of huge expansion to support increased production. This demanded regular change outs of equipment and materials that were now showing fatigue, thereby creating a risky environment.

The projects in Aberdeen were small and in the region of a handful of engineering hours, but all were interesting. There would be times when I would be sitting at my drawing board laying out new compressor piping in the morning when I would be pulled into a meeting to discuss a new project and asked to pack a bag and head offshore to a platform that afternoon for a few days.

Aberdeen airport at Dyce had a phenomenal sized area for helicopter operations. Dozens of flights out to the North Sea and back could be seen as inbound and outbound choppers filled the sky.

Visits to a platform in the northern waters of the North Sea would consist of a two or three hour flight, landing on the helideck high up on the platform, coming down some stairs into the accommodation quarters and checking into the arrivals lounge before being given a safety orientation of the platform, either by video or open talk. This would be the norm for first timers to that platform. If an engineer needed to spend more than four days on an offshore installation a safety course would need to be completed and passed to support the trip.

On three-day visits I would then be given a room where I would stay for my time out in the middle of the ocean.

There would also be occasions offshore when the area I needed to visit was closed off due to inclement weather. Dependent on wind direction two sides of a platform may be impacted by 100mph winds, snow and ice while the other two sides would be fine.

Food on an offshore platform could be considered some of the best in

Scotland and the executive chefs, that oversee the food, put out simply wonderful choices and a large variety of meals.

While there are always plenty of choices, there are also plenty of huge workers that line up to eat.

I recall sitting near a drill floor worker in filthy overalls collecting his dinner that would include a couple of T-bone steaks, spaghetti Bolognese, chips, gravy, baked beans, cherry crumble and custard... and a fried egg sunny side up. All mixed up on two plates. He sat there holding a fork in each fist and stuffed the lot down his neck in under ten minutes. Before I'd finished my soup he got up and walked over to the ice cream machine, clearly feeling a bit peckish, and filling a couple of wafers before heading off to the cinema.

Fitness rooms, pool tables and the cinema would offer a variety of entertainment. Televisions were uncommon in the bunk rooms.

String bags would be placed under your pillow and these were used to submit your laundry. They boil the crap out of everything and, because of this, you never take your Lacoste or Ben Sherman shirts offshore with you.

On a trip out to a Mobil platform, I returned from a sixteen hour day to see the string bag returned and sitting at the foot of my bed. Tipping the stuff out onto the bed, I picked up my new pair of synthetic winter long johns and held them up to the light. I could see they would fit perfectly over the legs of a Barbie doll.

One freezing cold morning and a ten minute walk to the area I was studying that week I took a short cut through an electrical transformer room to keep warm. The outside temperature was below zero and I was freezing my nuts off.

I had a lot to get through and chose not to have breakfast but was hungry. The warmth of the enclosure cheered me up and as I was about to exit the large room on the other side I stopped in my tracks. There, on the top of a short cabinet, was a plate piled high with a dozen soft, warm bacon rolls. I grabbed two of them, stuffed them into my pockets and high tailed it out of the door into the cold. Leaning against a handrail looking out to sea at several other distant platforms and vessels, the rolls tasted really good.

There's something about going offshore on your own. A sort of pride that surrounds you in the knowledge that the operating company have assigned a considerable amount of funds towards your efforts. They pay you for your time on the platform and for travel time. And on top of that you get to have dinner with someone who likes to eat his custard mixed in with his gravy.

Back in the Aberdeen office, results and dimensional data from the site survey are used to develop new P&IDs and, consequently, a new piping general arrangement. The design would be discussed with other disciplines and the project management team before finalising with the client.

Once all parties had bought into the design, the piping GA and isometrics would be completed, checked and approved before issuing to the pipe fabricator.

This type of project modification may take just three weeks to complete, while others may require a larger team and a much longer schedule.

# 1987

Foster Wheeler prepared for an office move from a sweet position downtown to a building near a fishmeal factory at the harbour. A move, that wasn't getting too much applause.

I received a telephone call from Alan Eddy, the Matthew Hall engineering manager on the Brae Bravo platform project I'd left prematurely. Alan asked me if I was interested in re-joining the Brae Bravo team and taking an offshore assignment to be part of the hook up team out in the North Sea. They'd asked for my name and I weighed up the options of a two week on, two week off well paid rotation or a desk job down at the fish factory.

I gave notice and left Aberdeen in the car on a Friday to prepare for a couple of weeks off with my son.

I then had to fly back up to Aberdeen for a one week offshore survival course at the Robert Gordon Institute of Technology, just outside the city centre.

There are a number of academic, written and strenuous, physical exercises that have to be passed over the five days. And passed comfortably. Offshore survival training is no walk in the park and folk who sign up for this fail on a regular basis, often at the cost of their position of employment.

The RGIT have a purpose built swimming pool where I would spend the next few days. The thirty metre (one hundred feet) long by ten metre (thirty-three feet) pool is fitted with an integral wave-making facility. There is no shallow end and halfway along one side is a structure that provides a series of diving platforms at three different levels up to a height of ten metres. At one end of the building set into the wall are two enormous fans, each the size of an air intake on a Rolls Royce jet engine. Water temperature is maintained at a higher temperature than that of the North Sea. Can't have guys dying from hypothermia in a training scenario!

Fixed to the ceiling of the swimming pool building is a steel structure and series of chains and pulleys twenty metres (sixty-six feet) above the water to support the fuselage of an old Sikorsky S76 helicopter.

After a day of classroom and academic stuff, it was time to hop into the trunks, zip up the survival suit and do some practical stuff in the pool.

Climbing the stair tower to the top platform and leaping into the cold waters, eight of us bobbed around in the water. The wave machine kicked in and so did the loud fans. Lights went out as a cable and harness were lowered down from the helicopter. As if this wasn't enough, pool staff stood on the tiles holding hosepipes, flushing cold water onto us. We all had to stay afloat long enough to be rescued. The suit provided sufficient buoyancy and this first exercise was really about staying afloat in the swells and not crashing into each other till it was our turn to get rescued. When my name was called out by a lifeguard with a megaphone, I swam across to the harness, grabbed it and tried hard to get each leg into the slings. Sadly, this didn't quite go to plan and one of my bollocks was agonisingly caught up in the harness while the mechanical team started winching me up towards the helicopter. I was crying out in pain but could not be heard above the sounds of the fans and wave machine. As I stopped next to the platform, I scrambled out and away from the harness holding my nuts and trying not to vomit.

Activity number two didn't go too well and, with the possibility of losing a testicle, I managed to pass the test.

The next activity was a little more intense. We were all told to stand at the side of the pool. The helicopter fuselage was slowly lowered from its position beneath the ceiling and onto the surface of the still waters. Still wearing the survival suit we jumped into the pool and swam through the open door of the helicopter before finding one of the sixteen seats to buckle into.

When we were all settled into a seat the chopper was slowly winched back up to its original position beneath the ceiling. The waves kicked in, the fans began blowing and the lights went out. Much like the agonising anticipation of a popular Disney World ride, we all sat there, shivering and gripping the sides of our seats, while squinting hard. After what seemed like a lifetime's wait the mechanical lever was pulled and the helicopter went into freefall. Two seconds later we hit the surface of the pool, and hard. Descending into the frigid gloom of the dark, turbulent, chlorinated waters, the fuselage started rotating about its axis until we were fully upside down in the water and about twenty feet beneath the surface, still strapped into our seats. We had to unbuckle, squeeze through the tight window opening and swim to the surface.

With one or two chaps panicking and needing assistance from the staff who were already in the water, I unbuckled and glided towards the open doorway where I darted out and shot up to the surface of the water to grab a much needed breath of air. And again, some bastard was targeting me with pressurised water from the hose!

Thankfully, I passed that test and after another day of written stuff moved onto day four.

The morning consisted of more playing around in the pool and an opportunity to correctly right and overturn an inflated life raft which, again, was no easy task. In the afternoon, we were driven out to one of Aberdeen's harbours and all climbed into a lifeboat.

Chugging out of the choppy bay into open waters, it wasn't long before we were throwing up. This, predominantly, due to the fact that we were situated in the bottom of the craft and could not see a horizon.

A life size dummy wearing a survival suit was tossed into the sea. I was asked to take the control of the vessel and in a sort of keyhole shaped manoeuvre make an effort to ease up beside the dummy where another chap would drag it into the boat. Five times I tried and five times I ran over the dummy. Holding back vomit and attempting the rescue for a sixth time it was critical that I didn't run over the dummy again. But, I did.

Onto effort number seven, daylight fading and the possibility of failing the entire week's course.

But, everything then fell into place. I glided up to the dummy and he was, at last, hauled into the lifeboat before we all struggled back to the port.

A fifth day of successful exams and tests and after a tough week I passed the course and was given the green light to go offshore for my assignment.

After a week back home I was then back up to Aberdeen again and a helicopter flight out to the Marathon Brae field to start my first two week assignment with the hook up team.

All previous visits to several offshore platforms had increased my knowledge, protocol, safety and etiquette of a chap heading offshore for a more, prolonged assignment. I was excited.

As the helicopter approached the Brae Bravo platform, the visibility was excellent and I could see the huge platform standing on its steel jacket, isolated in the middle of this huge expanse of ocean. Floating off to one side of the platform was a support vessel called Britannia, owned by a Swedish company called SAFE. This floating hotel was to be my home while offshore in the Brae field.

The helicopter descended onto the helideck and I deplaned and checked in. After finding my room and a good night's sleep, I grabbed a quick breakfast and showed my face in the office.

Chris Leida, my supervisor and a great guy, asked me to first resolve a piping issue, apparently of utmost urgency. I was happy to help and felt a sense of importance surge through my body.

I took directions and found my way across the bridge onto Bravo's accommodation module and after a ten minute walk tracked down a chap called Barry Talbot. There were a series of offices in the module and Barry was one of the managers based there. Barry greeted me and showed me to the kitchen. On the floor was a large box containing a coffee machine. It had been sitting there for three weeks and his entire team could not get a cup of coffee until it was hooked up.

So, this 'utmost urgent' task was to unpack the coffee machine, review the existing plumbing and electrical systems in place and draw field sketches to depict the arrangement. The sketch should reflect all the materials necessary to connect the machine to the potable water supply, and more importantly, allow someone to collect these materials from the offshore stores. Both Barry and I stood there laughing our socks off. This was clearly a set up, *but if a job's worth doing...*

With a pad and pencil I drew up some sketches and got them signed and approved before heading off to the warehouse for the quarter inch diameter copper piping and valve materials. A pipe fitter was sourced and the machine was hooked up before lunchtime, with plenty of smiling faces around me.

I settled down and got used to life on the platform, based in an office type environment with plenty of folk I had worked with back in the Tottenham Court Road offices. I was assuming tasks and activities that included field verifications on piping systems a little more interesting than quarter inch copper capillary tubing and tiny needle valves.

The employment structure on an offshore workforce rolls up to the Offshore Installation Manager (OIM). It is he who is ultimately responsible for delivering the platform to the client and supporting a safe environment in operations. Below the rank of the OIM are a number of supervised levels including oversight of worker's safety, hook up, environmental, fire detection, firefighting, mechanical installation, piping, electrical, control systems, insulation, heat tracing, security, telecoms, civil & structural, diving, marine, pipelines, travel and logistics. These folk can amount to more than three hundred hookup souls offshore and, really, a small village.

Safety is absolutely critical on the construction phase of a platform, even before the installation is live and there are several rules and regulations to follow that must never be compromised.

There are one or two huge structures on a production platform that essentially provide a structural blanket for all drilling activity. These are known as the drilling derricks. One of the several areas of piping I had been assigned to field check was the utility piping up in the drilling derricks. The highest point on any offshore platform is usually the top of these derricks. The walk from my office location on the SAFE Britannia, across the bridge and up to the top of the derrick took me about forty-five minutes. Unfortunately, there were no bacon sarnies to be found anywhere along the way.

The top mechanical section of a drilling rig is known as the *crown block*. It sits about one hundred and fifty metres (five hundred feet) above the main deck of the platform and, once up there, the view is extraordinary. On a clear day, it is possible to see one hundred kilometres in any direction and pick out many vessels and other offshore platforms. Below you and off to another side of the installation is the helideck, which sits above the accommodation platform. An incredible sight looking down to a helideck and on one or two of my utility checks choppers would come and go below me. I relaxed for a few minutes to take it all in.

Immediately across the other side of the platform towards the hazardous areas is the long flare bridge that moves unwanted gases to the flare boom, a safe distance from the operating areas of the decks and well away from harm to any operators.

The discharge of these waste gases is a contentious issue for what these days appears to be every individual on the planet. Fossil fuels like oil and gas, if they are to be extracted and utilised as a trade-off for the energy sources the world needs, have to be burned. When burning these fuels, carbon dioxide is emitted. Oil companies around the world are investing an unprecedented amount of time and funding on restricting the discharge of

$CO_2$ into the atmosphere. One important piece of information is that, to capture greenhouse gas emissions, an operating facility has to first be in place and the facilities within that fossil fuel burning facility, before a process is established to remove the harmful $CO_2$ gases. After recycling and redirecting the gases into other areas of the chemical process, the residues that can no longer be utilised are emitted away from the platform through piping known as a flare line. This flare line, sometimes twenty-four inches (600mm) in diameter is surrounded by a supporting steel structure and can be positioned horizontally on a bridge, or up and away from the installation at an engineered angle of anything between thirty and forty-five degrees to the horizontal.

The prevailing wind directions are important when early engineering studies are conducted, in an effort to orientate the platform correctly. The position of facilities considered when preparing the plot plan of an offshore platform, along with the flare boom include the helideck, large exhaust stacks, cranes, drilling derricks, boat loading and offloading and the two lifeboat stations at opposite ends of the platform.

When finally arriving at the crown block my job was to ensure that the small diameter air, cooling oil and cooling water piping was positioned correctly and ready for commissioning and start up. In a back pack I would carry with me a binder filled with all the plot plan and isometrics, pipe support drawings, a small mirror for detecting hidden items like missing nuts and a small, metal hammer. The hammer is used in field checks to lightly tap on stud bolt nuts securing the bolts between flanges. By holding your ear close to the tapped joints it was possible to determine if the nut was properly tightened by hearing a slightly different pitch to the note. This observation would allow me to conduct these checks and balances, but only if a chopper was not taking off or landing, of course, when you can't hear diddly squat. A small torch for gasket material identification and feeler gauges would complete the list of small tools I'd take with me. Any missing materials like nuts, bolts, U-bolt supports, insulation, angle iron, valves, plugs, caps and instrumentation would be recorded on the drawings and returned to the construction team responsible for assembling all that stuff in the first place. And let me say now that people cut corners in an effort to finish their work. These modules I was working high up on are built at various overseas locations. The tight schedules of fabrication and assembly are often driven by the fixed departure of the sailings. Work is usually incomplete and has to be finished in the field where costs are sometimes ten times that of costs back at the module yard.

I really don't like heights and when up in that sort of exposed environment with the wind and rain crashing against the steelwork, it is all too easy to yellow off the drawings and pretend the checks have been done in an effort to get back to a pot of hot coffee and the warmth of the engineering office. But that really isn't the point of my job, is it?

It is important that I check everything, right down to the correct number of nuts on a U-bolt pipe support guide or anchor. And that the correct valve is installed and also installed in the correct configuration. Some valves like check or non-return valves are marked with an arrow depicting the direction of flow of the fluid. Some pipe fabricators or installation contractors get this wrong, including installing a ball valve with a 'pressure side' advisory that's not always how you initially think the valve should be installed. Laziness costs lives in our game and it's critical that any individual engaged in quality checks, a) knows what they're doing and, b) acts accordingly.

Insulation sometimes inhibits the audit of a piping system by covering key components. In such cases, a suitable note must be written on the isometric to reflect the items that could not be checked. Sometimes, it's prudent to bring an insulation installation supervisor to the location to remove some of the insulation in an effort for the Hookup piping engineer to tick that box and move on. I would check the entire library of drawings in the bag before heading back to the office.

The environment of an offshore platform is not for everyone. Depression can grip a person offshore at any time for any one of a number of reasons. Being away from loved ones, agrophobically isolated in a large expanse of water with no sight of land, having financial difficulties or experiencing family problems.

With Christmas approaching I was about to complete this particular offshore assignment and counting the days. One Sunday evening I had showered after a particularly mucky day out on the platform, changed into fresh gear and eaten in the dining room. Grabbing an ice cream I headed back to my desk to close out some paperwork. I was down at the small end of the cone when, over the loud speaker system, came a message that sounded like there was some urgency in its delivery. The details of the message were not obvious to me because my Swedish is a little bit sketchy.

The entire crew of the SAFE Britannia is Swedish. Yes, even the chef.

What followed was the alarm identifying the audible instruction to grab a life jacket and head to the lifeboat muster station.

Muster Stations are where oil workers gathered in the event of an emergency and a definitive location on the structure, normally close to either one of two lifeboat stations located at each opposite end of the platform.

I grabbed a cold weather jacket that was hanging up in the office, and threw on a life jacket. Rushing down to the lifeboats was not a new thing. Thankfully, every Sunday there was an organised evacuation drill and everyone on the floating Britannia instinctively knew what to do. I was on my own as I headed down the stairs.

As I stepped outside the enclosure, the night was dark, incredibly windy and horizontal rain greeted my face like dozens of needles.

As folk shivered and gathered around the lifeboats and after a roll call of names, people started talking and passing on snippets of information they may have heard. The muster alarm continued as the collective group grew in size. Dark, windy and full on rain showers did not allow us any respite.

It was about two hours before any news. But it came in the form of a visually disturbing sight; the bright headlights of four helicopters could be seen in the distance heading towards us in the dark skies. A bit like something out of *Apocalypse Now* it was another half hour before the choppers were upon us. The noise was hard to bear as we all sought cover in and around the mustering area. The alarm was still active and, with the noise of these helicopters, it was almost unbearable.

With just two collective helidecks on the platform and support vessel it was clearly impossible for all four to land at once, if necessary. But in fact neither helicopter intended to land. Instead, they hovered above us and shone strong search lights down onto the surface of the North Sea. The swell could probably be described as a sea state five or six. If someone was in the waters, it was indeed a sad moment and unlikely that anyone would be able to survive such traumatic circumstances.

Another hour and the helicopters turned around and headed back to the beach. As the muster alarms ceased and we all headed back up to the accommodations, everyone was clueless as to what might have happened.

Back in the office after breakfast the following morning, activities resumed as usual. A meeting was called to formally pass on information about the previous night.

Quite sadly indeed, a chap on the Bravo platform had tried to commit suicide. The Swedish spoken announcement on the Britannia was a message to say that a worker had been spotted in the waters. Apparently, he had made his way down to the lowest deck on the platform, known as a *spider deck*. He had opened up a small hatch in the platform grating and, what must have been a terribly difficult decision, jumped into the sea to take his own life. Two workers on night shift watched in disbelief from a level above the spider deck and did not have an opportunity to get to him before he jumped, but immediately raised the alarm.

However, as luck would have it, the chap had not perished. Bobbing around in the frigid waters for a few minutes the swell kept bringing him back up to the steel platform. After about the fifth time of smacking his exposed head on the underside of the large steel beams, he gave up the effort, reached up and grabbed the frigid steel. The two witnesses had, by this time, arrived at the scene and pulled him back onto the spider deck where he lay there sobbing in tears, gasping for air.

An incredibly sad event, he was immediately released from his offshore contract position and was on the next helicopter home for a full medical examination back in Aberdeen.

Several weeks later, it was apparent that the lad from Lancashire was not even thirty years old and suffering from depression due to some heavy, financial woes.

Then, about a month later, he was issued with a bill of more than £150,000 to cover the huge costs of four military Sikorsky's deployed to the scene. *Sometimes, life just sucks…*

Just before I headed back offshore, I received a telephone call at home from John Bickell at Conoco. John had asked if I was interested in coming back to Park Street to work on a new project. With terrific timing, I agreed to see him for a chat a couple of days after I had returned from the Brae field.

It was a contract basis and John had asked me the question; would I be willing to take a CAD course the company would pay for?

Two dimensional (2D) AutoCAD systems had just started to get attention in the industry and kickstart a culture that was to stick around forever and start the process of replacing drawing boards with computers, in the engineering office.

Agreeing to the position with Conoco and, though a tad higher than he wanted, John accepted the same rate I was on four years earlier. So again, the same contract that Dad had... but different dates.

I had enjoyed the experience offshore, for the third time I had been asked again to return to a company I had already worked for before and was heading back to a normal lifestyle working once again in one of the loveliest cities in the world, London.

# 1988

A vacation first on the Portuguese Algarve was a welcome break after the offshore stint.

Landing at Faro airport, Hertz gave me a car with a large, deep, basket type roof rack. I threw the luggage into the roof rack and headed off down the road to a wonderful private villa set back in amongst the olive and lemon trees. An hour later I pulled up in the driveway and stepped out of the car. With horror I peered at the roof. There was nothing in the rack! In haste, I had made a stupid decision not to tie the luggage down thinking that the depth of the containment would be fine. But, of course the 100kph air flow while the car was moving lifted them out.

I headed back to the airport, cursing.

Sure enough, around one long bend I spotted clothes and flip flops strewn across three lanes of highway along with the two, bruised suitcases that hopped out of the roof rack, together. A car pulled up and a nice local chap helped me pick up the stuff while we put lives in danger by waiting for gaps in the traffic and ducking in and out of the lanes collecting pants, trunks and shaving foam before driving back to the villa and falling upon a well-earned beer.

The CAD course I signed up for at the Richmond School of Technology was just a week long. The software was AutoCAD, *Release 9* and I was excited at the prospect of learning the program and applying it to my work at Conoco.

I began learning how to draw circles, straight lines and shapes. I learned how to type text, move things around, delete stuff, copy and make changes.

There were sessions on choosing colours, thicknesses of lines, underlining text and creating a new drawing. Everything was completely different to what I was used to doing on the drawing board and, when I started back in Conoco's offices the following Monday, the drawing board had been replaced with a computer, keyboard, digitiser and a heavy, twelve inch colour monitor.

The work I was assigned to do covered several areas. Conoco's documentation to support proposals and feasibility studies were sometimes three inches thick and did not include much drawing content. The company believed the time had come to add more drawings to the books where each drawing might eliminate the need for a thousand words of narrative. I was assigned to a piping and layout study to provide eight, unmanned, gas recovery platforms for a specific lease in the southern waters of the North Sea. My work and CAD drawings would reflect the platforms, pipeline links between each installation and back to the beach and proved to be a valuable component of the project binders.

Since I had left the company four years earlier, Conoco had not taken on anyone to replace me.

While back in Park Street, I enjoyed the location of being able to pick up stuff for lunches and dinner from Selfridges on Oxford Street that has a wonderful food floor. I would be able to meet up with old workmates from other local companies, or simply go for walks at lunchtime around the streets of west London or Hyde Park. Marble Arch and Bond Street stations are just up the road so commuting by underground to these hubs is perfect. And there's always the good old Licensed London Taxi to get you around.

The team around me was not the most effervescent and exciting bunch of guys. In fact, they were quite boring. As I got better on the CAD, I would suggest to the management team to create more complex and visually alluring pages in the proposals to which they agreed. I started developing three dimensional images adding different font types and colours. Pictures of platforms with backgrounds of pastel colours started to take shape. I would spend an entire day creating a two dimensional flat, *but 3D,* view of a platform and copy it across to a library I built up over time.

I got to enjoy this new toy very much and was gradually getting better and better at it.

My peers thought it all looked good, too. Within six months I had received requests from other departments and folk in the company to create drawings depicting dozens of different perspectives and views of offshore platforms, pipelines, onshore terminals, drilling equipment, compressors, generators, steel jackets, modules, steel structures, accommodation quarters, knuckle boom cranes, freefall lifeboats and stations, flare booms and helicopters. It was like being back at school again and I simply loved the CAD stuff and wasn't missing my drawing board at all.

My second child, Abbie was born and life was pretty cool. I was a dad again, plenty of work on my plate and getting stuck into CAD. I was learning about Conoco's future exploratory opportunities, enjoying the company of good folk around me and getting paid well for it, too.

Conoco took on a few new folk. I managed to get Graham a position studying plot plan options on a new feasibility study for one of Conoco's northern, North Sea blocks. He was sitting next to me on a drawing board while I was on a computer. Jim Spires and Phil River joined the team as planning and cost engineers. As we were all on a seven hour working day, it was easy to get a few extra hours in from Monday to Thursday and take a long lunch on the odd Friday. The four of us would hit one of the local pubs and laugh our socks off for a while before heading back to the office.

We found a pub that sold a strong, real ale called Old Bill. Jeez, this stuff was terrific and we used to woof it down. But, after four pints you didn't know your arse from your elbow and tried to seek well-hidden passages back to the office from the bars.

Pipers liked spending their money on good living, high end products and fast cars. Dave had bought a brand new yellow, Triumph TR7. It was a bloody awful car but it was Dave's pride and joy. He drove to work every morning and parked it in a local car park. Roger didn't like Dave. He thought he was a mouthy, arrogant git.

One afternoon, Roger slipped Dave's keys from his jacket pocket and popped down to the car park. He opened the door and sat in the driver's seat. Roger moved the seat back a foot and tweaked the door mirrors, then came back up to the office. He replaced the keys in Dave's jacket pocket and went back to his desk.

The following day, same time, and Roger again popped down to Dave's TR7, moved the driver's seat back a foot, tweaked the door mirrors, tuned the radio to a station playing classical music and turned up the volume to max. Then, back to the office.

On the third day, Dave got called into a meeting. Roger grabbed his keys, jumped into the car, moved the driver's seat back, tweaked the door mirrors, tuned the radio back to the classical music station and hiked up the volume. Roger then left an empty McDonalds bag on the floor with a few chips in it, with a Big Mac carton.

Dave came up to me the following morning and asked me if I'd seen anything a bit suspicious happening in the car park. I asked him why and Dave answered, *"Mitch, I think someone's been driving my car at lunchtimes."*

*"Who would do that?"* I replied. *"Well,"* Dave went on. *"Not sure. But what I do know is that he's tall, fat, deaf... and likes Mozart."*

# 1989

Ryan had started school in Barnet and I was proud of his progress. One afternoon he came home from school with a red and white scarf. I asked what it was and he told me a schoolmate had given it to him as a gift. Heaven forbid, his new friend was an Arsenal fan. Bloody hell.

My dad, my grandad, his dad and my dad's brother and I all supported West Ham United. To see my son curled up on the couch with a Gunners scarf was like having a leg off. I told him to take it back to his mate the following morning, which he did.

*"Tell Jason, thanks but you can't accept it."*

Couple of days later and Ryan returned home with the same Arsenal scarf.

*"Dad, Jason's dad said I should have it."*

So from that day, Ryan very much wanted to be an Arsenal supporter and it was not my business to interfere and he's been a fan ever since.

Moving from Essex to Hertfordshire a few years earlier had clearly sealed that one.

I took him to an Arsenal game at Upton Park one Saturday. Deep within the West Ham supporters, we were both nearly crucified.

I wrote to the local, *Old Fold Manor Golf Club* asking for a membership. This was a huge thing for me and I had gotten to absolutely love the game of golf and wanted to play the game more frequently. Essentially too, in a comfortable environment without the challenges of lining up at dawn on a Sunday morning, just to get a tee time on a public golf course for 3.37 p.m. that same afternoon.

Old Fold Manor replied in writing and had set up an interview for a Tuesday evening. My plans were to go home from work, grab a bite, change into something appropriate and head up to the club in good time for the interview. However, that evening the trains were causing a problem and I found myself pulling up at High Barnet station just ten minutes before the scheduled interview. I had a choice: arrive for the interview on time in the flowery shirt and sports jacket I was wearing, or head home, change into the appropriate attire but arrive late. I plumped for the first option and headed straight to the club.

Mike Bish was the captain, a recognised property developer in the north London area and he interviewed me with his vice-Captain.

I was asked what I did for a living, and discussed a few things in my personal life before advising me that effective immediately, I would be given three months of complimentary golf at the course to improve my game and get used to the layout. Either playing alone or with a member of the club, it was a gracious deal, indeed and over that period I was to submit a number of signed, score cards.

Mike went on, *"Mitch, once the cards are in at the end of the three months we'll set up an interview with the entire twelve members of the committee. Just a word of advice when you attend that meeting; don't wear that fucking calypso shirt."*

As my work fronts and opportunities continued at Conoco there were always organised events. One such event that jumps out at me was a Thursday lunch celebrating *Beaujolais Nouveau* Day. The French release this annual wine in the month of November and many good folk in London get to sample a wine in November of that same year.

Conoco had secured a basement of a local wine bar and several of us were invited to participate in the festivities. There were hors d'oeuvres and a seemingly unlimited supply of the lovely French beverage. Bottle after bottle was uncorked and the event drifted well into the afternoon.

By seven p.m. there were still about twelve Conoco folk enjoying themselves but after seven hours of drinking red wine it was more than time for me to head home.

I found my way to Marble Arch tube station on the Central Line and entered the top of the escalators which are arguably the longest ones on the London tube system. About halfway down I heard that familiar sound as a train whistled into the station. I began to start running down the stretch of escalators. Now, anyone employed as a stuntman or simply completely sober having a crack at this would get into trouble very quickly. On the other hand, I did not fall into either of these categories but instead, was totally pissed having drunk more than a fair share of Beaujolais Nouveau.

About twenty steps from the bottom things began to merge into one

145

another and I completely lost it. I fell, and bounced down the rest of the escalators coming to a complete halt, laying on my back on that flat bit of the escalator as the stairs level out and disappear under the floor. My tie was twisted halfway around my neck like a scene from *Frenzy*, the sports jacket and shirt sleeve were in tatters and my left forearm, entirely bloody, from coming into contact with the metallic edges of the moving stairs.

Two or three folk rushed up to help and I can remember one woman saying, *"Oh, leave him, he's drunk."* So they did.

Getting to my feet and appearing on the platform I didn't quite make that train, which was fortunate because it was heading in the other direction.

I boarded the next train and had to go just three stops before needing to change at Tottenham Court Road to get the Northern Line. I grabbed a seat and fell into a deep sleep, almost immediately.

Next thing I knew was a London Underground station master giving me a shake. I looked up at the station name and could see I was in Epping. This is not good when you live in Barnet.

I crossed the bridge and waited ten minutes before grabbing a westbound Ealing train. I had about an hour before the train would arrive at Tottenham Court Road, so grabbed a discarded newspaper and desperately tried to stay awake.

It was after ten o'clock when I pulled up at Ealing Broadway.

I grabbed an eastbound train and stood up all the way to Tottenham Court Road where I changed trains and battled more escalators before heading north to Barnet.

It was nearly half past eleven when I arrived at High Barnet station. Deaf and dumb sandwiches for a week.

146

# 1990

As the months flew by, I was getting bored at the office. Although I had settled well into a position in demand from most departments of Conoco, the work was simply not technically challenging enough and I missed the cut and thrust of the schedule driven project.

I had called an old workmate from my office one morning to catch up a bit and we both threw a few names around. I had discovered that a chap I was up in Aberdeen with, Ray Cobalt, was on an exciting assignment in Caracas, Venezuela. I don't know what gripped me at that moment but I felt a senseless urge to get hold of Ray and find out a bit more.

I called the agency placing the piping chaps in South America and asked them for Ray's telephone number. The agency immediately asked me if I might be interested in a position out there. I actually hadn't thought about it but suddenly found my palms all sweaty. I said 'yes' and that evening could think of nothing else.

Caracas time is 4 hours behind the UK. I walked into work the following morning and had just removed my coat when the landline rang. It was the agent in Scotland. They had already spoken to the engineering client and had received immediate approval, and a reference from Ray, to offer me a contract of employment.

It was a Wednesday and a fax was dispatched to my office. I was asked to be on a flight that Saturday! I took my Conoco supervisor to one side and discussed the opportunity, including the minor fact that I'd be leaving the company that day! John was a tad sceptical but agreed to the move if I could find a suitable replacement before I left.

I gave an old workmate, Phil Caitlin a bell and he popped across town for an interview. By three p.m. it was all sorted and Phil had accepted a position. I headed home to find myself planning a new assignment in Venezuela.

The project in Caracas was an engineering and design phase of an ethylene plant, built on the banks of Lake Maracaibo, Venezuela. The engineering

147

contractor was a German firm called *Linde* and the client was the Venezuelan state owned oil company, Pequiven. I was assigned to the project as a checker.

My first three days would not be spent doing anything else but reading client specifications and standards. I was introduced to several key managers of which one, my supervisor, was a Yugoslavian called Jorge. Jorge was quite simply an arrogant, nasty, backstabbing twat who proceeded to make my working life in Venezuela, an infamously memorable nightmare.

There were eleven expats on the project of which seven were Scottish. We all lived about half an hour from the offices in an apartment block called the Altamira Suites. I had a gorgeous one bedroom apartment on the twenty-first floor, sixty feet in width and one side facing the city and entirely covered by sliding windows. On the rooftop there was a running track, a bar, an outdoor pool and a bubbling Jacuzzi under a deep blue sky with the northernmost Andes mountain range, a gorgeous backdrop. On the ground floor, another outdoor pool graced the long bar and restaurant, with several tables shaded by thick, grassy cabanas.

It was a stunning place to live and each evening, competing with the local mad drivers and a three car race from the engineering offices back to the suites, we'd all gather around the pool bar for a few beers. It was rude not to.

The choices of restaurants in the Altamira district was extensive, the favourites being one that had an awesome, pungent aroma serving locally cured sausage, pancetta and hams that were also hanging on hooks from the ceiling and an Italian eatery that had a dance area right in the middle of the floor for couples who fancied a smooch to the jazzie music while waiting for their zabaglione to be whisked.

But work was definitely a problem. In those first three days on the project reading specs and standards I had not paid special attention to the pipe supports. In the second week, I had made an error and assigned an incorrect pipe support to a six inch line hooked up to the underside of a small vertical vessel. Jorge hit the roof, pulled me aside and royally bollocked me. In fact he bollocked me every day for a week or more. I was on a downer and I'd only been on the project for a short while.

The rest of the *Linde* project team were fine and it appeared that the other ten British expats I was working alongside, including Ray, had good, decent supervisors.

I also had an unfortunate incident at one of Caracas' largest shopping malls.

The team had access to three vehicles and any one of the eleven chaps could use them. I went shopping on my own one Saturday morning and chose to head across town to a large mall. Access to the underground car park was possible when pressing the button at the machine next to the mechanical arm that rises and allows passage into the car park, like any other parking lot.

As I pulled up next to a machine and pressed the button, the ticket was not dispensed from the machine. I tried several times but still the ticket didn't pop out and the barrier stayed down. I then attempted to reverse backwards and head to another point of access.

But, right behind me was a guy in another car. He was not moving out of the way to allow me to back up. Instead, this twat was waving frantically at me to go forward. I would've liked to of course, but there was a small problem of this barrier in the way. I honked, he waved. After a minute of this, he threw his arms around and finally succumbed to the honking, reversed, turned and buggered off.

As I backed up I heard a loud bang. I sat there in a frozen state and as crime was pretty hectic in Caracas I half thought I'd been shot.

The vehicle behind me sped away as I cautiously got out of my car. I looked down and saw that my rear two tires had been punctured. I had not realised this when pulling up to the barrier, but as a vehicle pulls up to enter the car park, the wheels roll across a forward pointing bar with large teeth like spikes protruding from the top of the bar.

They are not, however, designed to support a reversing vehicle. The spikes had punctured the tires and I now realised that the chap behind me was trying to alert me.

No-one gets out of their vehicle in Caracas and that is probably why he chose not to tell me face to face. And when I started getting out of my car, he thought it best to get the heck out.

On the intercom system the car park attendant alerted the manager at the Altamira Suites who sent someone to help me get out of my dilemma.

Geographically, Caracas is positioned beautifully to make it easy to visit other exciting places quite close by. I became a sort of, unofficial, travel agent for the eleven expats planning trips away every second weekend and grabbing the opportunity to head to the airport right after work on a Friday evening. Venezuela's northern capital city sits right on the Caribbean and from the coastal airport, the highway connecting the city winds up the mountainside and past some of the poorest townsites in the country. These dwellings have no formal postal address and are constructed of materials with little defence against heavy weather conditions like rains, mud and heavy wind speeds and, sadly, all too often they are demolished and swept away after a storm.

A Venezuelan island off the coast called Margarita is a lovely place to escape the city. A hotel in Porlamar with a lovely pool for two nights, open barbecues, white sandy beaches and fresh coconuts filled with a rum punch. Value for money was extraordinary.

Every expat working in-country were there *without* a work permit, including me. We had entered as visitors and every sixty days had to leave the country and return to acquire another sixty day stamp.

One Monday morning, a very nice girl from HR stopped at my desk and handed me a return airline ticket for a long weekend on the Dutch island of Curaçao, all expenses paid. It's a rough life but someone's gotta do it.

Curaçao was an extraordinary place but, unlike Margarita and part of the Dutch West Indies, very expensive. One of my workmates was a smashing fella by the name of Scott Scrummage. We got on very well and he was one of the five guys who were on this particular trip. On the Saturday, Scott, myself and the other three lads spent the evening at a brothel. Now, before this appears a bit distasteful, I am well informed that the town of Willemstad has the only legal brothel in the world and as a recognized tourist attraction we all wanted to see it, but not participate. *Why not!*

Beyond the security gates and into the main building is a huge bar, restaurant and a dance floor. It is possible to enjoy a nice evening meal and some wine at this place without dropping your trousers. However, when Scott approached the bar and ordered a chilled bottle of Dom Perignon and a bucket of ice, the scene soon took on a different atmosphere and it was like bees around a honeypot. Hookers came from everywhere and we got stuck into some terrific, amusing conversations. The evening was a right laugh and after visiting Willemstad and a few hours laid out on a white beach recovering from the night before, it was back to Caracas and trying to handle my shite supervisor.

Another great long weekend, eight of us jumped in two cars and headed west for five hours to a town called Chichiriviche De La Costa. It's a sort of old, rundown fishing village and we all stayed the night in a basic hotel.

At the crack of dawn, right after breakfast, we wandered down to the waterside. Bobbing around on the water were dozens of long, narrow boats with outboard motors hanging off the back. We reserved two of them, each with its own weathered pilots who looked like they had spent their entire lives on the windswept waters of Chichiriviche.

The two boats left the mainland and cut into the waves, heading for an island called Casa Sombrero, the largest of a small group of atolls just a half hour's chug away. The weather gradually began getting worse and within fifteen minutes we were being battered with gale force winds. This was less than fun and I started thinking about a life jacket and the minor fact that we didn't actually have any on the boat. The four of us squealed and shuffled in our seats wondering if we'd ever see land again. Scott, became increasingly agitated and unlike three of us who were trying hard to contain our emotions and tears he was audibly about to throw the pilot over the side. We calmed him down before the clouds cleared, the waves dropped and in front of us was the most beautiful sight as the boat moved along calmer fronts and the palms of Casa Sombrero appeared on the horizon like a scene from *South Pacific*. Except this was the Caribbean.

The two old fishermen dropped us all off with our bags and coolers full of basic essentials for spending the day on a desert island: crisps, peanuts and beer. They would collect us close to sundown.

The island was absolutely gorgeous as we walked the beaches looking for that perfect spot. We found it on an isolated stretch of sand near some shady palms and there were no people to be seen for miles.

Towels were laid down, beer cans popped open and a small ghetto blaster cranked up a few Gypsy Kings tracks. The sea was warm and calm and in between cool dips from the heat of the sun we just chilled, talked and got a bit sunburned before the boats picked us up late afternoon.

Monday back in the office was, again, depressing. I was becoming desperately unhappy and deemed it necessary to put this to bed. I pulled my lead aside and asked to be transferred to another area. I had made one miscalculation on a choice of pipe support and Jorge was not leaving it alone.

To my mild astonishment, the project agreed and moved me off the checking team and into a design role on the board. I was assigned an area that included laying out a sixty-six inch diameter flare system and huge knockout drum. Suddenly, I was working on something I enjoyed and within a week I was impressing project management who stopped by on a regular basis to see how I was handling the new activities. Liking the piping design, they gave me a thumbs up on the study work.

An hour's drive from Altamira and at a slightly higher elevation from Caracas was *Junko Golf Club*. A few of us would take one of the cars and head out to play eighteen holes.

The course is positioned on the lower levels of the cloud base and young caddies were available to walk with us for a small fee.

My lad, Eduardo, took my towel and dunked it in the stream next to the first tee before hanging it on the bag. A few holes were played on this stunning layout before the clouds rolled in. Within a minute we were all immersed in thick cloud and this was a real pea souper. I struggled to know what to do next, standing over my ball in the middle of the fifth fairway, not even knowing what direction I should be aiming.

My caddy pulled a four iron from the bag and told me where to stand, adjusting my stance ever so slightly. As I prepared to swing, he adjusted my stance again, my aim, and then told me to go for it.

Hitting a golf ball when you can barely see beyond it is a strange thing, indeed, and after connecting with the ball my caddy quickly made a sign for me to drop another ball because the first one was well gone, into the thick rainforest.

The same thing for the next ball and at this rate, I could see me going through every golf ball in the bag before I held a putter. After hitting the fourth ball I got the thumbs up as the young lad smiled and made a sign that it was about five feet from the pin. What bollocks, I thought. Approaching the green I dropped the bag and walked forward to mark my ball. It was sitting five feet from the hole. *These kids are good.*

There were many other trips away but on a particularly tremendous long weekend, I organised two simultaneous trips for eight of the lads while the other three abstained, preferring instead to work extra overtime and hang around Altamira.

One group plumped for a deep sea marlin and tuna fishing trip in the

Caribbean on a private cruiser with crew included, while the others, including me, opted for a trip away to see the world's tallest waterfall, *Angel Falls*.

In the wee hours a Boeing 737 collected us from Caracas International airport and flew a couple of hours south to a small town called Ciudad Bolivar. We landed and taxied to the hangar before switching to an eight seater, twin turbo prop and climbed back into the skies.

The landscape surrounding the town was beautiful, as tall, isolated mountains with flat tops called *tepuys* graced the visual feast as I craned my neck towards the window. When the aircraft banked and lost the clouds I looked from the window and there, just a hundred feet below us, were the apex of these magnificent falls dropping nine hundred and seventy-nine metres (three thousand, two hundred and twelve feet) to the base. It was a simply overwhelming sight and I felt awkwardly emotional and close to tears among the other chaps who were high-fiving in the cabin.

We made three circles and were all told by the captain that only one in a hundred flights around the Falls were as visually rewarding as this one.

Canaima Camp, a UNESCO Heritage Site in which the Falls were located, was to be our place of stay for a couple of nights where we played football with some of the local kids. We grabbed a good night's sleep.

At dawn, we headed off on a day hike towards the falls, watching them from the ground this time as we weaved our way through the jungle. Occasionally, we came across some natural pools that offered opportunities for diving from a high rock platform into the deeper waters.

The entire weekend was an incredible experience and, late Sunday evening back at the Altamira Suites, all eleven of us met up for a late supper and compared stories. It appeared that I had chosen the right trip. The four guys choosing the fishing trip had evidently spent several hours throwing up into the Caribbean as heavy swells caused the chartered boat to toss and turn shortly after leaving the coast. To add insult to injury, not a single fish was caught.

My time in Venezuela came to an end and Matthew Hall were busy once again on another offshore platform with the Marathon Oil client. The Brae East project needed piping designers and I was offered a position on the drawing board as a senior piping designer. Even though the CAD market was opening up, not all engineering companies had made that costly

153

decision to change out the boards in favour of computers.

I was comfy with this as my experiences on the 2D systems at Conoco, while being fundamentally prudent to have gotten into, were really not the right tool to design the 3D piping systems for a large offshore project.

I was back working alongside good folk like Eldridge, with Ian Dill, Chris the Greek and Terry Healy. Frank Bourne was our design lead and a smashing bloke who kept the ring of designers happy in what we were doing, while also encouraging us all to meet the deadlines and complete the piping studies and general arrangements in a timely fashion.

I was given my own modularised area to layout. Offshore modular piping design has its own set of challenges and is very different from designing an area of equipment and piping on, say, a refinery or a gas plant.

The two restrictions that make such designs different are space and weight. Offshore modules do not have the luxury of infinite plot space to locate mechanical equipment, side by side.

The piping designer must first position the equipment in an organised manner using P&IDs and a mechanical equipment list. The drawing resulting from this effort is regarded as a preliminary plot plan. What follows is a series of piping studies local to each item of equipment. It is these piping studies that will reaffirm if the equipment arrangement on the plot plan is acceptable, or to determine if further plot study work is required.

Offshore modules may consist of three levels with each level ten metres (thirty-two feet) in height between the main steel decking. The length of a module could exceed sixty metres (two hundred feet) with a width of forty metres (a hundred and thirty feet). Such a module will therefore have seventy-two thousand cubic metres (two and a half million cubic feet) of volume and including the structural steel, mechanical and electrical equipment, the piping and auxiliaries could weigh more than five thousand metric tonnes (eleven million pounds).

When building an onshore installation like a refinery or gas plant, weight is not a key concern because the mass of land any piece of equipment sits on will take an infinite load. However, a production platform positioned offshore in the middle of an ocean above the surface of the stormy waters rests on a supporting structure where weight *is* indeed a critical factor.

Weight distribution and centres of gravity are cause for concern when considering transportation requirements and must be recognised when engineering the module and laying out the equipment and piping. It is therefore not unusual to have a substantial team of weight assessment engineers assigned to a project who will track the collective weights and *c of g* for all components from a fifty tonne (110,000lbs) compressor to a small three quarter inch diameter needle valve.

An offshore platform to be located say, in the Gulf of Mexico, may consist of anything between three and a dozen modules. Often, the modules will be *engineered* in offices based at one location in the world like the UK, the USA or the Far East. The *construction* of each module, however, may well be executed at other locations that could be halfway round the world from the engineering offices or the platform's final resting place. The decision to assign worldwide locations far from where these platforms will finally rest is essentially caused by one common factor: cost.

At the time of labour cost assessment, a platform module assembled in southern Italy would be cheaper than building the same module in Glasgow. On that same note a module built in India will almost certainly be cheaper than building it in Italy.

There are many dynamics when choosing a country to assign the construction and assembly of a five thousand tonne offshore module. If a billion dollars is at stake, it's worth doing the homework.

First consideration, what is the political stability of the country being considered? If stable, are there inherent union issues with construction workers where there could be a lot of down time affecting the schedule?

What is the voyage from the module's port of construction, to its final offshore destination?

Will it have to travel across politically sensitive waters or storm-prevalent parts of open water?

Where does the host country acquire its workforce from? Are there civil rights issues with low pay and poor conditions?

What testament does the operating company have that the module yard being considered has proven construction abilities in the past on other large projects?

And then, of course, there is the obvious question: How much would it all cost?

As soon as a reimbursable contract is awarded, it kick starts a work process where the manufacturers of all equipment and materials are informed where to send their products. These items may be built in any one of several places around the world and would need to be shipped either to

155

the module assembly yard, or the jobsite. Logistics of transportation, weather windows and scheduled delivery times will also have an effect on the overall plan.

So, the defining reason of engineering, design, fabrication, construction and commissioning of all components of an offshore production platform is down to cost.

It is remarkably cheaper to assemble at site all the offsite built modules and weld them out instead of building the offshore production platform, piece by piece, out in the North Sea, known as being *stick built.*

The costs boil down to hourly labour rates.

Offshore workers like scaffolders, welders, pipe fitters, insulation installation contractors and structural steel erection companies are, all, very expensive when they are employed at the offshore platform's resting place out in the ocean.

It is substantially more cost effective to build modules overseas and engage these resources in countries like China, India, Chile, Malaysia or Indonesia where rates are considerably lower and staffing is more abundant. The total installed cost (TIC) might be reduced from $12bn to a more reasonable, $7bn. These cost savings may allow the Operator to consider another development.

And, often, bonuses are hung out there as carrots to encourage the module construction and assembly contractor to get it all done ahead of schedule.

But, on rare occasions, it is not critical to get the modules built so quickly.

The Norwegian oil company Statoil lease oil rich land in Norway's deep water fjords. Several modules of an offshore production platform destined for the *Sleipner East* oil field located in Gandsfjord were in their final stages of global construction and transportation. They were about to begin their seagoing voyage to the fjord when the tripod-like concrete supporting structure known as a *condeep* (concrete structure for a deep water site) was floated out to the field on huge, air filled pontoons used as ballast.

Once at its desired resting place, the condeep would be slowly de-ballasted and lowered to the seabed. Then, shortly afterwards, the module support frame (MSF) would arrive from its construction site, quickly followed by all the modules. This was the plan.

But, as the huge concrete, supporting structure was floated out to sea, to the horror of construction workers, engineers and technicians supervising the massive structure's delivery, poorly constructed concrete walls in the structure failed and the six hundred thousand tonne beast started taking on water much faster than the pumps could discharge it. Within just a few minutes, to panic-stricken onlookers of hundreds of workers, the structure freed itself from its tethers and sank, unrestrained, to the floor of the deep fjord.

The US$3 billion concrete structure would sit there forever.

But in a remarkable act of resourcefulness, and with all the construction drawings in place, Statoil commissioned a new structure which was built and floated out to the field one year later. This, in itself, was an incredible feat.

The Brae East project sailed along and I was fortunate to work in the company of some good folk while enjoying the challenges on the design side. I was pumping out general arrangement drawing plans on a number of the more critical areas of mechanical equipment. There were some particularly challenging areas of design around some huge shell and tube heat exchangers with welded nozzles replacing the more conventional, flanged joints to eliminate the chance of leakage around joints in a process system with potentially fatal toxic elements of the service.

Several months into the project, one morning, the telephone rang. It was an agent called Diane. Incredibly, her agency had been asked by Kellogg Brown & Root to track me down and ask me if I was interested in working in Canada on a large, prestigious offshore project.

The Hibernia Development Project was a partnership operated by Mobil Oil Canada, Chevron Oil Canada, Gulf Canada and Petro-Canada.

The engineering consortium known as the Newfoundland Offshore Contractors (NOC) was also a joint venture made up of Aker Engineering out of Norway, SNC Lavalin in Canada, KBR from London and a Newfoundland based company called BFC.

Originally, the project was to be engineered out of Toronto, Ontario, but Canada's Prime Minister at that time, Brian Mulroney, in a last ditch effort to help the economically struggling province of Quebec, had supported a proposal to switch the project engineering activities to Montreal.

The agent told me to look out for a confidential fax with all the details of the offer. She closed out the conversation by saying that KBR had advised her to inform me that, if I were to turn down the offer, the reason must not be because of money.

As Popeye might say, *"well blow me down"*.

I was excited and eagerly pacing between my desk and the fax machine, trying to be inconspicuous, until the papers rolled out and I sought a private place in a café down the road to assess the details of the offer.

The details of the assignment were very good. There was a great salary, low tax rate, accommodation, company car, business class return flights four times a year, or cash in lieu. Included in the contract was a lump sum settling in allowance and other perks like costs for setting up home for rent, a great medical coverage, sick leave and generous holidays. This was an assignment from heaven.

The following morning I called Diane and advised that I would *not* be moving forward with the offer. I explained that there would be a lot of hidden expenses on my side and it would not be possible to cover these expenses on the base salary offered. If the moons were to line up I would need a 40% increase in the base salary.

Diane called me back half an hour later. KBR had accepted.

Off to Canada. Again!

# 1991

The next few weeks were spent selling the car, preparing a house for rent and saying goodbyes to friends and family.

I held a leaving bash at *Ye Olde Monken Holt* pub in Barnet… a great spot for a piss up and had many old piping muckers there alongside me.

There was something uncanny about that leaving do. It was as if I sort of knew I would not this time, be returning to England.

Before preparing for departure from the UK I needed to make a critical phone call. When I was last in Canada it didn't all go that well, financially. It was important that I checked my name and credit rating before arriving in Quebec.

I called a London law firm and a couple of days later they confirmed that there were no negative issues and I would be okay to step back into Canada without getting cuffed by the Quebecois gendarmerie.

Montreal, to the newbie, is a delightful experience in any season. But, it is especially lovely in winter.

Snow lies on the ground and the downtown street life still buzzes from multi-level underground shopping malls, while the Metro rail system shuttles thousands of people to work and back each day. The gems of Montreal though come in a number of packages; Montreal is a culturally classy place offering hundreds of choices of chic, international restaurants, lively or quietly tucked away piano bars, a variety of different museums, rock, jazz music, classical concert halls and stunning theatres. There are five-star hotels, quality bakeries and delicatessens, fitness centres, an exciting Formula One grand prix circuit and, of course, memories from the 1976 summer Olympic Games. The only Olympics I might add, that is famous for two records the residents might rather forget: a) the only Olympic Games that lost money and, b) the only Games where a host country did *not* win a single gold medal.

Below the ground level of these bitterly cold wintry streets is another incredible world. Floors on several different levels provide an arena offering hundreds of amazing, climate-controlled shops and amenities, cinemas, bowling alleys, gymnasiums and even more food outlets and restaurants.

I was very excited to start work on the new project. The first morning I put on a new suit, new shoes, new shirt and a new overcoat before heading out from the apartment and onto the street wearing a new hat, too. I had thirty metres (a hundred feet) to go to the nearest Metro station and not even halfway there I stepped off the sidewalk straight onto a section of snow disguising a deep pool of icy cold water. With two anaesthetised feet I found my way to the office and started my third era of working in Canada.

My position on Hibernia was to be an Area Piping Lead on the M50 Accommodation Super Module. The module consisted of several levels of accommodation and two lower levels with electrical and firewater equipment. Above the accommodation was a helideck.

I was also assigned design supervision and control of the overall plot plans for the entire Hibernia platform. This latter responsibility involved overseeing all platform facilities like cranage and laydown, two monstrous drilling derricks, the tall offset flare boom, large power generation exhaust ductwork plus platform escape amenities including two lifeboat stations and the helideck.

I was joining the project early on in its development and many studies were required to nail down the position of these facilities. There were also four other Super Modules assigned to Process, Drilling, Well Management and Utilities.

The term 'Super Module' was applied to each of the five modules. Each module weighed in excess of six thousand tonnes (13,200,000lbs). Throughout the four-year construction work process none of these modules were ever to be lifted by a crane. They would all be designed to *slide* into positions throughout their journey. First, once assembled and prior to sailing from their country of origin, then, onto their final destination resting on the module support frame (MSF) of the seven hundred thousand tonne ($1,540^3$lbs) concrete gravity base structure (GBS) at the Bull Arm deep water port on the east coast of Newfoundland. This was where the offshore platform would be hooked up before the entire platform structure was towed out to sea.

And if you have trouble digesting such large numbers, the total weight of the entire unit would end up close to seven hundred thousand metric

160

tonnes. To put things in perspective, the ill-fated ocean going liner, *Titanic* would weigh in at a little over fifty-two thousand tonnes.

3D computer design was just getting started around the world. The chosen system was the Intergraph 3D piping design system known as PDS. Piping designers would be given a desktop computer, a monitor, digitiser and mouse. Area piping leads like myself would be provided with a drawing board and desk, but no computers. Now, this was a strange approach as Microsoft products like Excel and Word were also just getting started. Therefore, the leads who had to develop the planning, the schedules, budgets and other numerous spreadsheets would only have pencils, paper and erasers to prepare the documents. Email had just about got off the ground too, but use of the email system was restricted to senior management. Of course it was.

I spent the majority of that first year preparing piping studies. One study was to prove that two cranes instead of three were sufficient to handle all lifting requirements throughout the twenty-five year life of the platform. Lifting, that might involve offloading from a seagoing vessel and moving materials to dedicated, accessible laydown areas marked out on the exposed top levels of the installation and cantilevered decks. Or lifting and moving equipment from one side of the platform to the other.

Another study was to determine the size of the helideck. This required information on the actual helicopter expected to service the platform.

The operating partnership had made a decision to introduce a company called *Agusta* out of Italy, to purpose-build a number of EH101 helicopters. The 'EH' would be an acronym for European Helicopters.

The studies involved sizing the helideck and establishing its precise position above the accommodation module. The intended position of the Hibernia platform was to be about one hundred kilometres (sixty-two miles) off the Newfoundland coast and not far from where *Titanic* now rests. The weather patterns for that area of the North Atlantic would have an impact on helicopter landings and take-offs, interrupting workforce arrival and departures and risking business capital.

Directions of prevailing winds and how frequently they might hit the area were also taken into consideration. I spent weeks discussing and studying options of north, west or south facing locations but the results were still proving difficult in making a decision. One option of arrangement included a rectangular helicopter maintenance area where a crippled chopper would have the opportunity to fold up its rotor blades and be rolled off to one side of the helideck while allowing another helicopter to land. All were feasible ideas.

It was clear to the project team that wherever the helideck was to be positioned, there would still be an inordinate number of 'down' days in one calendar year where helicopters would not be able to land or take off. Because of these unsavoury statistics the unprecedented idea of having two Hibernia helidecks surfaced.

One helideck would be cantilevered off the northwest corner of the accommodation module while the other helideck would be cantilevered off the southwest corner. These two separated options of landing would help increase the flow of transportation and reduce the offshore platform 'down' time, thereby saving enormous costs.

Using the drawings, a plastic model was built by the University of Western Ontario, based in the town of London. On campus, the *Boundary Layer Wind Tunnel* faculty was prepared for our visit. This faculty had provided aerodynamic feedback on a number of globally recognised engineered projects including vehicles, large aircraft, the NASA space shuttle program and a number of large passenger cruise liners, except *Titanic*.

I spent two full days at the university studying the wind patterns of Hibernia's structure using the concept of both one and two helideck scenarios, using a model that included one easily removable helideck.

The model was placed at the centre of a thirty metre (one hundred feet) long metallic tunnel with flat sides, measuring five metres (sixteen feet) in height by five metres in width. Along each of the two side walls and ceiling were hundreds of small cylinders about 10cm (four inches) in diameter buried within the wall that could move in and out of the walls when directed to do so by a computer program. The program would create similar sea patterns expected in that part of the Atlantic Ocean.

To identify wind movement a blower would distribute different coloured smokes through the tunnel as the computer program transmitted the signals to the cylinders which moved in and out of the wall surfaces, in unison, to create a desired weather pattern. Using the data it was possible to determine what the impact of turbulence might be from having these two helidecks in place at the same time, or indeed adopting just one helideck.

Videographers captured the entire experiment, a report was issued and results were discussed back in Montreal later in the week.

The results proved that, if two helidecks were built, the frequency of helicopter landings would increase over time, compared to having only one helideck.

However, cost and schedule also play a big part in the decision making process and, shortly after the trip to Ontario, the call was made to run with one helideck.

One morning, my piping manager Dave Churns called me into his office and sat me down. He explained to me that the senior project management of all five companies had agreed to run a social club throughout the life of the project and would I like to get involved?

I jumped at the idea and within three weeks was voted in as the President of the Hibernia Social Club!

The mandate was for the Social Club consisting of twelve men and women, French and English speaking to provide one social event every single month of the year. To boot, with such a joint venture we had a budget in excess of a quarter of a million dollars a year to make it happen.

I had never seen anything quite like it as such a lavish budget would provide amazing opportunities with some exciting, diverse events.

Around November and about the same time that the new Social Club was conceived, Dave had also pulled the five piping leads into a room and told us that senior management had agreed to support a competition to discover what department could create the best Christmas decorations around the offices!

As the five of us left his office, with smiles like Cheshire cats, I doubt a day went by after that when Dave didn't regret endorsing the competition.

Week after week, models were made and Christmas decorations purchased. Walls were plastered with tinsel and shining stars. We also had a team of model makers who could be commissioned, for a small price like a beer or lunch, to make anything you wanted. So, for a few weeks, hardly any progress was made on the Hibernia Development Project while most pipers were, instead, fully engaged in decorating our entire floor.

One team modified a meeting room to look like a barn with Jesus' crib tucked away amongst bales of straw. There were large, stuffed animals including a donkey and lights all around the windows with carols quietly emanating from discreetly positioned speakers.

163

Another team suspended a Hornby railway track from the ceiling. Positioned on the twenty or so metres (sixty-five feet) of track was a moving train that made a choo-choo noise when it went past a certain point. A red cloaked smiling Santa sat in the driver's seat while Christmas tunes blasted out of a few speakers.

As the weeks went by, each of the five piping areas were involved in preparing their corners of the office. Soon enough though, the client managers were seen wandering around the piping floor feeling very much like part of a Christmas pantomime, wondering how on earth the piping group had time to do anything else, like design piping for example, when investment in preparing such elaborate decorations was clearly taking a priority.

Dave was summoned to a meeting to explain why the project had purchased more lengths of silver tinsel than carbon steel pipe? The poor fella was clueless and another meeting with his leads to ask us to tone it down a bit had almost no effect as the euphoria surrounding this Christmas competition was now in full throttle and fast approaching the finish line.

Prizes were handed out and on the Sunday before Christmas, the piping floor was a clear winner from the other nine participating disciplines.

The floor was soon opened up after hours to families of employees working on the project to bring the kids along and come take a look. A constant stream of visitors wandered through the drawing office.

Needless to say, the pipers cleaned up and celebrated the result with an extended lunch at *Ruby Foo's* pub which happened to be five minutes' walk from the offices.

# 1992

I worked hard at every corner of the project in Montreal. I was busy managing the area of the piping team under my wing, preparing numerous piping studies trying to firm up the platform facilities while attending social club meetings for a substantial calendar of events.

There were about ten overall plot plans covering all areas of the project. Although the piping, structural and electrical designs were all electronically conceived using the elaborate 3D PDS, the set of plot plans were being developed manually on the drawing board. While this was acceptable, as soon as each drawing required modifications, a different person would be involved in making the changes. This essentially kick started an ever increasing variance in appearance for the drawings as one designer's pencil work was, evidently, grossly different from the next.

The drawings started to look like crap and, unfortunately, under my watch.

One week, I was under pressure in getting the drawings ready for a whole day's client review when I noticed the draughting work for the M40 plot plan was of a decidedly poor quality. The client review was due the following day and, with hardly any time to get the pencil work improved, I made a decision to redraw the entire plot plan myself in an effort to make it look half decent for the review. This meant working all day then staying late into the evening.

As the evening wore on it was evident that I would struggle to get the drawing finished in a reasonable time but chose to stick with the plan.

The afternoon turned into evening and the evening turned into night. For some reason, the temperature had shot up so I needed to remove my shirt. The drawing board was set up in its vertical position and standing next to the board, hour after hour cranked out the line work and printing.

Around three a.m. things were quiet. But I then heard the main double doors to the office squeak open, followed by the sound of slow, cautious footsteps coming in my direction, the only part of the floor that was illuminated.

As the footsteps approached, I started getting a bit unsettled. When they were almost next to me I leaned out of one side of my drawing board just as a security officer walked past.

Well, the poor bloke almost had a bloody heart attack!

Obviously, he had no idea someone was working at a desk in the wee hours of the morning.

Once the redraw was complete, I felt much better. But when the chap who worked on the previous changes, got into work the following morning he was not thrilled at his drawing being redrawn. He had little reason to be of course and should've done a better job, first time around.

As Hibernia moved slowly through detailed design, the schedule moved to the right and costs escalated from an estimated C$2.6bn to a staggering C$5.7bn. Then came the news that might be sending us all packing and heading back home; Gulf Canada decided to pull out of the project. As new investors were sought, it was apparent to the remaining owners and several contractors engaged in Hibernia that finding a replacement would not be quick.

As prime time news stories touched on Gulf Canada's withdrawal, word then got out that the escalating costs were predominantly caused by a large number of expatriated engineers who had moved to Canada from the UK, Norway and USA.

One morning, the *Fifth Estate* news team tried to enter the offices to get any snippets of information they could lay their hands on.

No-one has any idea to this day how it happened, but a copy of the assignment contract all the British expats had, was released to the press. One evening while watching telly, scoffing back some poutine and cheese on the sofa, there on the TV screen was my assignment contract with all the sordid details right down to the settling in allowance!

The *Fifth Estate* got their stories in order and aired the hour long program a couple of Sundays later. One of our American engineering managers was seen holding a hand up to the camera lens, asking the documentary team to leave immediately.

These negative stories only served to widen a sizeable chasm that already existed between the expats and local French Canadians who were not seeing any of these expenses. Soon enough, all local hires were lined up for an increase in their salaries.

166

As the project continued the piping group struggled to deliver some key deliverables and we all got to see the other side of our department manager. Pressure was building up across the piping team and most mornings there was normally a bun run. This is where someone in the team takes a turn to write up a list of breakfast goodies like sausage rolls, bacon and fried egg sandwiches, then head down to the nearest café and bring them all back to the office.

Well, in Dave's mind, this had to stop because it was disruptive to production. He called an impromptu meeting for the sixty plus pipers and held the ten minute meeting in the larger, elevator area. Everyone gathered and listened quietly to Dave begin ranting on, raising his voice and reaming everyone out while instructing us all to work harder. Overtime would be mandatory, late arrival in the mornings would be noted and daily trips down to get rolls and sarnies would no longer be tolerated.

At that very moment and before anyone had dispersed and returned to their desks, one of the elevators went 'ding', the doors opened and with perfect timing I stepped out of the lift with enough bags of breakfasts to feed an army. Dave had a cadenza and went a sort of purple colour. He gave me a royal bollocking in front of a congregation of giggling pipers.

As the social club's president, I was asked to be *Master of Ceremonies* at the project Christmas Party. It was held at the swish, Queen Elizabeth hotel on Rene Levesque Boulevard. There were a heck of a lot of folk present and I had bought a brand new white woven patterned shirt to wear and a brooch over my top button. The trousers were black, as was the jacket with one exception; one of the two sleeves was brown with three large, black diamond shapes. I looked the part of an MC.

As the evening progressed, speeches completed and dinner cleared away, I had been chewing over an awkward decision on telling a sensitive joke before I stepped down and opened up the dancing.

It was a decision that was not easy to make because the story, to be told at Christmas, had a religious component in it.

So, for all you readers that are not too bothered about such politically correct statements, here is the story I shared with one thousand folk that December evening:

There's a nail company. They make and sell, nails. One morning a meeting is called by the CEO and around the large oak table sit all the nine directors and shareholders.

"I'm here to advise," the CEO started, "that the company is presently suffering unprecedented losses. I'm not sure how this has happened but we most certainly have to turn this around or we'll all be looking for a job in six months."

"It is absolutely critical that we sell more nails," the CEO went on.

The CEO then directed his next comment at the marketing director.

"We're relying on you, Brian, in putting this right and getting us back on track. So, I've reserved a sixty second slot on prime time television this evening, around eight p.m. Please prepare something extraordinary for this opportunity. Let's all meet back here at seven a.m. tomorrow morning."

"No problem, sir," Brian confirmed. "I'll sort it."

With this parting comment the CEO closed the meeting.

That evening, the board of directors are glued to the telly and at eight p.m. the commercials kick in. There on the screen is a picture of Jesus Christ up on the cross. The camera zooms in on one of his hands and there, written in large stamped letters on the head of a nail, are the words WILSON'S NAILS.

With the CEO on the edge of his seat and a cold sweat emerging, he picked up the telephone.

"Brian, WHAT the fuck have you done? You can't do this, you idiot! It's over and we're gonna be banished from operating in the country again. This is a terrible position you've put us in and another thing, the switchboard has been jammed! What the fuck were you thinking?"

"Sorry guvnor," Brian said. "I promise I'll fix it."

"You'd better. Thankfully, I booked another slot at the same time tomorrow. Please get out there and correct this horrendous problem. If you don't, I'm gonna have to let you go, Brian."

"No problem, guvnor," Brian continued. "Things will be all right. Honest."

So, the following night the entire nation was glued to the telly.

Eight p.m. arrived and on came the commercials.

A serene picture of green fields, trees and hedgerows filled the screen. The camera pans first to the left, then to the right. And look, there's Jesus! Running, stark bollock naked across a field with two Roman centurions

168

*close behind, one of them shouting to the other...*
*"I told you we should've used Wilson's Nails."*

Being *El Presidente* was no walk in the park. I had meetings occasionally during working hours in the day and at lunchtimes and evenings discussing options for events. One such event was a riverboat cruise and dance on a smart boat on the St Lawrence River. The vessel was large enough to accommodate four hundred people for a fully served, sit down evening dinner followed by a party and dance on the lower level.

It was a Friday evening and the weather was glorious. I had made arrangements during the day, showered and shaved at the office before heading out to the port to hook up with the other guests.

I sat at a table of eight with many of my closest friends. We were allowed one complimentary carafe of red and one carafe of white wine per table. It proved to be a terrific evening especially when I pulled the head waiter aside, shook his hand and stuffed some Canadian dollar notes into his top pocket.

Following the gesture, both carafes on our table were primed the entire evening. However, on the table next to ours was the project director on the boat with a few client folk and their wives, but his table wasn't getting any more than the allotted quota of wine. One or two glances from that table and I had a quick word with the head waiter before the problem was soon resolved.

I continued to immerse myself in the project and worked heaps of overtime. The piping team had grown by about 50% and a dozen new designers had joined my team either permanently or on a temporary basis and I was continually making an effort to ensure all the newbies had what they needed.

Hibernia acquired new investors. Murphy Oil and the Canadian federal government replaced Gulf Canada and chipped into the project and, after a few months of a slowdown, we picked it up again and recovered the momentum.

# 1993

Detailed design moved into post engineering and dozens of folk were laid off from the project in Montreal. Module construction moved out to Italy and South Korea where four of the five super modules were built, while the other one, the Accommodation module, was retained in Canada and built at Bull Arm, three hours round the bay from St John's. I was asked to follow the project through to St John's, Newfoundland.

Packing up the van I headed out to Newfoundland and a week on the road before catching a fourteen hour ferry from North Sydney, Nova Scotia.

Leasing a house backing onto Bally Haly Golf Course, I settled down and with the other hundred and ten thousand residents enjoyed the much slower Newfoundland lifestyle from the faster pace of Montreal.

St John's is about five hundred years old and the town has a great character about it. Steep streets, brightly coloured terraced housing and a busy dockyard. There are fish and chip shops selling cod tongues and turbot cheeks. Pubs that stay open till four a.m. *screeching* you in with a local rum that is delightfully disgusting. Screw up the 'screeching in' words on a sheet and you are forced to kiss a puffin's arse. Lovely stuff.

Hot dog stands grace Water Street till the wee hours when a taxi will take you no more than ten minutes to your home.

I had a couple of pairs of trousers made at a men's clothing outlet called *Byron's*. As I stood in front of a full length mirror, not that I ever need a full length mirror, a very attractive young lady measured me up and while pinning and chalking up the details, she asked me, *"Mitch, what side do you dress?"* My first thoughts were to say… the bedroom on the left side of my house.

Not fully understanding the question I told her that I didn't have a preference. With that, the assistant walked away and Byron himself walked over to me and whispered in my ear. I was surprised to hear that the young girl was really asking whether my banana hung to the left or the right. It was fairly important when measuring up for a pair of trousers.

I had never heard of this before but in truth I hadn't had many pairs of trousers tailored, either. And what about all those trousers on the peg? I cannot recall any half decent menswear stores segregating their trouser sections to direct the customer to a sign that said *"discounted trousers for men who hang to the left."*

She returned and I said, *"The left side, Andrea. Thanks for asking."*

Nautical Nellies was a great pub and buzzing every Friday night. I made good friends as the establishment, packed out with Hibernia engineering and construction folk, handed out warm nibbles and snacks while folk got hammered and dreamed of early retirement.

The rest of the Montreal piping gang soon made their way across to St John's when engineering activities wound down in Quebec.

One Friday evening I joined the pipers for a boys' night out at a place called the *Victoria Station*. A lovely, five level pub and restaurant with bedrooms on the top floors. I'd had about four pints and we were all enjoying the evening so no thoughts of heading home just yet, when I considered having something different instead of a pint.

Steve asked me if I'd ever had a Southern Comfort and freshly squeezed orange juice. Short answer was, that I hadn't. The barman told me I was the first chap in three years to ask for one of these. He lifted a small glass up to the optic on the wall, and drew two shots of Southern Comfort before topping it off with the juice and ice. What a simply divine drink it is, too! Three more later and I ordered just one more before calling it a night.

The bottle was empty and the barman detached it from the wall support and replaced it with a new one. Laying the large bottle on its side on the bar, he removed the optic.

There, in full sight of us all craning across the bar to take a look, was the neck of the empty bottle of Southern Comfort, crammed full of dead bluebottle flies.

There was probably a full ten seconds of open shock before the place erupted in laughter. With one exception being me, of course. I really didn't think I'd make it through to Saturday.

Newfoundland was gearing up for an oil and gas boom it had never seen before. Until Hibernia the only game in town was fishing. That year, the

Newfoundland and Labrador Fisheries had placed a moratorium on the fishing of cod in the northern Atlantic. The industry had been decimated by this decision. There would be no fish and chips at the St John's tables on a Friday night for a long time to come.

Christmas approached and so did the annual Hibernia Christmas Party. It would be the last one conducted in Montreal before the project closed up the offices and relocated in its entirety, to Newfoundland.

The project director had paid me a visit to ask me if I would be prepared to once again host and emcee the party back in Montreal. I agreed and was flown back to Montreal where the project put me up in the QE hotel for two nights. A lovely gesture.

# 1994

Like all good things, they come to an end. Hibernia was no different and after three and a half years it was time to move on. I had loved every minute of the project and had acquired a tremendous amount of respect from my working colleagues and peers.

I was being relocated back to London where I was advised that, with no work in London, I would be released from KBR. This news caught me off guard.

However, Calgary was once more booming as the Oil Sands projects that had collapsed ten years ago, had opened up once again. As incredible as it was at the time, there was much more sensibility in choosing this option.

After a discussion with my manager, Arthur Barter, I would forego the business class return to London and KBR would replace this with a three week, paid driving holiday that would see me head west, out to Alberta. The costs of hotels and trimmings would be far less expensive than relocating me back to London on an expensive business class ticket. Furthermore, my personal belongings would be moved by road to Calgary instead of a much more costly shipping by sea to the UK.

After the ferry back to the mainland, the drive across parts of the eastern USA and Canada were spectacular. I hit Maine, Massachusetts and New York states before popping back up to Canada and spending a week around the general Niagara area. Visiting the Falls, the Sarnia hospital I was born in and a hidden gem of a small town called Niagara-on-the-Lake where some of the loveliest wines are made in that region.

Then through the northern central states and a few days in Yellowstone Park before heading north, up to Calgary.

When I submitted my expense claim for hotel costs, a week later, I received a call from Arthur. He had looked at the map and asked how on earth Yellowstone Park was on the route back to Calgary?

It was a terrific road trip and set me up for the new experience back in an old familiar city I never thought I'd ever see again.

Checking into a hotel, it was a fax machine that provided dozens of places to rent. Three days later I moved into a detached house in the southwest part of the city just off Elbow Drive.

Within a week of arriving in Calgary I had found a position at Colt Engineering.

I was assigned to a project as a CAD piping designer with a chap called Paul Dinkhurst as the area lead. He was suspicious of me right from the offset and managed to make my working life a misery, as he did most folk. I had not had much CAD experience so requested a drawing board which was to help me. I was asked to lay out a few areas and prepared studies for consideration and option. But my CAD skills, although improving, were slow.

Paul, a hardnosed, unsmiling and miserable tosser of a Dutchman, was impatient for me to finish my study. I was summoned to the Piping Manager's office, John Headland, another piping chap in a lead role who clearly had a severe charisma bypass. Colt was full of them.

I explained it as I saw the situation and was asked to continue doing what I'd been doing. That relationship was never to recover and I hated every minute of the project until I moved onto a Westcoast Aitkin Creek job where 2D CAD was the only tool available and the only pipers who did have drawing boards were surprisingly, just the piping checkers. *Why on earth would they need a drawing board?*

I continued to struggle with the 2D CAD work having not engaged in the software since my spell at Conoco. If you don't use it, you lose it and while immersed in a difficult area where I simply couldn't keep up with the program, it was a tough few months.

I could see how my area should be piped up but not having a drawing board or experience with the computer systems it was impossible to express my desires properly in the piping design. I was heading back to London for a week's break and asked for more time to finish my area. The project agreed that I would complete the design upon my return.

In a cruel reversal of fortune while abroad, and to support the ridiculous schedule, my area lead had printed off a copy of my incomplete drawing for checking. I returned from vacation to find the checkprint laying on my desk, covered in redline markups. I felt like I was set up and when the project was cancelled a few months later, I was released.

Piping projects can be made to be great or disastrous depending mostly on what type of individual is running each discipline team and department. There are plenty of technically acceptable pipers around. However, there are few who can provide leadership and support for a large piping team.

My methodology of leadership tries to bring people together, share information between us, especially schedules, recognise folk who have gone that extra distance to make an effort, and, basically, try to be a nice chap. I've been fortunate to have led many piping jobs and when guys return to my team after working with me before, it's a nice feeling. Don't get me wrong, I'm far from a perfect leader. But there are a number of things that help a piping team deliver the drawings and gain credibility after the project has finished.

First, always be open with the team. Hiding schedules and dates does not help anyone. The pipers need to know when information should be moved between the process and mechanical engineers, piping designers, stress engineers, structural designers, control systems group and vendors. They need to feel part of the team and understand all challenges because it's also rewarding if a designer completes an area on time. It's not fair, either, to give a fictitious date to a designer. Give him a copy of the approved schedule and let the designer plan his or her work.

A good lead must listen to the pipers. They are trying hard to get things finished and they will more often than not need leadership in moving forward.

Don't be forced by project engineers in issuing isometrics that do not have the supporting information behind them. Isometrics issued on time but not right will never be remembered by the client for being issued on time but they WILL be remembered for unnecessary costs and being crap. Issue quality drawings a tad late but with all the supporting information in place and the client will always remember the good product while unlikely recalling they went out late.

Some project engineers rarely help the pipers with the subject of quality and hinder progress by providing nothing but a plethora of incomprehensible targets and unnecessary activities. Often, project engineers do not have the necessary background in piping engineering and design and if things are not going well on the job they'll behave more like messengers, hopping around the floor passing information they've gleaned from the piper, to the project manager. But if things go well, it is the PE that'll receive all the accolades.

If the piping team haven't received all the critical stress engineering,

175

instead of the PE putting some pressure on the stress group they will ask you to spend time and create hundreds of lists of what systems are outstanding, what systems are more critical and what you can do to move forward. Rarely are project engineers seen to help the piping group by clearing holds and roadblocks. They just pester the crap out of you till you beat them to death one Monday morning with a baseball bat. I have been fortunate to have also worked with a few crackerjack PE's.

Many times, piping isometrics will have target dates that are unrealistic for everyone in the issue cycle. The piping group may be forced to issue drawings far too early when pipe fabrication contracts are not even in place and materials not yet in the warehouse. A good piping lead will understand what these dynamics are, consolidate with the supporting vendor data and make an effort to rise to all the challenges.

Calgary's major college, the Southern Alberta Institute of Technology, or *SAIT*, had many courses open to the public. I love to cook and had taken several cookery courses over time, including a 3-year certificate I had to postpone three quarters of the way through when I left England to go to Montreal in 1991.

Indian food is always special. But, I noticed that *SAIT's* brochure of part time courses did not have a single course offering tuition on the cooking of Indian food. I love to cook Indian dishes and wanted to give teaching a shot. I called the Faculty and went along for an interview.

A lovely lady offered me an opportunity by setting up a proper, practical interview.

I was given complete access to the college kitchens and amenities. All I had to do was to find at least twelve persons, friends and workmates, to come along for an evening. The Head of the Faculty would sit at the back and monitor my progress. I could choose a menu, buy the foods and *SAIT* would cover the costs.

I draughted up a detailed menu, bought all the stuff and one Thursday I opened up the arena to seventeen friends and colleagues for *An Evening with Mitch Jago* on North Indian cookery.

I bought several bottles of red and white wine and, along with the host who had one or two glasses over the course of the evening, everyone helped themselves, too.

I scrambled my way through the three hours over running by just fifteen minutes as I cooked eight different dishes, including some naan breads. It was a real hoot as everyone slowly got pissed and we all had a great time.

The Head of the Faculty sat at the back of the classroom and laughed his way through the entire process.

I got the job! In the next issue of *SAIT's* brochure was a course on Indian Cooking, served up by yours truly Mr Mitch Jago. I was to be paid $20 an hour and was thrilled at the achievement.

Unfortunately, there had to be a minimum of seven persons enrolled in the course for it to be formally sanctioned and over the next few weeks only five had signed up. I got to understand that this was not unusual and, regretfully, the course was cancelled, sadly, before I had the opportunity to take things further.

One Friday afternoon at Colt, the entire Westcoast piping team were called into a large conference room and systematically and alphabetically told from reading a list of resources if you were being transferred to another project, placed on overheads or let go. I was let go and, after many months struggling with the computer, I was actually chuffed to be out of such a useless company environment and poorly managed by the piping department manager, Harry Shortbread.

I took this opportunity to consider something I'd wanted to do for many years; entertain children. With a clear lack of such stuff in Calgary I started a bouncing castle business and named the company, *Bouncing Bubbles*. I bought a brand new, bright orange and black inflatable tiger from San Antonio, Texas with a great big striped, floppy head.

Contacting the Calgary Herald's small business department, I soon had a team of reporters around to the house for an interview and picture taking. The small business section of the weekly issue published a whole page spread on the business and, thereon, the phone never stopped ringing and my entire summer was taken care of with bookings.

Later on, I supplemented the tiger with an inflatable slide and set these pieces up at fairs, shows and birthday parties around the city and southern Alberta. I would either get paid as a lump sum for a day or two, or on occasion was allowed to charge a dollar for a five minute session. When the latter was agreed, I would make quite a few bob.

The Calgary Philharmonic Orchestra paid me to set up at an event that sadly, is no longer considered; *Mozart On The Mountains*. The CPO would set up in Canmore or Kananaskis Country on a warm summer's Sunday and the public would bring a picnic, chairs and blankets and sit on the grass listening to the gorgeous music of Mozart for a couple of hours, played by a full orchestra at the feet of the Canadian Rockies. This was a spectacular annual event and the two bouncers were in constant use.

The line-up of kids went back a hundred metres as I set two timers for precisely five minutes before each would ring loudly and all kids shuffled off the units before the next group of twenty hopped on. In peak times, twenty kids and twenty bucks every six minutes. This time away from the piping industry was a tremendous experience and I loved seeing the children's faces when they hopped around inside these bouncers.

But it wasn't all fun and roses…

One cloudy Sunday, I delivered the tiger to an address in the northwest part of the city in a new development. The large, detached house was built on slightly sloping ground but the back garden had not yet been seeded.

I inflated the unit, chatted to the Mum in charge and took off to another address where the slide was being rented. The heavens then opened.

I went back to collect the tiger three hours later and obviously, the kids were all indoors. The power had been shut off and the tiger had fully deflated, leaving the lovely orange and black unit looking like a children's swimming pool. The ground all around the tiger was a mud bath. And add to this the fact that it was all on a slight gradient.

I struggled to find purchase when rolling up the unit as my feet gave way and often I would slip, face down, onto the mud. It finally took me about four hours to get it back onto the trailer. Puffing and panting, I knocked on the front door to claim my fee and was curtly told to bugger off because the kids had not even got an hour's use from the bouncer. Departing empty handed and being blamed for a rainstorm I drove on to collect the slide where I also received no cash before arriving home absolutely knackered.

Canada is not a great country to set up an outdoor business. The season is unquestionably short and in that first year I made a few bucks between the months of May and October but after that, what then? I could hardly start selling three hour sessions with a foot of snow on the ground in minus fifteen degree temperatures. It was time to get back into piping.

178

# 1995

Out on some cold, miserable industrial estate on the east side of the city a small company called Calc Engineering leased an office. I joined their small team on the drawing board supporting a Chevron project and a revamp to the Burnaby refinery near Vancouver. The owner was a nice chap called Ron Impey, although he was careful on expenditure. This was obvious as soon as anyone entered the office to see old panelled doors laying horizontally on top of bins. These were our desks.

Ron had made an acquaintance with a chap quite high up on the Chevron Board and, as a result of some marketing and strategic dining, Calc Engineering had won a lucrative contract to provide small-project services to the refinery. Business trips out to the Vancouver area and a walk around the site were required before bringing the details back to the Calgary office.

Toward the end of my first month, Ron happened to be out of the office as I asked around the team when I might expect to get paid? A reasonable question after nearly four weeks of effort. The chaps advised me that normally, the last working day of a month the invoice should be submitted and Ron would pay a week later. Fair dos…

Just then the phone rang. It was the only phone and I was closest, so answered with, *"Good morning, Calc Engineering."*

*"Hello, Mitch,"* the voice replied, *"this is Ron. Is Keith in?"*

Keith was in and I continued to give Ron an update for twenty minutes on the area I was working on. He told me he would be in around eleven a.m. before I put the phone down.

Then, in an impulsive act of comedy, I immediately picked up the phone and said, *"Oh and by the way, where's my fucking cheque!"*

Well, the place collapsed in laughter as I put the phone down and turned back to my drawing.

Not ten seconds later, the phone rang. *"Good morning, Calc Engineering,"* I answered once again.

*"Hi, Mitch, I thought you were gonna pass me onto Keith? And what's this about a fucking cheque?"*

I was the last one to be paid.

# 1996

I found a position with a small, growing company called *Triad Engineers.*

The project was a new oil production installation in northern Alberta that was under scrutiny from the Ethics Board due to the client artificially elevating its stock value by telling porkies about the actual oil it had claimed to be present beneath the ground.

Newspaper reporters and television coverage jumped on this and, with discretion important, I told few people about the new venture I was about to become engaged in.

Even so, an engineering team was put in place to develop the project and I did my bit as a piping area lead for several months before the project was canned. I was also getting paid very late after submitting a monthly invoice so was actually pleased when it all went belly up. A recurring and common experience for projects conceived in Alberta. My last paycheque I received about six months after leaving Triad.

I subleased the bouncing business to a company called Astro Jump and joined a company called Duckworth, Price & Henderson (DPH). Small projects, good folk. The piping manager George Novotny was a pleasure to work with and I enjoyed my time there working with smart pipers like Bill Staples, Lorraine Shizecki and Peter Tarke. The project culture at DPH was slim budgets and small gas plants to be developed around rural Alberta. Each job lasted a few weeks and might include a visit out to a remote wellhead on some farmer's plot of land.

# 1997

I then joined Bechtel's Canadian arm of their organisation, *Bantrel*. They had a stack of work and I was immediately positioned as project piping lead on a bid for a huge Co-Generation Plant that was to be part of the Joffre expansion project near Red Deer for the client, Nova Chemicals.

To support the FEED development, and along with four other engineers, I was assigned for six months to Bechtel's Power division in Gaithersburg, Maryland near Washington DC.

The dear structural chap I was to share an apartment with, Dave Shaker, was a real nice bloke but clearly a sandwich short of a picnic. We were asked to book our own flights and plan to be in the Bechtel offices on a specific Monday morning. The closest airport was Dulles International and I secured an open return ticket with Delta. At a meeting in Bantrel's offices in Calgary immediately prior to flying south we all compared flight times and itinerary before flying out of Calgary. Everyone possessed tickets to Dulles, except poor old Dave who had purchased a ticket to DALLAS. A Texas based airport, being a couple of thousand miles from DC that wasn't much use to him.

When Dave finally got his destinations sorted, we shared a vehicle down in the States. He would fly home one weekend, while I stayed in DC and vice versa so that we would switch each weekend and not get under each other's toes. During the week, we shared the cooking until I suggested one day that I continue to cook for us from now on. This was essentially due to the fact that we went shopping to a supermarket and he said he'd do the dinner that evening. He bought a bag of basmati rice and a couple of artichokes. Wow! I thought, I'm in for a treat.

After unpacking the goods and cracking open a couple of beers, Dave then proceeded to heat olive oil, then throw in the rice, straight into the pan. While the rice was burning away, he sliced up the artichokes and threw them into the pan with the burning, uncooked rice.

The evening didn't end well except for the sound of the doorbell, when the pizza was delivered.

One Friday, Dave drove me to the airport. Dulles airport, that is. Not Dallas. We approached a toll bank with about twenty booths. There were no mechanical arms at the booths but, instead of slowing down, Dave accelerated through one of these booths. I asked why on earth he had risked a night in a DC jailhouse and he told me he had no change on him. Well, all the bells and whistles went off and I thought a chase would be on. Dave just carried on towards the airport. Imagine that kind of reaction in today's culture? We'd have probably been shot dead within ten seconds. A bit like Santino Corleone's demise in *The Godfather*.

Bechtel management were not very supportive of the Canadians in town. I was getting frustrated by secret squirrel stuff and being kept at arm's length from the local cliquey team who'd worked together for twenty-five years. I vented my frustrations but also learned how powerful the Bechtel Power organisation was as, week after week, we were given snippets of updates and, essentially, told to shut up or go home.

I loved that part of North America, especially in the Fall. The shopping malls and golf courses were wonderful, as were the quaint tree-lined neighbourhoods around Washington DC and Baltimore.

Georgetown was buzzing with nightlife of pubs and restaurants. The beauty in these three hundred year old communities essentially revolved around the fact that they were established and much different to Calgary which, less than one hundred years ago, had dozens of bat door saloons and muddy streets with horses tied up to rails.

The Co-Gen project was eventually awarded to Black & Veitch out of Chicago and the Calgary boys all returned home.

In the next twelve months, Bantrel's engineering department made front page news for the wrong reasons.

First, I was placed on a Texaco refinery revamp project down in Anacortes, near Seattle in Washington State. The design had gone pear shaped but I had managed to support the final issue of all the piping isometrics, poorly project managed by an arrogant American chap called Roy Gurner. A court case was pending and I was interviewed by a legal team and asked to keep the sensitive things, quiet.

I had then been given a couple of small Suncor projects to oversee in parallel. Both projects were based in the main Bantrel Tower on 6$^{th}$ Avenue. Nothing too dramatic and maybe two thousand piping hours each.

Meanwhile, over in a satellite office a few blocks away, the engineering and design for the monstrous Suncor Millennium project continued. This was a hugely prestigious project for the company and they had a cast of thousands working on it. A Chinese chap by the name of Don Chan was heading up the piping team and was struggling to retain control of the pipers. Changes were not being controlled and managed properly and Don had a tendency to go off the deep end on a regular basis, screaming to all within earshot.

Charlie Crown, a Texan, was one of several piping checkers who were under the gun to keep the numbers up and check a certain quantity of isometrics each week.

Jean Marie Dilligent, an Algerian Frenchman and a half decent piper but wasn't the most personable chap in Calgary, was a piping coordinator assigned to crack the whip and ensure the checkers were hitting their targets each week.

One Friday afternoon, when approaching Charlie's desk with notepad in hand to get the numbers, a row had developed. The pressure is on the checkers to check as many drawings as possible but, often, there were reasonable excuses for not hitting the targets. Late vendor data and constant process changes were the usual suspects. But, in the argument, Jean Marie accidentally knocked over Charlie's cup of coffee spilling the lot over his check prints.

Charlie had leapt from his chair and grabbed Jean Marie by the throat, forcing him down on his back onto the carpet tiles. As if that wasn't enough, Charlie straddled Jean Marie across the chest and continued to beat the crap out of the poor Algerian who was really only trying to do his job.

A couple of guys jumped in and pulled them apart.

Bob Mall, the piping manager, was advised of the incident and quickly shot across to the Millennium office to review the situation. As Jean Marie and Charlie were key pipers in the company, albeit contract, Bob made the decision not to sack them but give them a bollocking and separate them.

Back at the main office he pulled me aside and as my two projects were winding down asked me if I didn't mind switching to a role on Millennium and replacing Charlie Crown. Charlie would be re-assigned to another project in the main tower. I saw no issue with this and so relocated to the Millennium project.

# 1998

The next few weeks, things got back to normal and word had gotten around about the punch up. Meanwhile, Mike Izzard was an area piping lead on another small Suncor project in the main tower and was not managing the stress very well.

Well, one of the process engineers, Bob Shai, had made repeated changes to the roller boards. Backwards and forwards he would go to redline modifications to line sizes of a control valve set. The master roller board happened to sit outside Mike's office and, each time this chap appeared at the board with his coloured pencils, the red mist came up on Mike's face. After the fifth line size change to the same valves, Mike rushed out of the office, grabbed the back of Bob's shirt and air lifted the smaller chap up and over a desk while buttons popped off his shirt.

This incident happened fresh on the heels of the Algerian Franco-American incident a couple of days earlier. On this particular occasion, Bob Mall had no recourse but to sack Mike, which he reluctantly did, under supplementary pressure from Bantrel's senior management. That afternoon, Mike looked a lost soul, carrying boxes out to his car.

Punch ups, accidents and instant dismissals are rare but not unheard of in the oil and gas game and there are numerous stories to support each case.

One Friday afternoon in the early seventies, a couple of chaps working at Matthew Hall in London came back from the pub late and one of them was seen wobbling through the piping floor to his board, trying hard not to be noticed. This was going well until he negotiated a corner of a large plastic model in the middle of the drawing office and this was where it all went wrong. He caught the corner of the model and a large chunk of a piped up compressor area broke off and smashed onto the hard ceramic tiles. This was probably six months of model work killed off in five seconds and that guy got an instant dismissal.

Friday afternoons would, on occasion, not end well. Several chaps at Worley Engineering got back to the office after three o'clock. One chap, a tall, lively Scotsman called Doug, thought it was a good idea to open up and spray a fire extinguisher onto the other pipers. Instead of clear, cold water sprayed all over the place was a dark brown, stinking liquid that covered and spoiled just about every man's original drawing on each desk. The piping manager bollocked Doug and told everyone to clean up the mess before things got back to normal.

As explained earlier, when I was younger I had my fair share of extended Friday lunchtimes. In truth, they were not intended to rip off the company for a few hours but simply to enjoy an end-of-week social event with a few good old workmates. If there were no design emergencies in the office, often, a few guys would congregate and enjoy a few beers before going straight home after.

Timesheets were often submitted on a Monday morning then and could reflect time off taken on a Friday afternoon. But when timesheets are approved on Friday mornings or even a Thursday, it's not that easy to modify the sheet once approved and faxed off to the agent, so Friday drinks were less common.

Sorry, I digressed a bit there.

After switching across to the Suncor Millennium project, I worked as a checker on a tall, vertical vessel. The Philippino piping designer on that area was fairly green behind the ears and hadn't much of a clue on how to pipe up the item of static equipment. His design supervisor was busy looking after other activities and allowed the designer to run loose on the area for three months without being overlooked. This is criminal. Such lack of supervision can put back an area nine months behind schedule.

Piping to and from nozzles was running straight out and over the handrailing of local, circumferential platforms with no opportunity to support the piping. In such situations, any nozzle on a vertical vessel that has a piping system attached, the piping must turn away from the nozzle and run up or down the side of the vessel. This allows an arrangement of supporting structural steel known as a *welded attachment*, to be connected to the vessel and thereby provide an opportunity for a bolt-on support for the adjacent piping.

The design was on a 3D CAD Bentley system called AutoPlant. I checked the area over a period of a couple of weeks, marked up the check prints and handed it back to the designer for him to update the model.

# 1999

Around this time as the project started to get into a busy isometric issue phase a brand new, prestigious project was gearing up in Calgary.

Syncrude's upgrader facility about 75km (forty-five miles) outside Fort McMurray in northern Alberta was about to get considerably larger. Upgrader Expansion One, *or UE-1* as the project was crowned involved a 25% increase in the production and sales of synthetic sweet crude oil to bring production to a massive three hundred and sixty-five thousand barrels a day (bbld).

Due to the sheer size of the project a joint venture was orchestrated that involved a number of engineering contractors. Under the management of Kellogg Brown & Root (KBR) out of Houston two large firms, Fluor and SNC Lavalin, headed up the Calgary-based engineering project along with an environmental company, Veco, and other smaller indirects.

Four silos were created to oversee the entire scope of work. In addition to the three silos covering the process system streams being engineered was a fourth silo and huge component of utilities and offsites (U&O). The organisational structure was set out such that Fluor piping leads headed up the process silos while SNC Lavalin were to oversee the U&O piping work. My name had been pencilled in for a lead role with SNC.

Malcolm Mayhew was the manager of piping at SNC and he took me out for lunch to discuss the position. The hourly rates in Calgary for pipers were anywhere from $35 to $50 but yet to be seen in the city was a rate of $60, or one dollar a minute. Malcolm took me to lunch and offered me the lead position at the rate of sixty bucks! I immediately agreed and we shook hands over a glass of port.

The next few weeks went by as paperwork was secured and I was now ready to give notice to Bantrel.

I have always been a very cautious chap when it comes to divulging work opportunities to others around me. Several times in the past, I've seen positions almost stolen from under someone's nose as a close workmate hears about an opportunity and makes a last minute call to a lead engineer he knows and slips into the role instead. I therefore choose to play my cards carefully and keep them close to my chest.

I wanted to speak to my department manager Bob Mall, first. In trying to call him, I heard he was up in Edmonton on a business trip.

I found out where he was and dragged him from a meeting to take my call and allow me to give notice. Bob was very gracious in hearing the news, thanked me for being the first person I contacted and wished me well in my new role on the UE-1 project. The news was probably a bit tough on Bob because Bantrel had also submitted substantial proposals and bids for chunks of the UE-1 work but, on this occasion, the Calgary firm was overlooked.

The following day I called Bob's deputy and someone who, at the time, was a good friend of mine. Graham Mayhew was Malcolm's brother and did not take the news very well. On the telephone, he reamed me out for not letting him know about my interest in the new position. This conversation caught me off guard and we finished on a sour note that would have a defining moment in our friendship. To this day, I have not really understood why Graham had taken that approach.

I had always gotten on well with Graham but from that moment, due to his soppy response and preferring a negative onslaught of abuse instead of well wishes, we never socialised together, again.

I had bought a smart, four-bedroom house in Braeside on a quiet, established tree-lined street to rent out as an investment. After having the place painted, cleaned and ready to move in, an ad was placed in the newspaper. It was an exciting few weeks but, alas, enquiries did not lead to much.

One day I received a call from a gentleman interested in the house. When I met him that evening, he brought with him five young lads around eighteen years of age. He was the manager of Canada's national water polo team. The five boys standing on the lawn in shorts and flip flops were half of his squad of ten. With no other options of tenancy I made a decision to show them the house and agreed to read their references, which were all fine. But a team of boy teenagers in one house concerned me.

An arrangement was made to meet up again on the Saturday morning and sign the lease.

On the day before, I stopped off at the house after work to get a few final things sorted and remove the FOR LEASE sign from the living room window.

A car pulled up next to the lawn and out got a family of four. Husband, wife and two young kids. They had seen the ad in the window and were interested in taking a look. I advised them that a lease was being signed in the morning. However, I didn't mind showing them around. They loved it of course and asked me to join them at a coffee house where we discussed their desire to lease the house for two years.

I was in a bit of a jeppy quandary and undecided on who to choose as tenants. On one hand was a deposit paid on a twelve month lease but the house would be full of young scrotes probably partying all night and pissing off the neighbours. The other alternative would be to discard the water polo team in favour of a text book, ideal family who would be there for two years at least and who were unlikely to piss off the neighbours.

Business is business and I plumped for the family. The manager of the water boys was not amused by my about turn. It wasn't personal.

When arriving the following weekend to collect a banker's draft and hand over the keys, a moving truck was already on site and the pathway leading up to the front door was packed solid with furnishings and personal items.

Mr and Mrs Horsewinkle shook my hand and handed me a batch of cheques, none certified. I reminded them that certified cheques covering one month's rent and a damage deposit was necessary to move in, along with eleven post-dated cheques. They tried hard to swim over it all but I was having none of it. Either, certified cheques would be handed over to me now, or the chaps unloading the truck would be reloading everything back onto it. Mr Horsewinkle was furious and Mrs Horsewinkle had to calm him down.

I asked him to get the correct funds together and give me a call when he was ready. I then got in the car and drove off, shaking from the confrontation.

The following day, we were all back at the house, certified cheques flying everywhere. Two sets of keys were handed over with large portions of smiles. Everyone was happy.

Three days later I received a call from Mr Horsewinkle. He was not a happy camper. Apparently, there had been a sewage backup in the basement and people were walking around, knee deep in Richard the thirds. I shot over to the house and took a look. It wasn't good. Furthermore, what could not quite be hidden was the fact that cousins of the Horsewinkle's were squatting in the basement and sleeping on flower patterned mattresses, now soaked in brown shite. I nearly threw up. This time, the tenant gave me shit for the shit in the house and the other shit from the cheques.

After extensive investigation of the underground sewage piping it had emerged that the City of Calgary had received a number of faxed complaints over the years from the previous owner of the house. Evidently, the roots of nearby poplar trees had penetrated the concrete underground lines, resulting in major blockages.

It took a large pit eight feet deep, a bulldozer and replacement sections of piping to sort out the problem. The ground work cost me $3,500.

I met up with the previous owner for a beer, showed him the pictures and faxes. He had *forgotten* to disclose the drainage problems and apologised. Having lived there for seventeen years he felt bad about the entire episode and wrote me a cheque for $3,000. Sucking up humble pie I had to pay for the Horsewinkle's temporary accommodation in hotel facilities. His cousins paid their own way! A frikkin' nightmare, and I had wished I had stayed on track to have the polo team in there. Although this would not have solved the problem of where their horses would've resided.

# 2000

I started on the UE-1 EPC project in January and immediately enjoyed the new position. Apart from the sixteen new and modified facilities under the U&O banner my role also included overseeing the overall, integrated plot plan, and real estate for the UE-1 expansion project.

Intergraph's 3D Piping Design System (PDS) was the chosen design platform to develop the project.

Although I had learned 2D CAD in the earlier years I had not practised 3D CAD which was an entirely different animal as mentioned earlier. I still had a lot to offer regarding manual plot layout and study work so convinced the project to give just one person a drawing board.

Alan Lawrence worked for Fluor and was the overall piping lead heading up all four silos. I had worked with Alan at Fluor in the early 1980s and without a doubt he remains one of the smartest, nicest and most helpful piping leads you'll ever meet in the business. As an SNC Lavalin area piping lead this time around he supported my position as best he could given the dynamics and politics of a complicated joint venture project where Fluor resources held down the senior positions of the project.

I set up the infrastructure of my U&O scope and attended meetings on schedule and budgets of piping engineering hours estimated to complete the project. Establishing a list of documents to be delivered to the client helped understand what my activity plans would look like while setting out the project technical requirements.

A staffing plan was created showing a gradual increase in resources to a peak in twenty-four months before tapering off down to project completion in the fourth year. I prepared an office layout and interviewed fresh resources while making an effort to recruit onto the project, designers I knew and could rely upon.

Getting the right people was a nightmare. There simply were not enough solid folk in Calgary to support each position. The project made a decision to introduce two ideas to UE-1 that would help.

First, the project acquired Canadian federal government approval to

190

supply open ended work visas that would allow the project to recruit designers and engineers from overseas.

Second, and not so fortuitous, was that a percentage of the engineering work would be outsourced to India.

Both decisions would prove to have a profound impact on the engineering arena in Calgary.

In an effort to bring more pipers to Calgary, Malcolm visited London for three weeks and set up a hotel suite for interviews in the Hyatt Carlton hotel, Kensington. The results of this trip were deemed positive and within a few weeks piping designers were issued working visas and flocking across the pond to Calgary. In addition to Malcolm's efforts, a number of agencies were commissioned to help boost the workforce.

Over the first twelve months the piping team increased from one to sixty. It was a huge project and the estimated total installed costs (TIC) started escalating from the $2.6bn to something approaching five billion dollars. The Project considered all options on how to cut costs.

The decision to outsource large scopes of work to India, would be an attempt to offset the costs of dozens of resources moving across to Canada on expenses from places like the UK and Australia.

# 2001

Fluor had opened an engineering office in New Delhi and had offered the option to Syncrude, of using their satellite offices and trained staff of engineers and PDS piping designers. The project would have an opportunity to save costs by incorporating a much cheaper US$10 hourly rate for resources in India than the US$50 hourly rates being paid to folk in Calgary. The UE-1 project was not the only global project of its size to introduce outsourced engineering work to low cost centres, or as it is known at Fluor, high value engineering centres (HVEC). Projects around the world began to adopt the same ideas and, soon enough, India was very much on the oil and gas engineering map.

While this approach made the bean counters very happy the subject of outsourcing was to have a lasting impression on the culture of engineering around the world.

I threw a dinner party one Saturday night and also invited Malcolm over to thank him for offering me the role on the project. I had planned a smart, Japanese evening making my own sushi and sashimi dishes. I enjoyed warm sake and had bought a nice bottle to accompany the small Japanese cups. The bottle was the size of a normal bottle of wine, 75cl and had a metal screwed cap, so no good to heat up in the microwave.

Instead, I chose to loosen the cap and lay it down in a baking tray before sliding it into an oven on the lowest setting. Sorted.

Continuing with the dinner preparations, folk started to arrive. Beers and bubbly were dished out in the first hour and, later on, it was time for a small cup of sake. Out of sight from others, opening the oven door, I removed the tray and stood the warm bottle on the kitchen island bar. I placed the small Japanese cups alongside and we all gathered around the island, nibbling on a few snacks.

Using my bare hands I held the warm bottle and tipped the sake towards the cups. Well, we all gazed on in shock as the sake shot out of the bottle at a rate of knots and straight onto Malcolm's chest and silk waistcoat.

Holy fuck!

Poor Malcolm leapt off his stool and reacted like he'd had a bucket of iced water dropped on his head. With us all bemused but starting to see the funny side, I gave the poor fella a towel down before cracking open a can of Kilkenny for him.

Bit more chit-chat, more beer and half an hour later we were all ready for that sake before sitting down to dinner.

Very carefully, and with all straining to see what happens next, I tipped the now much cooler bottle of sake towards the small cups. We were all standing or seated in the same position as before but with amazing repetition and velocity, the sake once again spurted out of the bottle and straight onto Malcolm's chest. I couldn't believe it!

We all surmised that it must have had something to do with the reaction from the lower temperature of the bottle and the higher temperature of the sake.

*Malcolm stuck to Kilkenny, thereon in.*


Work fronts increased in Calgary and the UE-1 working visas continued to be issued while the resources settled in. Malcolm would personally drive the new recruits, fresh off the boat, down to Fluor's brand new offices in Sundance.

One Monday morning, I stepped into the reception area to meet Malcolm and a new materials controller was introduced to me. Clive Forester had just arrived from London, with his wife, and Malcolm introduced him to me.

Clive was shaking uncontrollably. I assumed it was nerves.

However, what was also evident was the smell of alcohol on his breath. He'd probably gulped down half a bottle of scotch whisky for breakfast. I looked at Malcolm in disbelief as he left the building.

I showed Clive to his desk and left him to settle in as I scuttled off to a meeting.

An hour and a half later a couple of pipers tapped on the glass of the meeting room, beckoning me to come out. They quickly showed me to Clive's cubicle.

Clive was flat out on the floor and barely coherent. The paramedics had been called but he was having trouble stringing more than one or two words together. It was clear to me that he was elephant's trunk and Mozart.

The paramedics showed up quickly and checked him over. The supervisor pulled me aside and advised me that the diagnosis was pretty simple. Clive was absolutely pissed.

They stuck him on a gurney anyway and moved him out to the ambulance where folk gathered, gawking at yet another pissed up piper. It wasn't even Friday!

My new materials manager spent the rest of the week in hospital. On the Friday, I called Malcolm and then Clive's agent, Ron Hinchcliff, advising them both I would be releasing Clive from the project. The guys were reluctant to agree but my position was really, untenable. He had to go.

While I had been in the position of seeing guys come back from the pub a bit worse for wear, turning up to work drunk on the first day of an overseas assignment was a little off track!

The challenges in the office expanded as I prepared scopes of work for sixteen units I would be leading while submitting personnel approval forms (PAF) for endorsement.

When there is a lot of work around in the piping sector and the hourly rates skyrocket, senior designers come out of the woodwork. While most folk who join a piping team would have been recommended to a piping lead, there are a few who slip through the net.

I was heavily reliant on Malcolm's interview tour de force in London and agencies springing up all over the show. Most pipers I took on were very good but others were not. As I would point out on more than one occasion... *they might be slow but they make a lot of mistakes.*

I hired a chap to lay out a simple plot with two pumps and six inch piping. After two site trips and six weeks of nothing, he was sacked. There was a Scotsman by the name of Jim McAlladin who visited the Syncrude jobsite with a camera, but failed to apply for a camera permit for use in an operating area. When randomly pulled aside by a site patrol vehicle, he lied and gave his supervisor's name. Billy Flitt was his supervisor and a character who insisted the numpty Scot go and apologise in person to the permit office, which he did.

The huge brown field UE-1 project had very few brand new areas of real estate but many expansions to existing facilities. As it progressed, it was clear that there was limited plot space for new buildings, equipment packages and its piping on the operating facilities.

The project slowly moved forward and plans were drawn up for me to visit the New Delhi office to see how our HVEC colleagues were faring. I organised a round-the-world ticket taking me through London where I would surprise my good friend Gary's wife, Jane, by showing up as a surprise for her fortieth. I would then fly onto Japan and enjoy forty-eight hours in Tokyo then head back to Calgary. This journey would be less expensive than a straight return flight to India and back.

The Fluor offices in New Delhi are magnificent. Low walls separated the cubicles and each person was given smart furnishings and state of the art computers and monitors. The designers had been trained on the buttons and the entire team was very organised. On the negative side was the fact that the resources were not all experienced in piping design.

On the first lunchtime I stood in line at the cafeteria. A caterer had brought in plenty of wonderful food. The doors to the lunch room were opened and all the food laid out on decorative table cloths. After a while I looked down the line and the ten or so in front of me were looking back at me. I asked what we were waiting for, only to be told that they were all waiting for me! That's the Indian thing: incredibly polite, calm, gracious and professional people.

I attended a few meetings and met lots of folk in that first week before taking a weekend off and paying a visit to the city of Agra and the opulent, *Taj Mahal*. The other visitors had been driven out to Agra the previous weekend. Fluor had offered to drive me there but I wanted to do it all alone and take the train. This request did not go down well and the Fluor managers tried to change my mind at the dinner table one evening. Apart from sitting in a car for six hours each way, the train systems were established by the British and I wanted to grab the opportunity to sample the infamous Indian railway system where six million people are employed.

The managers backed down so, with another piper who also wanted to tag along, we took the Rajasthani Express west, to Agra.

India has a vibrancy not close to anywhere else in the world. With one and a quarter billion people, Indians take up more than one fifth of our world's entire population. In country, it often seems that they are all walking with you and watching your every move. There's no escape in India. Garbage is everywhere and small children are covered in dirt. Rats are seen popping in and out of hidden nests while droves of pigs wander across a plethora of railway tracks.

Industry continues while vehicles ignore road traffic law and avoiding driving into the odd sleeping cow in the middle of the road.

1960 must have been a terrific year because that was clearly the last time anyone could buy something brand new!

The architecture is amazing with many structures more than a thousand years old. When walking through Old Delhi you are immersed in everything it has to offer, especially the street life with its wonderful side of the street food stalls known as a *Dhaba*.

The Taj Mahal proved to be an extraordinary place to visit. Perched above the Yamuna River the structure took twenty-one years to finish and was intended as a burial place for Mumtaz Mahal, the deceased wife of the Moghul Emperor Shah Jahan who commissioned the project.

The bill came in at a whopping US$10 billion! That was in 1653 so in today's money it was probably the same cost as an English footballer moving from Reading to Stockport County.

The streets surrounding the Taj Mahal were filled with poverty stricken families and shoe shops.

I spent two hours in an Indian textile shop selling silk carpets and negotiated prices for two gorgeous items which they professionally wrapped and prepared for the long journey home.

I travelled back to Canada business class with a good piping chap and one of my leads, Terry Cahill. The journey through Tokyo allowed us a weekend in this bustling city.

Now, as already attested to, I love Japanese food and checking into a hotel on the Friday afternoon we dumped the bags into rooms the size of a mouse's earhole and headed out on the town. Wandering around gazing at a variety of eating establishments we grabbed a couple of beers in a bar before stumbling upon a terrific looking sushi bar.

That was the moment Terry tugged on a sleeve and told me he did not eat Japanese food! This piece of information was actually dispatched a bit late when a stopover in Japan was scheduled. Respecting Terry's constraints we continued along the street and ended up in Tony Roma's Rib House. I laughed my socks off.

He promised me that Saturday evening we'd give a sushi bar a shot. So, after seeing some sights during the day, Saturday night was a hoot and we found a great place that sold fish and cooked meat for Terry. Walking home after a few beers and sake we both needed a quick stop at a toilet and wandered into the reception area of a five star hotel. Quickly strutting past guests and staff we dived into a couple of adjacent traps and locked the doors. After a few seconds I looked at the wall and there was a digital keypad, text written, of course, in Japanese. There were about eight different buttons and I gave one of them a push. Nothing. I pushed another and a sharp burst of warm water shot right up my arse! I leapt off the seat.

Crashing back down, I pressed another button. The toilet flushed. One more button: a pair of soft, woman's hands came up from below and started rubbing Johnson's baby oil onto my balls.

*I wish.*

The entire business trip was a great experience. On the last morning I managed to squeeze in a trip to the Tsukiji fish market, at the time the largest fish market in the world. Dozens of three hundred pound tuna lay in suspended animation on the tiles of partially frozen ground, half covered with a layer of icy fog. Four-wheeled flatbed mini-trucks thrashed around the place and if you were not careful it was easy to have one's legs chopped in half at the ankles.

Back home in Calgary I was trying hard to manage the people, project and piping activities. I had a team of close to sixty-five in Calgary while the team I was also responsible for in New Delhi was slightly more than seventy. There was an organisation chart reflecting a number of area leads or *lieutenants* but for things to run smoother for me I needed to delegate more activities and responsibilities down the line. My project manager was a Texan and a delightful chap. Sid Clearing gave me plenty of support and everyone liked Sid.

As time moved on I was stressed up to my eye balls and needed a diversion after work. In the south of Calgary is a comedy club called *Yuk Yuks*. I discovered that Mondays was amateur night where drop-ins were accepted and the club was open to the public. I went in one Monday evening.

It was a good, solid look into the art and craft of making people laugh. The structure of the evening was such that the professional comedian gave a one hour presentation to the amateurs and would take the stage at the end of the evening. If they wished, the dozen or more amateurs would then take turns to pull pieces of folded paper from a jar of which eight of the papers would have the numbers one to eight written on them and the others would

197

be blank. If you picked a blank, it was not your turn to stand up on stage that night. If you picked a number six you were the sixth person up… and so forth. You could choose to pass on picking a ticket.

I tagged along to amateur night for a month of Mondays to learn all I could about stand-up comedy. I found the professionals, both male and female, to be complete, arrogant twats. Each of their acts would include abject swearing and vile, crude, disgusting narrative. What was even more shocking was the fact that many of the half-filled nightclub, laughed.

But not all of them.

I believed I could do a bit better by choosing subject material that did not include throwing in the 'f' bomb or discussing women farting in the bathtub. Not that there's anything wrong with that, of course.

Five weeks in I made the nerve racking decision to summon up the courage and pick a piece of paper out from the jar. I picked out '1' and would be the first one up on stage.

Looking at my watch I had only ten minutes before going on. *FFS.*

But in truth, I had used the past few weeks and prepared for the moment. I headed backstage and waited for the MC to call my name, *Mitch Elliott.*

On the call, my heart pounded as I walked out onto the stage to strong applause as the heat and light from a thousand bulbs shone down on me. Apart from the MC I couldn't see a single person and had to act as if I was not blinded. This was not easy. But a comedian can hardly walk out to an audience with his hands over his eyes shouting, *"Oh holy fuck, what's that light?"*

In my allotted five minutes were stories about shopping, Calgary and engineering. It all goes so fast and in amongst it all… was quite a lot of fun. The good news was that I was making people laugh and that experience was absolutely mesmerising. As the minutes progressed I gathered more confidence.

It was an enthralling evening and as I walked off stage to more applause I knew I wanted to do more comedy.

I attended a few more Mondays then took the plunge and entered a competition. The rules stated that I had to stand up for a minimum of four and a half minutes but no more than six. I prepared each evening actually setting up a video camera on a tripod in the lounge. The length of my act was in the higher time frame but I saw no reason to come close to the limit.

On the night, Yuk Yuks was hopping. The place was packed to the rafters and I recognised familiar piping designers all over the place as word had got around I was appearing at a comedy club. I was scheduled to go on in ninth place out of twelve and I wished I was number one because the extra hour or so's wait was almost too much for my ticker to handle. As number six came off I moved to the rear of the stage and tried to breathe deeply. Seven and eight came and went in a blur and I was poised to stroll on.

The MC chose that moment to natter and toss a few funnies out to the crowd. It seemed like an eternity before he switched focus and introduced the next act on; *"A very warm welcome for… Miiiiitch Elllliiiioooott."*

I bounced on and shook hands with him while he handed me the mobile microphone. Within a few words of starting my well-rehearsed six minutes, I stopped in my tracks. There in the middle of the stage was a large potato. I carried on but could think of nothing else but to get rid of it.

I bent over, picked up the King Edward and tossed it well into the dark and way over to the back left hand side of the room. I have no idea what possessed me to do this but it got a raucous laugh from the audience. About the same moment as the laughter broke out, the sound of shattered glass reverberated through Yuk Yuks.

I maintained focus and went through the routine. No swearing, no sexually explicit narrative. There was no 'f' bomb and no reference to women's raspberry ripples, labia majors, tradesmen's, vaginal fluids, or foreskins of large penises. It was straight up comedy based on day-to-day stuff. People were laughing. This was great.

When in competition, a light man holding a board with two coloured bulbs is assigned to assist the comedians. He is positioned close to the bar around mid-point around the club and easy for the comedian to spot. You can choose the frequency of when the lights are flashed to provide warning of when your time is nearly up. I asked that he flash twice yellow when I was thirty seconds away and one long red light when I was fifteen seconds from the six minutes.

I recall seeing the red light as I signed off and stepped from the stage to substantial applause.

Waiting for a decision I grabbed a well-deserved pint. Something I decided against before I went on.

The decision came and Mitch Elliott had got the most laughs and was a clear winner but the daft bastard was disqualified from the competition for being just three seconds over the six minutes.

In truth, I thought it was a bit harsh. Two hundred piping designers thought it was a bit harsh, too. However, I got good reviews from the colleagues and several of us went out for a few beers at the end of the night. All in all, a great experience.

# 2002

Back on UE-1 things were not going too well. Cost estimates had gotten out of control and Sid was moved on with other engineering managers. Attrition gripped the project as guys from overseas got homesick and went home. Schedules drifted to the right and material deliveries were late. Discipline leads were changed out as I struggled to hold onto my position.

The existing, operating plot space owned by Syncrude was huge. Probably two kilometres by one. The majority of the UE-1 project affected half of the existing plot with many units being revamped or expanded within the plot. It was like trying to squeeze three pounds of crap into a two pound bag and the project was suffering because of this.

However, immediately north of the existing units was an entirely vacant piece of Syncrude owned land. I had been studying the possibility of changing the whole dynamics of the project by ditching the ideas of modifying each existing unit and instead keeping them as they were and using the new real estate to the north, to develop the new unit plot space.

There would be a necessary piping link required between the new and existing units and that would be secured by introducing a brand new east-west pipe rack to the south of the new real estate.

This idea had some merit for a number of reasons. First, the constructability of the new units would be safer and easier to expedite. Second, modifying an existing facility and adding new equipment and piping to a live, operating unit is essentially hazardous and puts lives at risk.

Third, by building a brand new, self-contained operating facility it could be constructed, commissioned and mechanically complete, ready for start-up without the need to interrupt the operations of the existing facilities next door, thereby saving huge costs.

Three viable business options that supported safe construction and an advanced schedule by not having to integrate unit shutdowns into the equation.

I continued developing the study and over one entire weekend finished the site plan off on the drawing board before getting help from one of my designers in turning the pencil study into a 2D CAD drawing.

I then called a meeting to discuss it with Alan Lawrence and my project managers. The idea was deemed positive and gathered momentum. I could sense the wheels being greased for a meeting with Syncrude.

The project management team had a few project engineering coordinators and Roger Forth, a long time Syncrude employee, was assigned to help me sell the idea to the Project and Syncrude's senior management in a formal presentation set up for one Friday afternoon.

The moment came when we had five minutes to sell the idea and, as I stepped forward, Roger took the microphone. I liked Roger but he was not a salesman. It needed the east London car dealer touch.

The passion from Roger's sales pitch was underwhelming and grossly insufficient to sell it to the team. After all the hours and effort in preparing the study and summary, it was all out the window in just five minutes.

The oil and gas business is littered with stories like this. Stories of hardship, joy, elation, achievement and morale crushing decision making.

# 2003

But UE-1 rolled along through detailed design. Vendor drawings came in late and everything continued to move out to the right. The IFC isometric issue phase arrived and our U&O piping team was struggling to make the numbers. Fluor called upon a posse and brought four additional guys up from California to help me out with some key activities. Fred Sharma was one such fella. A short, white haired Japan-born Californian, Fred helped me with schedule and planning while I was assigned to getting isometrics out the door.

When Sid was released, along with several other folk, the entire engineering management team was re-organised. A new chap, Rodney Blackball, was assigned to U&O as the new engineering manager. Rodney was a South African hard-arsed military chap without the first idea how to run an oil and gas engineering team and as much use as a chocolate teapot. The first meeting with the discipline leads he advised us all that he was parachuted in to fix the problems on the project. Big yawns.

It wasn't the project that needed fixing but more like Rodney. Any individual who tells a team he was parachuted in is not going to gain the respect of his team. In fact, it would have the opposite effect as pressures mounted and all departments struggled to finish the project on time and on budget.

Issuing isometric drawings is probably the hardest task of all and I had over eight thousand to get out. Week after week I was dropping behind on the counts. I knew my position was under threat but Alan was sticking with me and because of his support I was focusing all my attention on the project.

One Friday afternoon, Rodney comes striding into my office, sits on one seat and throws his feet up on another. He tells me he's been asked to fire my arse!

At that very moment it was like a whole shitload of weight was lifted from my shoulders. I responded by saying, *"Go ahead, Rodney. You are more than welcome!"*

Rodney responded by telling me he was not going to release me but instead, was going to let me stew for a while longer. He went on to tell me about a movie he once watched in South Africa called *Bullet-Head*. Rodney pointed his hand and fore finger at my forehead in the shape of a gun and said, *"That's where we are."* Tosser.

That evening I went home and fought back tears. I had never been so stressed out in all my life and considered resigning on the Monday. I cracked open a bottle of red wine and spent the next two days giving the whole situation some serious thought.

In a nutshell there were just two options. I could throw in the towel and look for another position elsewhere. After all, there was a stack of work in Calgary and I wouldn't have trouble finding one.

Or, I could finish the job I'd signed up for and see it through to its inevitable conclusion.

Not sure if it was the Chianti Classico or a bit of soul searching but everything fell into place. By Sunday I knew what I had to do.

I called Alan at his home and told him, no matter what, I'd be seeing the project through to the end unless the project sacked me. He was pleased that I called and happy with my decision. He had also asked if I wanted to formally raise Rodney's confrontation on the threatening behaviour to HR. I said, *"Nah."*

On Monday I strolled into work a better person. Stronger, resilient, confident and ready for fresh opportunities and to get the job done. Rodney was air lifted out just a few weeks later, after upsetting one of the female project assistants with his aggressive attitude. His parachute in a carrier bag.

Things turned around and I signed off the last of the eight and a half thousand isometrics in February before joining a construction team up at the Fort McMurray jobsite.

The post engineering site team was huge and sufficient enough for the project to commission a Boeing 737 to take us all up there on a Monday morning and return us back to Calgary on the Thursday evening. It was a pain getting up at four on the Monday but a pleasure having a three day weekend, every single week.

The team mostly consisted of good men and women I'd worked with over the last three years.

The majority of the field exercises included *rerating* of existing piping where new tie-ins with higher temperature and pressure values connecting to existing piping materials, demanded changes to the existing piping.

Fort McMurray is a town that has expanded exponentially over the last thirty years and probably half the population happens to come from Newfoundland. There were plenty of social gatherings and I shared an apartment with Greg Shaker holding the occasional beer and pizza night indoors while one or two ice hockey matches were shown on the box.

Billy Flitt was also up there with us and if you don't know Billy, you haven't been in this business. Billy is a guy everyone just loves to bits. Very Scottish, very funny and very good at his job, it was good to have Billy around. I had worked with him in Aberdeen and later in Venezuela before offering him a position on UE-1.

The five months up at The Fort were enjoyable but after nearly four years on the project I was more than happy to give notice and head back to Calgary.

I decided to take six months off and travel the Far East and Australia. Stories for another book.

# 2004

After returning to a busy Calgary around the spring time, I joined Fluor's permanent staff piping team and settled onto a Quebec based project for the oil company, Ultramar.

I enjoyed several visits back to the French speaking Canadian province I'd always enjoyed when on Hibernia, but in these trips, I got to visit the wonderfully quaint and unspoiled city of Quebec City. I stayed at the Plaza hotel and visited the refinery across to the south side of the St Lawrence, near the town of Saint Romuald.

Quebec City has some wonderful little French style bars and restaurants and walking around the city is easy with plenty to see.

The activities for one of my visits included some field checks and extensive piping study work using the results from the field checks and a 20% accuracy detailed estimate on material costs.

I had a plot plan, line list, piping and instrumentation diagrams (P&IDs) and I had also brought out my drawing instruments, too. The trouble was, it was Easter weekend but the work couldn't wait.

I worked hard to crank out piping transpositions, or what some piping folk know as *line shoots*. Essentially, this is where a designer takes a P&ID and plots the routing of a piping system onto a scaled plot plan. This exercise, of course, can be done on a computer or a hard copy drawing. Let's assume the piping system is a medium pressure steam distribution system supplying steam to a number of users identified on the P&ID. The steam line would be plotted along the pipe rack which is a good location to support all distribution and collection piping systems, because the pipe rack structure provides adequate support for all lines snaking through a process unit. Elevated between four and eight or so metres above the ground, a pipe rack is designed to allow grade access beneath the rack for maintenance personnel and/or vehicles to service pumps or valve stations.

Once the main header is sketched in, all the branches from the main header to the equipment users can then be added according to the schematically shown lines on the P&ID.

Once the steam lines have been added, the same approach is taken to show other piping systems on the same transposition. Systems that might include services like oils, gases, waters, air, condensate and flare or blowdown. There are also several other systems like cooling water supply, cooling water return, utility water, treated water, demineralised water, potable water and oily water.

In truth, there might be forty or more different piping systems routed on a transposition. Eventually all the lines are drawn and line numbers added. Using the scale value of the plot plan (normally 1:100) and a scale rule, the lengths of each line number are measured and noted.

While a plot plan is effectively what it says, a plan, it is not immediately obvious what the lengths of piping are in vertical planes. This is where the designer adds a contingent for drops and rises, including the values in the noted lengths. A document is then written up to list all the assumptions and clarifications built into a spreadsheet of quantities the Estimator can use to apply costs.

I finished the work late on Easter Monday and soon enough was back on the plane to Calgary. The Ultramar project was then suspended and closed down when the client required more time to ascertain the costs. Wonderful.

A very sad note coming out of all this; one of the discipline leads, Marc Rheingold, a Civil engineer, joined me on a couple of pleasant evenings out while in Quebec City. However, a year after the project was suspended he chose to take his own life. This, apparently due to the pressures of the project. Incredibly sad, we just don't know what surprises life churns up and must always recognise any emotional issues close colleagues might be having. Our business is full of such stress-related stories.

# 2005

After a few months involved on a boring Shell estimate, Fluor had little work and I made a decision to move on to something more interesting. I hate sitting around waiting for projects to start and prefer that I seek them and not they seek me.

I had been offered a position at IMV Projects as piping lead on a FEED phase for the Primrose SagD project for the large Canadian client, Canadian Natural Resources Limited (CNRL).

I spent the first six months waiting for the project to roll out, eager to get involved and contribute. My time was utilised setting up the administrative side of the project while preparing job books, folders and e-drives.

IMV's Piping Manager was Doug Trench. It is fair to say that Doug came from a background of drawing office management where he would wear a white coat, walk around with a clipboard and know exactly what to do when the supply of staples was running low in the cupboard, or a desk had to be organised for a new starter.

Unfortunately, Doug's knowledge of piping you could write up on half a napkin. While he was a very nice chap, as IMV grew both in stature, staffing and recognition in Calgary, the position of Piping Manager really needed someone with a deep oil and gas background who could apply his experience and skills to the position.

Such a position also demands skillsets in people management, control and maintenance of company procedures, abilities to prepare proposals and cost estimates for a potential project, equipment layout and study to support a site plan or plot plan. Appreciation of client specifications, piping material line classes and standard detail drawings.

Now, on the surface, this might not appear that important to a chap who's working for the company as a project piping lead. But, in truth, it is *vitally* important because a piping lead needs support from his manager in these areas listed above.

I simply didn't get support from Doug and he did not have a clue how to run his piping group.

# 2006

I found that my life was lacking something but I didn't know what. The negative time at IMV Projects allowed me an inordinate amount of time to assess my life and my marriage. My second marriage, at that.

One Sunday afternoon after a quarrel at home, I jumped in the car and headed out towards the mountains to be on my own and think. On a Springbank country road I stopped and got out. I was upset with myself and everything around me. I just didn't know how to make things better.

Just about then, a strange thing happened. As I leaned against the car enjoying one of the best views I'll ever have in my lifetime looking out west towards the foothills of the Rocky Mountains, a small single engine aircraft flew over the car heading in a westerly direction towards the foothills. I hopped back in and followed it. The little plane landed at Springbank airport.

I parked and walked around the buildings, taking in a few more Cessnas landing and taking off. I was immersed in a whole new world. A village of aircraft, pilots, an air traffic control tower, hangars, car parks, taxiways and two runways running east to west, and north to south. I was absolutely besotted with what I'd stumbled upon and wandered into the Calgary Flying Club to chat with Spencer, the resident desk manager. Two hours later I was signed up for a private pilot's licence!

Over the next twenty-four hours I could think of nothing else but learning to fly. I handed over $5,000 and received an itinerary for ground school three evenings a week and Saturdays. The large deposit would go towards fees covering the schooling, reading material, flight charts, aircraft usage, flights with an instructor and aviation fuel. I was advised that the CFC would 'chip away' at the deposit as the weeks went by.

Ground school commenced that week and each subject we touched upon provided a magnetic attraction towards my inquisitive mind. Subjects of soft field take off, short field landing, airport circuits, engine mechanics and propeller, power and cruise, flight control and management, aircraft operation, elevator and wings, rudders and flaps, fuel and oil, air traffic control and communication, airspeed and slow flight, stalling and engine failure, oxygen and hypoxia, navigation and cross country, controlled and uncontrolled air space, instrumentation and cockpit. The list was endless but I had never been so excited in all my life. I was forty-eight years old and this seemed like a terrific time in my life to take up flying.

Without a shadow of doubt the hardest subject of all to grasp, was the weather. This included cloud formations, air density and pressure, temperature and winds, decision making on the ground, decision making in the air. I had to keep re-reading the exercises in an effort to fully appreciate all components on the subject of weather.

It is a scientific reality that if a vehicle travelling on a road surface at fifty miles per hour (80kph) with a head wind of 20mph (32kph) the true speed of that vehicle remains at 50mph. However, an aircraft travelling at the same air speed against the same headwind will reflect a true air speed of 30mph, or A minus B. This, of course, is a simplistic approach to air speed. To understand the speed of an aircraft more precisely, it is important to have an understanding of calibrated air speed (CAS), equivalent air speed, (EAS), indicated air speed (IAS), and true air speed (TAS). Open ended *pitot* tubes installed on the fuselage of an aircraft point forward into the oncoming atmosphere and calibrate the air density that will be reflected on the air speed indicator (ASI) instrument dial on the dashboard. Complicated stuff it is and air speed is just one of dozens of subjects and many weeks of ground school invested into the weather.

After a few ground school evenings I began some actual flight tuition. The time had come when I would start flying an aircraft. My instructor was a great fella called Jason Lakmanetz. On the first outing Jason would take control of the aircraft taking me through some of the basics I had also learned from ground school. Soon enough, I was handling the Cessna 172 with my instructor always ready to assume control, should it be required. And it was required, frequently.

Jason would often refer to my flying as *dramatic* by turning the wheel too quickly or applying power too strongly. I would taxi too fast but speak too slowly to air traffic control (ATC).

Me, speak too slowly? I've never been told that in my life but there certainly was a language barrier when the ATC team tried to understand my Essex English while I tried hard to focus on the speed at which ATC would relay instruction back to a pilot.

*"November-sierra-tango-you-are-cleared-for-takeoff-head-north-then-east."*

I got to learn the phonetic code and always checked out the aircraft systems before taking it up. Having an engineering background helped me assess all situations and apply the right attention. A few checklists were typed up and reduced in size on a photocopier before I laminated them in transparent plastic covering.

I can tell you that there are exactly a hundred and five checklist items between the moment you collect the keys from the CFC desk clerk to the moment you are cleared by ATC to start rolling from the aircraft's stationary position next to the club. Then, there's another thirty-five things to do prior to take off. Dialect and accents are key to building a short term relationship with an air traffic controller. Repeating statements are to be avoided but on occasion are necessary for each party to fully understand an instruction. It is mandatory for a pilot to repeat any instruction given by ATC and always starting with the aircraft call sign. An example is *"sierra x-ray papa you are cleared for take-off"* spoken by the controller, immediately followed by *"sierra x-ray papa, cleared for take-off"* confirmed by the pilot.

A Canadian aircraft call sign is five characters in length always starting with the letter 'C', followed by an 'F' or 'G' and three letters. The example used above is a Cessna 172 aircraft registered with a call sign of C-FSXP. This particular aircraft was affectionately known as *sexy papa* within the Calgary Flying Club.

It is incredibly daunting moving through a long checklist while the instructor sits on the co-pilot's seat eating an apple. You can't rush things but try to ignore him being there while you mentally address all one hundred and five items.

Adapting a true sense of quality from my engineering occupation, I learned on the flying side to take everything cautiously, gather as much knowledge as I can both on the ground and a thousand feet above the ground while stimulating the new passion I had immersed myself in.

I was loving every day. *Flying is for me!*

The CFC supported all my efforts and Jason went up with me at least three times a week. I became familiar with all characteristics of flight and increasingly learned to control the aircraft in a safe and proper manner. There would be times when Jason would congratulate me for my flying skills after a two hour session. But on other occasions we would be up for just half an hour before he would be bringing us back in because my coordination was crap and everything I did was incorrect, or I was too anxious and my ATC interfaces were pathetic. He'd notice that I was not in the right space and simply not up for the job on that day.

I would be frustrated at my performance and critical of myself, applying extra effort to my ground school and homework. Drinking was forsaken the night before a flight and I wouldn't even have one sip. This was tough sometimes when I had organised a flight on a Saturday and there was a boys' night out on the Friday. I'd be out drinking cokes and lime.

One of my checklist items before going up was to ensure that the Cessna had sufficient fuel. The fuel tanks are built into the two wings of the aircraft with the fuel inlets on the top. I would heave myself up and use a wooden dipstick to check the levels.

One flight with Jason, I turned onto the taxiway and headed off to runway 25. As I rolled along at a fast walking speed I noticed I had left the dipstick on the top of the engine canopy, right in front of the windshield. Jason noticed and a few seconds later the dipstick fell off. Instead of leaving it he asked me to step on the brake while he popped out to pick it up, avoiding a propeller that would take his head off. But before making this manoeuvre he called into ATC to advise them of his intent.

*"November victor uniform, over."*

*"Go ahead November victor uniform."*

*"November victor uniform request to stop taxi and pick up a dipstick, over."*

*"Manoeuvre approved; anyone we know?"*

Over the next few months I became adept at flying the aircraft. My ground school was also coming on in leaps and bounds, although I had chosen to sit three more times to cover the weather.

Irrespective of wind direction and runway assignment the circuit and traffic pattern around an air traffic controlled airport is anticlockwise, or *left-hand*. A left-hand pattern supports a left seated pilot to visually check his surroundings within the circuit. This is internationally recognised directive. On commercial jets where two pilots are necessary, the co-pilot sits on the right.

A pilot will always try to take off and land into a head wind. If there is one single runway then there will be two opportunities, to land and take off from one end or the other. If an airport has two runways, one perpendicular to the other, then four opportunities present themselves for take-off or landing. Springbank airport has two runways and four designations: Runways zero seven (07) and two five (25) at each end of an east-west strip. While runways one six (16) and three four (34) are positioned on the north-south direction.

One Saturday morning I felt great as I drove the twenty minutes out to Spring bank. I checked out *sexy papa* and prepared to take her up with Jason in the co-pilot's seat, as usual.

Taking off towards the east from runway 07, meant an east to west wind direction. This particular flight was to include four or five circuits. After touching down on 07, I brought in the flaps and powered back up before the aircraft rode into the clear cool sky. At an elevation of five hundred feet I slowly turned to the left and straightening out on this *crosswind* leg of the circuit continued to climb towards the thousand feet level before another left turn brought me in parallel to 07. At a thousand feet on this downwind leg I was about to check in with ATC just as Jason made the call.

*"Sierra x-ray papa,"* he announced.

*"Sierra x-ray papa, go ahead."*

*"Sierra x-ray papa, looking for the option."*

*"Sierra x-ray papa, option approved."*

The option? What on earth was he talking about?

Jason then asked me to land, leave the runway and pull up on a taxiway, which I did. As the engine idled and I waited for the bollocking, my instructor then told me he was jumping out and walking back to the club on foot, leaving the aircraft *and my life* in my own hands.

The time had arrived for me to take my first solo flight. Holy crap.

I smiled and thanked him for the opportunity. He instructed me to do one circuit, land the Cessna and head back to the flying club.

I was back on the waves with ATC before preparing to take off again. This time on my Jack Jones.

In those short five or so minutes between Jason leaping out and bringing the aircraft back in, the wind direction had changed and ATC guided me across to take off from runway 34 as the wind was now out of the north. At first, this caught me a little off guard but that is where ten months of training kick in and I had no issues with the switch.

Up in the air on my first solo flight, I kept looking across at the seat next to me. There was no-one sitting in it and as I glanced to the empty two seats behind me too, a huge feeling of elation overwhelmed me. I landed SXP perfectly bringing the rear wheels down, right on the painted number 34, taxied a few hundred metres and brought *sexy papa* back to the Calgary Flying Club, unscathed, completing the manoeuvre by parking the front wheel of the aircraft precisely on the yellow mark intended. I had been flying ten months and secured a profound achievement of my first solo flight.

After the FEED phase of Primrose came to an end I received a call from Fluor again and was soon back there heading up a new project for a Saudi Arabian company called SIPCHEM.

Unlike IMV, I knew they had experienced pipers, good procedures and a great project.

Sipchem were developing some land near Jubail, Saudi Arabia. A chemical installation was to be constructed consisting of three defined plants. An acetic acid (AA) plant, a vinyl acetate monomer (VAM) plant and a utilities and offsites (U&O) facility. My responsibilities were as area piping lead on the VAM plant. The American petrochemical organisation *Du Pont* was the Licensor.

The client positioned themselves in Fluor's offices as I started recruiting a couple of piping area leads. Colleen Velcrose was first on the list. I had worked briefly with Colleen in the late nineties at Bantrel and I'd heard that she might be interested in a position on the project. I'd met Colleen a few other times at various social functions and found her to be a great communicator and she'd be lots of fun to work with. Fluor have every second Friday off and Colleen came in for a chat on one of these Fridays. I gave her the lowdown on the project and she agreed to join the team as one of my area leads and deputy.

Colin Treefall then came in a few weeks later. Playing golf and socialising with Colin was the only interaction I'd had with the chap. We had not worked together in the past. I reckoned he'd also be a good guy to have. I had an instinct that the three of us would be able to set out the project well and take it from start to finish. The Fluor New Delhi team would also be engaged in a large part of the design.

214

# 2007

I continued to enjoy the flying stuff, taking Cessnas up on my own on a regular basis, while booking Jason in to help me with other parts of the curriculum I was coming to terms with. Cross country and navigation is a huge part of flying and I soaked up the ground school each week. Messing around with flight charts, mental arithmetic, distances and geography was a treat as I strived to get ever closer to the finish line.

Then came a real hiccup and interruption to my efforts. Jason left the CFC to take a position as a pilot with Ken Borek Air up in the arctic. This was a real blow as I felt I was about three quarters of the way through the course. I was assigned a new pilot who had only just joined the CFC. Peter Krautslich was a German national living in Calgary. He had moved on from his position as a helicopter pilot taking tourists up for sightseeing tours in the Rockies.

From day one Peter wanted to change the way I flew an aircraft. His instruction was very much different from Jason and the very last thing I wanted was a switch in training methodology. I had been flying for about fifteen months and, soon enough, each week and each flight I thought I was losing touch and drifting away from ever achieving my goals and a PPL.

We started arguing. We argued on the ground and up in the air. Imagine: a German and an Englishman with a strong difference of opinion a couple of thousand feet up in the air trying to control a 1968 Cessna. Believe me, this was not a good thing. On one almost laughable situation we had booked a four hour slot on a Saturday for a cross country trip around southern Alberta.

Well, we got lost!

We had disagreed on where we actually were while looking for *Vulcan* airport and a scheduled stop in the flight plan. We didn't stop there because you have to actually know where it is before landing. It was a good half hour before we found our position and tracked it on the flight chart. Worse things have happened and often bad things start out by folk being lost or coming down after an engine failure.

After six weeks of this rubbish I had had enough. I made a decision to approach the general manager of the Club and ask his thoughts. It had been eighteen months since I enrolled with the Calgary Flying Club, fifty-seven hours of flight, months of ground school and around $20,000 in costs. I had also passed the two required written examinations (one of them, in a second attempt!).

Pierre Van Der Veld was a cracking guy and had only just assumed managing control of the Club's interests. I explained my flight plight and told him it was becoming very difficult working closely with Peter. Pierre fully understood the situation and pulled the three of us into a room. Essentially, he agreed to move Peter's efforts away from me while stepping forward and offering his own services to see me through to the end of the course. This was a simply terrific decision and Peter was comfortable and gracious with the new arrangement. We shook hands while he apologised to me for not being able to make it happen.

Pierre had worked with Jason for several years and knew his style of training and tuition. After a couple of flights with me, he could sense I was close to taking the final test.

A Flight Test includes a tense, three hour examination entirely in the seat of an aircraft. He therefore assigned me a sort of coach to fine tune a few specifics. Marie was a very pretty blond woman of Scandinavian heritage and I prayed she would not be a distraction. There was nothing this lady didn't know about the mechanics of an aircraft. She walked me through the unwritten stuff related to a Cessna 172 while Pierre took me up in the air to conduct exercises including slow flight, stalls, rapid descents or dives, precautionary and emergency landings or what is also known as a *forced* landing. This is one of the most daunting exercises a pilot will ever have to do, even in training.

Three thousand feet above the ground, without warning, the instructor pulls back the power and the aircraft engine thrust is cut to a dribble. The plane immediately loses height and after first reaching for a pair of clean underpants the pilot then has to make several decisions very quickly. He must first look for a place to land. Is there reasonably flat terrain and a field nearby? If so, are there any elevated electrical and telephone cables obstructing access to the field when ready to touch down?

From what direction is the wind blowing? Are there any tell-tale signs of direction, like dust from a moving vehicle on a dirt road? One end of a lake that shows the calmer waters is a sign that the wind blows away from the smoother waters.

A herd of cattle will usually stand with their faces into the wind. What about smoke from a cottage or a flag? If it's a field as the chosen destination, are there any ploughed furrows that might snap off the undercarriage if landing against the direction of the furrows?

Essentially, the pilot has about three minutes to prepare and bring his aircraft down safely. In the exercise with Pierre, I would get to about three hundred feet above the ground and power back up. This manoeuvre in itself is not easy as southern Alberta's foothills of the Rockies are rarely flat but peppered with hills, rivers and lakes. I recall one nerve racking exercise on a solo flight practising forced and emergency landings. I had covered the checklist (yes, there are also emergency checklists to be used) only to find myself in a sort of large bowl of grass and roadways but surrounded by hills. I had been focusing attention on the landing site but not enough attention to getting out after powering the engine back up to full throttle. While breaking out into a cold sweat I chose the best route out of the bowl and ended up clearing the trees by only a few inches. I was hyperventilating as my sweaty hands gripped the control wheel. In such situations it is absolutely critical that the pilot does not draw back the control wheel or stick too far or too fast as to lift the nose excessively would put the aircraft into a stall.

It's all over if that happens because there is not enough of the minimum five hundred feet height an aircraft needs to get out of a stall by sharply moving the control wheel forward and dropping the nose.

While the Sipchem project had its usual challenges, about a year in I made a fundamental mistake which pissed off senior management. It was a mistake I was to learn from, going forward.

Projects conduct model reviews at various intervals along its journey. Early in design, midway through design and towards the back end of design. They are generally known as 30%, 60% and 90% model reviews. Some project managers will modify this criteria, because they can.

It is as such critical that all parties are ready to attend the review and that all the ducks are in a row.

The Sipchem project was six weeks away from the big, 60% model review with the client. But it was evident that Piping would *not* be ready for the review. Pipe modelling was behind, changes had gripped the process engineering work (now, there's a surprise) and stress engineering still had a long way to go. Instead of battling through the difficult times and getting on with it I wrote an email to senior project management advising that the review be put back six weeks.

In my experienced viewpoint I wanted to raise my hand earlier rather than later. As a piping lead I have always been honest as soon as it is apparent that milestones cannot be achieved. But, on occasion, these things don't work out as they should.

The following afternoon I walked into a meeting where everyone gave me deaf and dumb sandwiches. *I asked Alan Lawrence how my email had been received.*

*"Not good, Mitch. The grenades have stopped, but the flame throwers have started,"* he said.

Now, while I may have had a good reason to send this email, there are always those who prefer to cover things up and take the easy road.

The Fluor project director replied to the email. While the underlying tone of his message suggested he was pissed off he wanted to know the reasons behind my proposal to postpone the model review?

I responded, providing the support requested. Things settled down and after the furore from the email it was all soon forgotten. I almost lost a job because of my impetuosity but because the model review was correctly put back six weeks, the project supported my position.

I learned a few things from this experience. First, not to shake up a project team with email bombs. I write lengthy emails to get my points across and not everyone likes long emails. I have worked with managers who also write long emails and managers who don't write any. This is because they don't send emails down to lesser folk like me who report back up to them. They'll only write emails to the folk they report up to but on many occasions their writing skills might be like that of a six year old.

If things may get delayed or postponed, they inevitably will. And project management will make that call, not the lead piping supervisor. Second, there are few reasons to piss senior management off, no matter what valiant reasons there might be hanging out there. Go with the flow, allow PM to have their day and let *them* recognise their own mistakes. Third, as a contract lead piping supervisor, I was not aware that one of the key bonus payments being made from Sipchem to the Fluor senior management working on the project was paid up, after the 60% model review had been conducted. My email killed off that bonus. *Oh well.*

Back at the Flying Club, Pierre had helped bring me up to a satisfactory level of flying ability where he was now confident I could book the flight test. I was to have a two hour lesson on a Friday morning followed by the flight test twenty-four hours later on the Saturday.

Gladys was a qualified and esteemed flight examiner whom frequented the CFC each week, testing pilots. She was the person assigned to taking me up. The lesson went well with Pierre on the Friday and on the Saturday morning I drove to the Club feeling fairly confident but with an edge of controlled, nervous anxiety.

The weather was good. No clouds, but a moderate north northwest wind. The flight test takes about three hours and the work process is meant to touch on every aspect of flying. I would check out the aircraft, taxi out to a runway, take it up in the air and from that moment I would simply follow instructions from Gladys.

My take off on runway 34 would take me in a northerly direction away from Springbank airport and across the gorge of the east flowing Bow River below. Once levelled out, Gladys then asked me to head towards the town of Madden, about 30km from the airport. I had been to Madden in a Cessna before and the townsite lies almost exactly due north of the airport. But, on the morning of the test, the NNW wind direction had caught me off guard and I suddenly found myself well east of Madden in an area I was not familiar with. I had been up in the air for about seven minutes and for the second time in my life piloting an aircraft, found myself lost.

In these situations, the examiner does not revise the instructions but sits and observes how the pilot handles the situation. Silence filled the cockpit as I struggled to understand what part of western Canada I actually was in.

I was anxious but also focused. For the next twenty minutes I went into a recovery mode flying in large 'squares' while trying hard to find things on the ground that were evident on the flight chart I was holding in one hand. I was just about to advise Gladys that I was done and that we should head back to Springbank when I spotted a substantial dogleg type directional change for a long string of large electrical pylons running in a

219

north-south direction. This change of direction was right there on the flight chart and I was back in business.

As I corrected my flight pattern I whispered across to Gladys, *"Things can only get better now on in."*

After that shocking interruption I continued in a positive manner, accepting all the instructions along the way.

But late on in the test, one manoeuvre caught me out. Gladys asked me to enter slow flight, followed by a stall. This procedure takes a few minutes to complete and, as I closed in on the final part of the exercise, the Cessna's nose was very much up in the air and I have to wait until the aircraft stalls and the nose drops out of the sky.

With my air speed rapidly dropping, as the nose dropped ahead of me a pilot is meant to push forward on the control wheel, thereby breaking the stall. But in a regretful moment and less than a fraction of a second, I reacted by ever so briefly pulling the control wheel towards me. This rearward movement accentuates the stall and makes things worse. I realised my mistake of course after I had done it and immediately corrected my mistake with a forward movement but knew I couldn't hide my small, but potentially disastrous, error.

I finished the flight test and headed back to the airport arriving four hours after we started out, which included a sightseeing tour around southern Alberta.

I sat down with Gladys as she immediately advised me that I had failed the test on just one issue; the incorrect manoeuvre to get out of the stall.

She also said that I was about one minute away from failing at the first hurdle but was pleased that I rediscovered our position near Madden.

An opportunity then presented itself. When a pupil fails a flight test it is mandatory that a lesson be conducted afterwards to address those activities failed in the test. This would then be followed by another flight test focusing solely on those failed items.

At the CFC that Saturday was one flight instructor, Ian, who thankfully did not have any plans. With some swift conversations with Gladys, an aircraft was checked out and I was back up in the skies, heading west, out to the foothills with Ian in the right seat. We climbed to two thousand feet which is the mandatory minimum height above the ground to practise stalls. I entered slow flight, the aircraft slowed down below sixty knots and I raised the nose. As is typical with this kind of exercise, the aircraft started vibrating before the nose dropped like a rock. Some aircraft are furnished with a horrible loud siren when a stall is approaching. Once the aircraft had entered the stall condition and we started dropping out of the sky I immediately cranked the control wheel forward and broke the stall, thereby levelling out the aircraft. He gave me two thumbs up and we returned to the airport and parked the plane.

Ian signed me off and, within the hour, I was back up in the skies again with Gladys for flight test number 2, but this time with SXP under me.

Up to two thousand feet, into slow flight and my third stall of the day, everything went well and another two thumbs up before back at the CFC Gladys gave me a hug and advised me I had passed my flight test. Holy crap, I had done it!

I was so close to tears and had to contain myself as there were hugs all round and the staff members present that Saturday, along with a few pupils, all congratulated me on a wonderful achievement. In truth, it was an amazing journey and the Calgary Flying Club were an integral part of my achievement.

I had spent the last twenty-one months and had $21,000 invested in this fantastic, but expensive, hobby.

The following Monday back at the office I ran through the stories. More pats on the back.

Mike Reiter was a betting man. The other pipers in the office knew this, too. Mike often chose to slip out for half an hour and place some dosh on a horse or two. There was never much of a hoorah when he came back or listened to the radio as results came in. Except one Friday…

Mike came back around two p.m. grinning like a Cheshire cat. He had won £1,250 and the look said it all. This result had made his week and he was about to go on vacation for a well-earned two week holiday to Portugal. After work at five p.m. he took several folk down the pub for a couple of beers before most headed off in all directions to homes in London suburbia. There were four chaps left and, come Monday morning, this is how the story unfolded…

Mike suggested going across town to The Inn on the Park hotel restaurant for dinner. The other three of his pals nodded. The Inn on the Park restaurant enjoyed a Michelin Class III notoriety and was regarded as one of *the* best restaurants in the capital.

A taxi dropped them off and they settled down at a nice table. Lobster appetisers and caviar were ordered along with a nice French white wine and shots of chilled Russian vodka. Consommé soup came next followed by some wild boar pate and a sorbet.

Chateaubriand steaks were perfectly flamed and some spectacular Gervray Chambertain burgundy served up by a gentleman wearing a pair of white gloves.

The port and cigars came out with a walnut platter of stilton, wild strawberries and a few glasses of Sauternes.

Four hours into the dinner Mike went to the loo.

After a few minutes, the other three asked each other if they'd seen Mike return from the toilet. No, was the short answer.

The cigars stopped.

After each of them spent time looking under table cloths and around the restaurant and hotel for Mike it was clear that he'd buggered off and left his three muckers with a bill of more than a thousand pounds!

This happened in 1979. You could've bought a house in Rochdale for that. No-one knew Mike well enough to know where he lived and what his home telephone number was.

Mike walked into the office seventeen days later and three guys almost choked him to death before he signed in. By lunchtime they were all laughing and recapping that Friday. That's the thing about a few pipers; they get over it and move on. Mike sorted out their costs.

The Sipchem team had *finally* sat through the 60% model review and started issuing drawings to a fabrication contractor. There was discussion on assigning one or two people to the jobsite in Jubail. Colleen was keen to go and was a bit upset when the project advised her that females were not allowed an assignment in Saudi Arabia. The Saudi laws and strict regulations would not allow an expatriate woman to be assigned a position in their country.

In late September, the project was approaching its peak in isometric issue, the client was happy and design was winding down. Each month I started reducing the piping team and letting one or two pipers go a week. This is the negative side of being a lead piping supervisor. Great to give people jobs but soon enough we have to release them, too.

Once a month Alan Lawrence would call a meeting with all his project piping leads. There were about twelve projects and the room was normally full. One of the things Alan would do is update us with opportunities for an assignment outside of Calgary, should we or other pipers be interested.

The meeting in September 2007 had a different flavour. Fort McMurray would always be an option, quickly rejected by everyone in the room. No-one wanted to spend time in Fort McMurray unless necessary. I had already spent five months in The Fort, four years earlier, and believed I had done my time there.

One other opportunity was discussed. There was a project starting up in South Africa. More hoots and jeers from the leads as they all touched on crime, murder, apartheid, security, safety and where the project was located, in a remote part of the country. They would prefer to go to Fort McMurray!

Fluor had been awarded the management contract (MC) from Sasol for a brand new expansion project to their existing refinery in Secunda. Known as the Sasol growth program (SGP) the engineering, procurement and construction (EPC) contracts had been awarded to Foster Wheeler Wood Group, UHDE and Fluor, respectively, out of their Sunninghill offices.

The meeting adjourned and I sauntered back to my desk. I went and sat alone in a coffee house over lunch just gazing out of the window. My thoughts drew me halfway round the world and it was evident by my emotional reaction that I wanted to know more about the South Africa project.

Alan had mentioned that Phil Chalk was down there running the project. Phil was a well-respected Fluor project director who had contributed towards the success of UE-1. I knew him well and liked his particular style of management.

So that afternoon I wrote an email asking him if he was looking for piping leads. I gave it an hour before hitting the send button.

The following morning I logged on and noted that I had received an email back from Phil. It started: *"Hello Mitch, great to hear from you. Yes, we are looking for a piping lead and would love to have you down here…"*

Those words would change my life forever.

I approached Alan Lawrence and discussed my desire to give this opportunity a shot. I reminded him that, after all, he did ask! Alan agreed to give me all the support I required.

Sipchem was winding down but there was still a heck of a way to go. Hundreds of isometrics still had to be issued and I was under pressure to increase the production to a much more significant level. I reassured the project teams that I would see the project through to the end while negotiating a possible assignment in South Africa.

I had a telephone interview with the engineering manager in SA, Solly Ismail. The interview went very well. HR in Calgary soon got involved and I was requested to pull together reams of paperwork including police clearance certificates and professional qualifications.

I then had to sort out my assignment package. The Fluor, single-status relocation package was very good indeed. I would be able to secure a nice home in Johannesburg. A car would be provided along with costs to cover fuel. I would receive eight weeks paid vacation a year. All SA taxes would be paid while taxes in Canada would also be reduced to a 'hypothetical' tax band while in SA. A settling in allowance equivalent to two weeks wages would be deposited into my bank account. I would be able to ship a certain amount of belongings out to SA or carry four suitcases with me on the Business Class flight ticket down there. On top of all this was a per diem that would support expenses for day-to-day living like food, beverages, restaurants, wine and a beer or two. Twice a year I would also receive an all-expenses paid return flight to my city of origin, Calgary.

# 2008

On Sipchem, my position was a 'contract' lead piper on an hourly rate. For this assignment I needed to switch across to a staff position which meant negotiating an annual salary based on a forty hour week. This part of the proceedings was not easy and I spent a couple of weeks going backwards and forwards between Alan and Phil. In the end, Fluor agreed to the salary I asked for as long as I didn't expect an increase later in 2008. It was fine with me and I could live with that.

Except for a terrific 50th birthday party at home, the weeks leading up to my departure were stressful when considering personal and occupational emotions. But once I was in the business class lounge at YYC with a glass of champagne, it was as if a huge weight had been lifted from my shoulders.

Just prior to accepting the position in SA, back at the Calgary Flying Club, I was actually days away from signing an agreement with seven other pilots to lease a brand spanking new four-seater, single engine, state of the art Diamond DA40 aircraft. I was excited at the thought of part owning the plane but, of course, such an agreement would slide me into a pair of financial concrete wellies like nothing else on earth.

The rest of my life as I knew it would be secured in the fact that I would have an aircraft to enjoy flying around western Canada including flights through the Rockies to Vancouver or down to other locations like California. But I would also be working seventy-five hours every week, paying for these pleasures. It was time to move on.

A Fluor driver met me at Tambo International Airport and rushed me straight to the offices in Sunninghill. I was quite knackered and could've done with a hotel room for a few hours. The HR manager immediately asked to see the stamp on my passport. She was furious with the twelve-month stamp and like a racing driver rushed me back to the airport where, through the back door, commandeered an immigration officer who stamped my passport again, with a five-year work visa! This was a first for me as I went with the flow answering questions along the way. After a couple of hours signing paperwork with HR, there were still no signs of a hotel as Fluor had been asked to get me out to Secunda as quickly as possible. It was like I was the first fire engine arriving on the scene of an inferno. Not the sort of hectic start I was hoping for in South Africa. After all, I was just a piper and not delivering a kidney.

The two-hour drive to Secunda took me past some pretty poor areas. Corrugated iron shacks in townships, fields of maize, trucks of coal and one or two power stations. The town of Liandra is an hour out of Secunda and not a place I would want to spend a long weekend.

Secunda is a townsite 165km east of Johannesburg overlooked by a huge refinery owned by Sasol. It was early evening and my accommodation for a few days would be the Tiffany Guest House. The couple managing the establishment were cool and the following morning, I was delivered a small Mercedes by Fluor to use as my own personal car for a few days until a more permanent vehicle was assigned.

I got to see Phil again and meet the entire management team. My position would be the piping engineering and design supervisor representing Sasol overseeing a number of areas of the SGP.

With the three large engineering houses engaged in the EPC work, Foster Wheeler Wood Group, UHDE and Fluor, the project had decided that I would be based in the FW offices in Midrand, Gauteng about forty minutes from Johannesburg and half an hour from Fluor's offices in Sunninghill. My role was to provide support for the FW scopes of work which were more than enough for one piper representing Sasol. I was looking forward to the opportunities and was confident in the fact that my engineering and project management teams were also happy with these plans.

My very first weekend in South Africa, I packed an overnight bag and headed off to Kruger National Park. The weather in April was perfect, dry and in the mid-twenties. The four hour drive took me to a town called Hazyview on the southwest corner of the giant, world famous game park. I signed in at Numbi Gate, collected a map and drifted slowly through the first sections of the park watching cautiously for any sign of movement in the bush.

South African wildlife is diverse in species but, arguably, the most sought after sightings are what African nationals refer to as the *Big Five*.

226

Water buffalo, rhinoceros, elephant, leopard and of course, the mighty lion.

Occasionally, I would stop, drink something cool from the flask and grab a few handfuls of nuts while I pinched myself and appreciated the wonderful arena I was in. The camera and binoculars were always close at hand as I took dozens of pictures using telephoto lenses with my Canon Rebel EOS xsi.

I had learned a few collective nouns before heading into the park.

A *tower* of giraffes would appear above the treeline and slowly amble out from the bush and onto the road. A *sounder* of warthogs would dart and sprint through undergrowth as if they were escaping from confinement. *Troops* of baboons dominated the trails on parts of my journey as the male leader looked majestically in control of his large family while I strained my eyes looking for that elusive *crash* of rhinoceros.

Three or four hours into the park I arrived at Skukuza Safari Lodge, a large, secure plot of land offering a variety of dwellings ranging from terraced suites to small detached rondavels, a round, thatched-roof building with a single bed and bathroom. I checked in and was given a map of the grounds and directions to my accommodation for the weekend.

After dumping the bag and a quick shower I wandered through the resort and down to a pub restaurant deck overlooking the Sabie River, ordered some spaghetti and sipped a cold beer. The sun was setting off to the west end of the river. I had read about the existence of malaria-borne mosquitos in Kruger and saturated my exposed areas of skin with a high deet creamy compound.

I gazed down and across to the other side of the bank where a couple of elephants were fussing over some banana leaves. A hundred metres upstream and a few crocodiles were half immersed in the flowing waters, cooling off after a hectic day of rest and yawning.

After the sun dipped below a horizon of trees and sky, I sauntered back to the room with an ice cream. That one single evening on my own at Skukuza was an incredible experience that I would always remember and cherish. One week in South Africa and it felt like it was meant to be.

I settled into the project, and participated in a number of refinery related safety courses. The ring road around the Secunda installation was 12.5 kilometres (eight miles) and I was given a few guided tours including the large areas that were about to undergo significant engineering, design and

227

reconstructive expansion.

After the second week I headed back to Johannesburg in my little hatchback to spend a couple of weeks in the Midrand offices preparing FWWG for the following two years of responsibilities. The Merc was switched out and keys to a brand new Toyota Avensis were handed to me. I arranged a meeting with a charming lady called Minka Hilton. Minka was going to find me a home while I was in Johannesburg.

I looked at a few places that came within the allowable budget and each one was huge! Some had permanent living quarters tacked onto the side but isolated sufficiently where servants and staff would reside while taking care of the cleaning and maintenance activity. I found this concept amazing and clearly a throwback from the apartheid era when the black residents of South Africa would serve to 'help' the white minorities.

After looking at properties in many diverse communities I settled on a wonderful, detached house in an estate called Villa Vitelli near the Fourways area to the north of Jozy and a walk from a great Irish pub, *The Brazen Head*.

The following day I signed on the dotted line with the owner and landlady, Karen. A lovely English lady who had moved to SA with her husband many years ago. They would be perfect landlords!

So, with a trip to Kruger under the belt, a new jam jar and drum all sorted I thought I'd do a bit of work! Shuttling between the Fluor Sunninghill offices and Fosters out at Midrand, I caught up with a few meetings on plot development before heading back out to Secunda for the rest of the working week.

In that first month it was evident that many Fluor folk had been assigned to the MC project from Canada, Europe and the USA. Seeing costs skyrocket, Sasol made a consolidated decision not to assign such a large Fluor team to the MC.

In an emergency meeting called by Phil, he advised the MC team that in the coming days many people would be released by the MC team and re-assigned back to their home office. We all stood there aghast, looking at each other.

One by one, we were pulled aside. I was no exception and was asked by HR, a straightforward question: *"Mitch, have you signed a lease on a house yet, in Johannesburg?"*

I had of course, and advised HR of such. Just four days earlier I'd signed on the line and committed to a twelve month lease contract for 24,000 SAR a month.

HR took that thought away and I would have to wait to hear if my time was up in South Africa and if I would be heading back to Canada after just a few weeks.

Realising the severity of the situation and having little control over decisions being made up at that senior management level, I packed a bag and headed out to Kruger again for a long, public holiday weekend.

I had learned a lot from my first weekend in Kruger and chose to travel light, this time, even though I would have three nights away. This time I chose to head to the most southerly gate at a townsite called Malelane. Arriving close to sunset I checked in at the Mhlati Guest House where Jan and Eric made me very welcome, indeed. Eric, a native English South African, was a building developer and was busy constructing one or two properties on the adjacent, prestigious *Leopard Creek Estate*. Jan was brought up in Southgate, north London and ran the Guest House that had five lovely, detached chalets all furnished with African décor. Each unit was located around a heated swimming pool.

After a pot of rosy lea and a ginger snap on the terrace, I hopped into the shower before shaving and heading out down towards the park gates that sat on the northern side of the Crocodile River. In the twilight, I pulled up on the bridge and got out. As I leaned on the bridge handrailing I could see a couple of crocs wallowing in the water.

These moments are so big in my life, it is hard to stay unemotional when miserably attempting to describe it all.

Fifty paces from the bridge is a stunning restaurant called *Hamilton's*. A simply gorgeous place and pictures of successful Big Game hunts and kills decorated the white-washed walls.

I sipped a pinkish cocktail at the bar and sat down to a dinner of turtle soup and wildebeest.

I slept like a baby among the therapeutic sounds of the constantly mobile pool cleaner called a *creepy crawly* and a host of garden crickets out to play.

After Jan's breakfast I could hardly move! Saying goodbye to my new friends I entered the park gate two minutes later. The trusty map was close at hand as my new car took me through new trails, stopping to take pictures of zebra, hippopotamus, giraffe and wildebeest.

The birdlife of Kruger was magnificent. The binoculars helped pick out lilac breasted rollers, glossy starlings, saddle billed storks, bat010as, guinea fowl, vultures, ground hornbills, ostrich, bald eagles and fish eagles known in the UK as *ospreys*.

The Lower Sabie Rest Camp towards the east side of the southern area of the park put me up for two nights. That evening I would not be covering myself in mosquito repellent as I did at Skukuza and hiding under the duvet. I had gotten used to the insects and simple sprays were adequate.

Kruger National Park's roads and trails are mostly developed and tarred. However, off road trails are also common and provide a diverse approach to tracking down wildlife. As my second weekend at Kruger came to a close, I had seen elephant and buffalo but three of the big five remained curiously obstinate.

Back at the office I attended a plot plan review that had been under development by Foster Wheeler for six months. The review was attended by Sasol, FW and other colleagues in the MC team. About twenty in the room sat and tried to put to bed, the equipment arrangement of the new plot. I picked up on a few problems…

Essentially a large, twelve metre (forty feet) wide existing pipe rack with two levels ran past the designated plot. Many of the lines on that existing rack required take-offs into the new utility plot. Therefore, a new ten metre (thirty-five feet) wide pipe rack would be required to deliver the piping through the new plot space.

Immediately at the front end of the plot were a number of buildings. These buildings were assigned to administration, operations, maintenance and reliability. Other than the odd water and air line, they were buildings that did not require any process piping. Therefore, the new pipe rack ran 50m past the buildings before coming close to any mechanical equipment requiring piping hookup.

Now, this to me was an ineffective and costly waste of pipe rack where dozens of lines would run on an extra 50m of pipe rack they really didn't need to.

I could see an opportunity to reposition these buildings to the back end of the plot while all the mechanical equipment and other piping users would be located at the front end of the plot. Not an unreasonable approach and this idea had the potential of saving several million dollars in excessive piping materials. Especially, with many of the lines being of exotic material and large in diameter so costly in unnecessary construction.

I chose the right moment in the meeting to raise my observation. After all, I was new to the project and many of these Afrikaans folk had been working together for years. I had to tread carefully on this one.

I raised my findings and we discussed them. Most of the attendees were cautious of modifying the plot plan because it had progressed to a point where piping design was already underway and the relocation of buildings and equipment would have an adverse effect on the design and the overall schedule.

The teams went away to consider the opportunity. While a plot plan review was the forum to discuss equipment layout, it may not be the best place to discuss impact from potential changes. That subject would have to come later after serious review and consideration of the decisions made.

Back at the MC offices, a high level decision had been made on the future of the MC team and folk were now referring to this as *MC-Lite*.

Regretfully, my position was one being removed from the new, smaller team. But, instead of shipping me back to Calgary I was asked if I would accept a position with the Fluor EPC piping team based in Sunninghill? They needed leads and had a shit load of work, so I accepted of course. Arrangements were made for me to switch across to the engineering contractor... from the management contractor.

I was to retain all existing privileges and contractual components of my current assignment package like the car, house, holidays and salary. I was lucky; many other folk were given notice from the project and soon after the decision, returned to their home offices in Texas and California to be given notice from the company!

My new position at Fluor SA as an area lead piping supervisor started immediately. I was to look after the engineering and design of several units on the SGP. John Roquefort would be my piping manager and as things turned out, would prove to be one of a very short list of Fluor piping resources who were civilised, respectful and gave me the time of day.

On the flipside I was soon to find out that many of the Fluor managers in South Africa proved to be belligerent, abrasive, argumentative, non-cohesive and downright nasty, backstabbing bastards.

Apart from that, they were okay.

While work proved to be challenging, as if this wasn't enough, I had some real brahmers around me to deal with. I had a team of piping designers and area leads working for me and many of the area leads enjoyed slating and rubbishing their own colleagues in front of me.

This was clearly a concern and it cultivates hatred, disrespect, disloyalty and distracts the piping team from their mission of providing a quality product.

One of the area leads, John Taylor, chose not to befriend me but treated me with contempt every day. First of all, he was saddened by the fact that John Roquefort, a smart and suitable man, had accepted the position of Piping Manager.

JT thought that he should have been the man for the job having been at Fluor thirty-five years. Then, six months later when I was handed one of the key lead piping positions on the SGP, JT was again upset. This resentment was evident each day and after a few weeks of this, I pulled him into a room. It was time for a little chat.

I asked JT why he was so pissed off with everything and everyone around him. He told me about John R's position and admitted that he thought he was the better man for the job. He went on to discuss other pipers whom he thought were not fit for a position on the team. He whinged about the client and he ripped into me for taking his lead piping engineer position.

I waited till he finished and said this to him;

*"Thanks, John, tough shit... now get over it. If I ever hear you complaining about another piper again I'll have you moved from my squad, immediately. We need positive folk on this project and not people trying to rubbish the group or, for that matter, any other member of the project team. We are not all perfect. We are who we are and it's teamwork that gets us through the horseshit on projects. If we continue to see any glass as half full instead of half empty, we may even get to enjoy being a piper each day!"*

I left the meeting room. I had gotten my point across and went straight to lunch.

I was a little bastard when I was a kid. Throwing stones at neighbours, dropping spiders down my mum's blouse and replacing the mint cream in my dad's *After Eight* chocolates, with salt.

When I was three my year old sister Debbie was crawling on the carpet when I switched on the vacuum cleaner and ran the unit over her hands. It wasn't a nice noise.

I remember my grandma running around the back garden trying to find me in the dark, wintry night. At seven, Mum took me shopping in Ilford town centre. Mum was about eight months pregnant with our younger sister and she had bought a water pistol for me. It was poking out of the shopping bag. While Mum sat us down in Lyon's coffee house and went back for the cup of tea she so desperately needed, I retrieved the pistol from her bag and filled it with chocolate milk shake. Before she got to the table, I had already hammered half a dozen people in the café, ducking down behind the seat like some sniper on a mission.

Screams and howling as I was escorted from the café with a tearful Mum close behind.

We hopped on a bus once and I told the bus conductor he looked like my cuddly golliwog. That didn't go down well, either.

At eight years old I pushed my baby sister off the couch onto the floor and broke her collar bone. Six months after it had healed, I did it again. But the other collar bone broke this time. When nine, I threw a roof tile at a neighbour I didn't like. He was fifty feet away but it was an amazing shot as the broken tile caught him in the head and he bent down screaming, wiping blood from his forehead.

I ran home and asked Mum if I could have a bath. She smelled a rat as I was always reluctant to climb into a bath. Ten minutes later, the boy's dad knocked on the door and from the right side of a locked bathroom door I could hear the commotion downstairs. Another talking to, a smack and an early night.

I was caught and reported swearing in our local park when I was ten. At the age of eleven I followed older kids to a local football match at Ilford FC, then tried to show off with some mischievous behaviour, but overdoing it just a tad when I lobbed an empty milk bottle over a tall fence and onto the pitch. The game was immediately halted while five hundred folk looked at me. I was ejected by the police and reported to my headmaster, Ken Aston who was the Chairman of FIFA at the time and lectured me in his smoke filled office at Newbury Park Primary School.

Mr Aston had written to my parents and invited them to his office on a Saturday morning, an hour before watching me represent Newbury Park in a football match. He had awkwardly recommended to Mum and Dad that their son see a psychiatrist. The day would not end well. We lost 8–0.

Dad was watching the box, dozing on the couch one evening. He was wearing a pair of PVC slippers. I opened up Mum's handbag and got out the box of pink, swan vesta matches. I cautiously slipped a match into the seam of Dad's slipper and lit it before placing the matches back in the bag. Behind the armchair I watched him snoring through the hinged gap of the door. As the match burned down to the slipper it must've been a full ten seconds before he suddenly leaped eight feet in the air and hopped around the lounge, dropping the 'f' bomb more than once. I got a right bollocking and went to my room, earlier than usual.

When I started out at Ilford County High Grammar school for boys, things could only get better. I was in the top half of the class for studies and results but I messed around a lot, frequently getting into trouble. Childish stuff and I took a while to grow up and stop showing off in the classroom, impersonating teachers and classmates.

At Christmas time the teacher would stand at the back of the class while I took the chalk and pointer, walking around the blackboard reverberating comments back to the laughing class in the accent of our Biology, Maths and Chemistry teachers.

I represented my school in chess, tennis, swimming, gymnastics, cricket just once and football. And even basketball on a couple of occasions when the rest of the school had been down with The Plague.

Mum and Dad would come and watch me play football every Saturday morning whether Ilford County High were playing at home or away, rain or sunshine. My folks were incredibly supportive in that area of my life. However, they were fairly innocent in the understanding of my schooling and therefore I never got too much pressure to do homework and spend an evening in my bedroom reading *Macbeth*.

Each class had about twenty kids. In each form room where our main desks and books were all retained was a piece of hardboard about twenty-four inches by eighteen inches covered in a sheet of lined paper. It was known as the Reprimand or *Rep* Board. Down the left side of the sheet were the twenty names of the scholars in that form, while across the top were all the fourteen or fifteen weeks in that particular term.

If anyone got into trouble during a class, the teacher of that lesson would ask the individual to bring the Reb Board at the next break. He would place his initials in one of the fields corresponding to the name of the trouble maker and the week of the term.

*"Jago, bring me the rep board,"* was usually a common statement coming from any teachers.

If it was signed three times in any one week, the teacher who was to place the third signature in that field would draw a bold line around the outside edges of that rectangle indicating a detention was required. This meant staying after school for one hour on the following Monday.

Two to four detentions in any term would mean simply two to four extended Mondays. If, however, a fifth field was signed out, a choice of the cane or loss of privileges would have to be made by the individual.

In the first term of my third year at County High I reached that moment I was not to forget. I had messed about too many times and a fifth detention was what I got. I made the decision and went with the option of loss of privileges. This choice was made simply because I was frightened to death of getting six of the best from Frank Young, our headmaster. I had heard stories of his methods and thought they were all a load of bollocks but wasn't in any mood to find out for myself.

One afternoon, I'm sitting in a history class discussing Stephenson's Rocket when my Games master Noel Martin entered the class. Having a quiet word in the ear of our History teacher I was pointed out and asked to leave the room.

Mr Martin had asked me why I had chosen to accept loss of privileges for my recently acquired fifth detention? I explained that I didn't fancy having Frank's stick across my arse six times. He walked me to Mr Young's office and along the way explained that the upcoming Saturday morning was a critical cup match against Fairlop School and he wanted me in the side. In this short, thirty second walk I was 'encouraged' to change my mind and ask Frank for the stick, instead. The two adults discussed the opportunity and Mr Martin went on his way while I was invited into the office, partially in shock.

The door was closed and I was asked to stand next to a big old armchair with both hands on the arms of the chair facing the wall. Behind the armchair hanging on the wall was a large picture of a Royal Air Force Spitfire. Sadly, pressed next to this wonderful image was a piece of reflective glass instead of, non-reflective glass. As I stood in tense preparation of what was to come I could see a reflection of Frank the Head flexing the stick at the back of his office. It appeared that he was about fifty feet away. In a few long strides I watched and squinted as he pounced on me and thrashed that half inch thick bamboo stick at my arse.

Let me tell you right now, it fucking hurt beyond belief. Frank reeled away and wandered back into position for a second effort. *'Whack'*, number two was administered. *'Whack'*, number three hit home on precisely the same spot where numbers one and two had landed. Four, five and six came along and I left Mr Young's office visibly shaken and in tears before heading back to hear the last few paragraphs of Britain's railways.

Everyone knew what had happened and left me alone to finish off my crying, quietly at my desk.

I'm not sure if this was a corroborated effort between my Games master and School Headmaster but that Saturday, I was on the bench and didn't play even one minute of the match.

Since that unfortunately memorable moment, every time I watch the Marlon Brando movie, *Mutiny on the Bounty*, and Richard Harris gets two dozen lashes I remember that day in Frank Young's office. I don't watch the movie a lot.

Two weeks later and just one week out from term end, I reached another sorry milestone and managed to see the sixth week of reprimands. This time I did lose loss of privileges which meant I would miss a key league basketball match. No-one stepped forward to help.

I was soon back at Mhlati with Jan and Eric and another dinner at Hamilton's before diving once more into Kruger Park before sunrise.

This was my fourth visit in as many months. Up at the crack of dawn I began the day slowly drifting through the park. I had now become well familiar with the southern areas of the park and always enjoyed the experience.

On one of those off road dirt trails that take you away from the beaten track for half a kilometre, I parked up for twenty minutes and sat there just gazing around. With no-one else near the car I opened my window and took in the surroundings. Lots of tall, heavy trees and bush broken apart by the yellow, dirt trail surface.

About twenty metres from the car was a large, old jackal berry tree. As I gazed up towards the main fork of the tree about ten metres above the ground, my heart stopped. There, resting and asleep in the fork with its face towards me, was a large, male leopard.

I fumbled quietly for the gorillapod, a small flexible tripod for all situations, threaded it onto the camera, switched out the lenses and prepared the correct exposure settings for the picture.

Resting the tripod on the open window door frame and settling into position I took a few pictures of the still peaceful, sleeping cat.

With the camera ready for that rare and special moment, I placed my right arm on the outside of the door and with one swift movement, banged the door with the palm of my hand. Immediately, the leopard's eyes opened sharply and he looked right at me. *Click, click, click...*

I grabbed some unforgettable images with his round face filling the frame. He didn't take his eyes off me once as I continued to take a stack of pictures. If this were happening in the seventies I would have used up about thirteen, thirty-six picture reels of Kodak film! Thankfully, the days of hundreds of wasted, out of focus prints are well behind us. The day of the leopard was a memorable occasion and I was absolutely ecstatic.

Regretfully, today's culture suggests we now take thousands of pictures instead of hundreds, retain them on our cell phones but never have them printed!

I have to say that I still do print pictures. Come February or March each year I gather all the images from the previous year on memory cards, cell phones, laptops and email. I sift through them all and pick out close to two hundred of the best images. I then get them printed online and they're delivered a week later before I place them in albums. Great memories and will probably be the first thing I take with me to escape a house fire. After the wife, of course.

Back at Fluor's offices I continued to support the project and offer my comments to the plot developments and piping design, while supporting a small team of pipers on the Sasol project. I was also battling relationships with other prima donnas in Sunninghill.

In weekly project meetings, while I was getting sufficient support from my American engineering manager, the project manager Graham James was proving to be difficult and obstructive. From the north of England, I won't hold that against him. However, he was a miserable, inflexible jerk who was unsupportive in his management ethics. I first wondered how he had risen to the levels he had in Sunninghill but as I got to know other managers in that office, it was clear there was an evident trend throughout.

I also think that he had been railroaded by Phil into taking me on as his overall piping lead when the MC Lite team was endorsed and my position, renegotiated.

Week after week, my comments in any meeting, though confidently delivered and well-intended, were criticised and efforts made to overturn them. I was dealing with a cliquey environment and it was occasionally embarrassing and without the fortunate open support from my EM, would have been detrimental to my position.

One specific, contentious issue was on the subject of a project requirement to provide an estimate of piping quantities and costs. I had attained a fair amount of experience in this area but the methods adopted by the project team were, simply, ineffective. The previous project piping lead had used only the 3D PDS Model to obtain the quantities. At any time in the middle of a project this approach would only take care of *modelled* piping components. But to understand the true costs of a piping project there is always a tremendous amount of *non-modelled* piping and other quantities of components to be considered in any estimate. These include pipe, valves, flanges, fittings, insulation, electric or steam heat tracing, bolts, nuts, gaskets, piping special items, standard pipe supports, special pipe supports, field supports, welding components like rods, piping connections to instrumentation, hydrotesting fluids and labour.

There may also be modularisation and transportation costs although these may well come under the construction banner. Furthermore, costs associated with operational activities like corrosion monitoring and assessments must be included in the estimate.

I prepared a detailed sheet showing all these items and how the project should acquire an estimate of quantities, when there was no model.

P&IDs do not always reflect the entire scope of piping, either. Where a drain connection might show a short branch from the header into a valve that says CHD, there is a world of unknown piping associated with this identification.

The Closed Hydrocarbon Drain system may have its own P&ID but has not yet been developed. The piping estimate must also take into account this unknown piping and components when expecting the drain to be piped to an underground collection system so thereby demanding a heck of a lot more materials than anticipated.

In an Estimate, P&IDs should be colour coded to reflect the afore-mentioned approach and retained for future reference. Finally, there is the estimate of piping engineering and design hours that get rolled up into the final product. Hours that include effort in engineering office locations at home and overseas in outsourced locations, site support and visits to vendor shops and module assembly yards, along with quality audits and reporting.

The piping estimate issued for the SGP fell well short of the requirements and GJ was coordinating the efforts across all disciplines. Unfortunately, he had not taken into account much of this stuff noted above.

A much more effective approach would have been to actually spend some time with the lead piper working the issues and deriving the supportive information.

There were no P&IDs marked up and no basis issued to each discipline. Sasol and the MC Lite team would see through this in a New York minute and as such, my proposal was to revisit the estimate again.

This idea was met with certain scepticism. The new kid on the block had thrown a spanner in the works and it was not possible to avoid the elephant in the room. The Estimate simply had to be revisited. And it was. But this time, it was done correctly resulting in another cross against my name.

Although I enjoyed the Sasol Growth Project, the arrogance I was becoming acquainted with was rubbing me up the wrong way at every turn. None of the managers had a compassionate bone in their body as I would be grilled on piping issues and have to continually support my own experience and decision making. You see, walking onto a project immersed with folk who'd worked together for years and years I was always going to be on a sticky wicket.

Projects are executed in many different ways. We have all heard the comment, *"that's what we've been doing for years"*, or *"in the eighty-three years I've been in this business I've never seen it done like that"*. If they are not set up correctly, projects can be spoiled very quickly.

# 2009

Schedule is one of, if not *the* most contentious, discussions a piper will have on any project. A lead piping engineer will need to have the experience and background knowledge on knowing when key milestones are to be met. When setting dates he will need to be assertive with his project management team, stress engineers, piping designers, materials engineers and material controllers.

He'll need to know when stress are making excuses and playing games or being serious about not hitting deliverables. He'll need to understand that plot plan issues and line lists come after P&IDs.

Rules of engagement for the three model reviews should be written and understood by the piping lead before project management pull the wool over your eyes and publish concrete targets that cannot be achieved.

There is a fine line between having justification in getting work completed late due to changes sweeping down through the project, or simply in the fact that the piping lead may not have the right team in place.

I've seen lead piping engineers sack designers on the spot for not doing their job correctly. Often sadly, when the lead piper is under so much pressure from above without the effort of pushing back. Designers have too much protection these days and appear to work less hard than they did in years gone by. They sit around chatting, listen to stuff through headphones and spend inordinate amounts of time on the internet and twenty minutes of every hour outside the office, smoking. Piping leads probably wish smoking was still allowed in the office. More work might get done!

With engineering offices located in downtown Calgary it is not uncommon to see guys during working hours, wandering around doing a bit of shopping. No-one these days gives a shit and if a supervisor pulls someone up then the individual will probably go and work somewhere else. That's the culture we see in busier times but not in all cases.

It is not easy any more to sack someone on the spot. Not that I endorse such behaviour, either. If a situation gets so bad that immediate dismissals must be considered then it is likely that the lead piping engineer was not doing his job correctly in the first place.

As work progressed in Fluor's offices and I tried hard to accept the incompetent folk around me while enjoying working with so many good, decent folk in Sunninghill I soon realised that a full year had passed by since I moved to South Africa. I soon found myself immersed in another occupational change.

The reduced scope of work that the MC Lite team had been working on soon expanded to a point where the MC team, once again, needed additional support. I was pulled aside by Phil and advised that I would be leaving the Fluor piping team and returning to the MC team. I was overjoyed by this decision as this essentially meant that the folk from the Planet Zog and who were giving me a hard time, I would now be overseeing and auditing. Furthermore, the move would keep me in South Africa for at least another two years.

The twelve month lease at Villa Vitelli was also coming to an end and I found alternate accommodation. The new position with the Fluor MC *not so lite* team also allowed me to lease a home in Secunda under the Fluor stewardship. I found a smart, furnished place in a street called Jakkalsdrai where I would stay when in town and head back to Joburg at weekends where I was now spending more time.

I continued to soak up the challenges of the project and attended model reviews held by Fluor, Foster Wheeler and Uhde with visits to their Indian offices in Pune, Gujarat.

I soon gained more respect from my Fluor MC colleagues and Sasol engineering and management. With this confidence came more responsibility. After those nine months under the Fluor EC umbrella, with the move back to Fluor MC I was now once again, very much enjoying the project.

I was increasingly beginning to further settle down in South Africa and found myself in a country where the year round climate is considered one of, if not, the best in the world but was freezing my nuts off in the month of June. In all my years in Canada I cannot remember ever feeling cold because the infrastructure doesn't allow it. This time each year in Joburg, people put up with a shit load of hardship because central heating is not a given. A few strategically placed gas heaters and an electric blanket was just the ticket.

Working at Worley Engineering in Wood Green in the early eighties there was a lovely Turkish piping chap on the board called Errol Shevket. He was more affectionately known as *earole shaving kit*.

Errol had bought a lounge suite in a furniture store down the road from the offices. Several weeks later the couch was falling apart so Errol went back to the store and asked to return the products for a refund.

The store turned down the request and several times over the course of a week he tried again and again by approaching different managers. You could see the strain on Errol as, each day, he grew more frustrated and angry.

One dark, early Sunday morning before the birds were up and well before shopping cultures dictated increased opening times, Errol went back to his favourite store. He had bought a stirrup type pump with a canister, foot pedal and hose.

Errol emptied the contents of a one gallon tin of shocking pink, oil-based paint into the canister under the protection of the relative darkness of the front entrance.

Standing in front of the locked doors of the department store and feeding the hosepipe through the letter box, he aimed the hose at a nearby disply of leather seating furniture. With his right foot pumping up and down, he waved the hose around. Word has it that it took Errol almost half an hour to clean out the canister before shuffling back to his car and off home.

The guys in the drawing office were falling apart laughing after one of them had inadvertently discovered this rather unfortunate but hilarious act of vandalism by reading about it in the local newspaper the following week. Errol denied ever being present that Sunday morning.

Golfing holidays were always popular with the boys. One particular trip to the Costa del Sol on the Spanish Riviera was memorable. Eight of us rented two cars at Malaga airport, chucked the luggage in the trunks and tied up the golf bags to the roofs. They were tied down with those lethal looking elasticated ropes with sharp hooks on each end.

It was agreed that the first vehicle to the El Paraiso golf resort would get the San Miguels sorted, the chaps in the second vehicle would buy them.

242

I drove one car and Roger drove the other. We raced along the beautiful, winding Spanish coast road and up around 120kph Roger's car pulled up next to me. The guys were all pointing to the roof. I pulled up and got out. Everything was tied down and stable.

*Of course, it was a ploy.*

I caught Roger's car again and sailed past them. Once again, Roger closed in and the guys were pointing to the roof of our car and looking much more disturbed. We both pulled over and eight of us got out.

Apparently, the front end of the four golf bags on the roof of our car were gradually lifting up as the car increased its speed. With the elastic ropes at their limit the bags were standing up vertically while I was doing more than a hundred clicks an hour. As the car slowed, the bags gradually lowered. If they'd have come loose the results could've been disastrous losing too many balls before the week had started.

A quick refit and we were back on our way.

The week was rolling along nicely. Golf, smart attire, dinner, bars, beers, night clubs.

During one of the rounds, we were playing a par three on the back nine, positioned right next to a large lake. The gorgeous lake looked like it had plenty of folk enjoying a number of water sports, including speed boats and water skiing. The green was the other side of the teeing ground and separated by a sizeable, but shallow, part of the waters. A wooden foot bridge carried golfers to the green.

Four of us played our tee shots immaculately and headed for the green. I followed the other three golfers and about halfway across the bridge one of the two wheels on my golf cart got caught up on a handrail post. The removable grip that should've been tightened to the rest of the frame with a wingnut came free in my hand. The golf cart tipped over and 14 golf clubs and a ball retriever all slipped out of the bag and into the lake.

I stood there, speechless. The other chaps were already on the green and hadn't seen what had happened.

I shouted to the others who made their way back onto the footbridge. Removing my shoes and socks, I stepped into the foot or so of water and amongst the reeds. One by one, I fished out each club.

Almost done, the four ball group behind us arrived on the tee when one of the chaps shouted, *"Hurry up! Put another ball down, you cheap bastard."*

# 2010

The SGP engineering had started to move towards the fabrication and construction phase of the project. Model reviews had begun and there were a plethora of changes coming from the process engineers. Now, changes are common in the energy industry, just like anywhere else in the world. As human beings we put up with a constant drizzle of change throughout our lives, both on the personal front and at work. It is essential that we accept changes, especially if they are out of our control.

When changes hit a large oil and gas project halfway through the development, the consequences can be enormous. Costs can double in size from a modest $5bn to more than $10bn.

Engineering accounts for approximately 10% of the total installed costs (TIC) while the remaining 90% is assigned to materials of construction like mechanical and electrical equipment, piping and valves, concrete and steel. If changes start appearing after construction begins, the schedule will move to the right and senior management heads will roll.

Piping design covers a multitude of arenas. Once a project is conceived and a plot plan established, with preliminary flow diagrams passed across from the process engineers the piping designer can begin. Years ago, this was very much different than it is today. I'll try to explain.

If you've got this far in the book and have no association whatsoever with the petrochemical industry, then you probably have no idea what a piping designer is, or what he does?

There are many oil and gas facilities dotted around the country. We drive past them on a regular basis but may not always notice. The first thing that is visually striking when gazing at a refinery is the tall flare stack emitting black smoke into the atmosphere. Many flare stacks these days do not have that smoke because hot steam is injected into the gases prior to their discharge rendering the discharge, smoke-free.

The oil and gas facility will always have a diversity of mechanical equipment sitting at ground level or elevated on steel structures. Vessels, drums, tall towers, pumps and compressors. Generators, flare stacks, heat exchangers, air coolers and gas or steam turbines. This equipment is connected by thousands of metres of steel piping. Collectively, all of this piping will appear sort of silver in colour which is attributed to the stainless steel or aluminium cladding that covers the insulation. Insulation protects the pressurised fluids moving through the steel piping from freezing.

In cold places like Canada, and other similar weather related environments, insulation on its own is not enough to prevent freezing. Additional precautions are required to maintain temperatures of the fluids. Heat tracing satisfies this requirement. Heat tracing can be found in two forms; small capillary tubing wrapped around the outside of the steel piping but inside the insulation is one option. A supply of steam flows through the tubing thereby maintaining a desirable operating temperature of the service moving through the piping. The other alternative is electric heat tracing or EHT. This is where electrically charged wiring or coils are wrapped around the surface of the steel piping, again beneath the insulation.

Underground utility corridors for pipelines, steel and high density polyethylene (HDPE) piping, cables and fibre optic systems are positioned by piping. The designer will also confirm the size and grade elevation of the plot space while orientating the plot to suit criteria like prevailing wind direction versus potential vapour clouds and emissions.

Off to the side of a refinery is an area called a Tank Farm dedicated to storage facilities. Often, these facilities are huge and cover several hundred square metres. Essentially, this offsite storage area accommodates a number of large, circumferential tanks that could contain products like crude oil, diluted bitumen, gasoline, aviation fuel, paraffin, liquefied natural gas, diesel, condensates and water. Other gaseous hydrocarbon products like butane, propane and hydrogen may also be stored in special, purpose built containment like long bullets and spheres.

Each storage tank must be positioned certain distances from its adjacent tank. Normally, one full diameter apart. The land or plot space surrounding the tankage will have containment walls built to a specific, engineered height and the plot space shall be of sufficient *volume* to contain 110% of the contents of the largest tank, should it rupture and release the product.

Once a plot plan has been secured and approved by the client, the piping designer may commence his design.

Within the Process Engineering group is a sub-team called Process Graphics. These folk are normally not certified engineers but essentially computer assisted draughtspersons who will develop drawings called flow sheets. A flow sheet may have another title like piping and instrument diagram (P&ID) or process flow diagram (PFD).

The information on the P&ID is depicted pictorially, not to scale, but rather as a schematic. It very much depends how much piping is associated with the equipment, but one P&ID drawing will be broken out by an area on the plot plan that might include one, two, three or more items of mechanical equipment. Each equipment on the plot will have piping and electrical connections and it is these piping connections both in and out of the equipment that will also be shown on the P&ID by the process graphics team, with the engineered assistance, of course, from the process engineers.

Before any pipe modelling has started a good designer will take a look at the area he wants to design. The plot plan might show mechanical equipment that includes two stacked heat exchangers, one vertical vessel, a couple of pumps and a steel structure called a pipe rack. The pipe rack is about six metres (twenty feet) wide with the same height and can stretch along the centre of a plot. The pipe rack is necessary on a process unit to accommodate all the piping that travels between distant equipment on the unit plot plan, normally located either sides or towards one end of the pipe rack.

Using a 2D electronic copy of the plot plan, the CAD piping designer will create a separate layer on the drawing. Taking the relevant P&IDs, covering the five items of equipment, the larger diameter piping will be addressed first. Each line will be transposed onto the plot plan by showing a single line routed from equipment A to equipment B, using the pipe rack if necessary, where the locations and distance between equipment may demand it.

Line after line, the designer will consider adding them to the layout. Once the larger lines are routed, the smaller two inch and below piping is added to complete the piping transpositions. The results are evident; an intelligent, smart and carefully considered piping arrangement that is safe, economically and aesthetically acceptable.

After the transpositions have been completed for that specific process area on the plot, the piping designer may start modelling the piping in the 3D CAD platform chosen for the project.

A number of CAD platforms are used throughout the industry. AutoPlant, PDMS, PDS and more recently, Intergraph's SmartPlant 3D (SP3D) and Aviva's E3D piping design software.

Back in my time as an apprentice I spent several weeks working in the fired heater group. I worked with a chap called Alan Smith who was to become a good friend.

Alan's pencil work was sensational. He would use three different size retractable pencils for all the single lined, twelve inch and below piping. 0.5mm thick leads for piping ¾", 1", 1½" and 2" in diameter. 0.7mm for sizes 3", 4", 6" and 8", then 0.9mm for the 10" and 12" piping. The centrelines of double line piping (14" and up) would be 0.3mm while the two outside edges would be drawn with 0.5mm leads.

Piping line work on the board was fairly straightforward. The designer had all the tools at his disposal. All he had to do was to stand next to his drawing board and think about how the piping should be laid out.

But of course, this draughting approach no longer exists. The world of computer modelling has gripped the engineering and design culture and taken over our piping design. The world has accepted this and you won't see a drawing board anywhere these days unless the Antiques Roadshow is in town.

Today's 3D pipe modeller, on one hand, does not need an eraser, draughting tools and scale rules. But he has other obstructions that plague his progress.

As briefly touched on earlier, when describing the components that make up a line number on a P&ID, a material line class identification provides the piping group with a library of information relevant to the materials of construction. Piping materials found on a hydrocarbon project would include carbon steels and low temperature materials, stainless steels, incoloy, chrome-molys, inconels, duplex, polypropylene and high density polyethylene for underground firewater systems.

Other materials include kunifer (copper, nickel and ferrous content), copper, copper nickel, glass reinforced plastic (GRP) and fibre reinforced plastic (FRP).

In addition to the materials of construction, material line classes provide the piping designer with the piping components available in size ranges. The components that make up a line class specification for any given piping system are as follows:

Pipe
90° long radius elbows
90° short radius elbows
45° long radius elbows
3D, 5D and 10D bends
Equal tees
Reducing tees
Concentric reducers
Eccentric reducers
Raised face weldneck flanges
Blind flanges
Ring joint flanges
Orifice flanges
Slip on flanges
Gate valves
Globe valves
Check valves
Ball valves
Butterfly valves
Needle valves
Plug valves
Weldolets
Sweepolets
Thredolets
Nipolets
Bolts
Gaskets
Pipe nipples
Strainers
Steam traps

The ends of the piping are prepared for a number of seals and closures; butt welding, socket welding, screwed and flanged.

Due to the wide range of pressures the process engineers require, flanged joints may have numerous choices of flange pressure ratings:

American National Standards Institute (ANSI) driven:

150 pounds, *symbolised with the hash tag (#)*

300#

600#

900#

1500#

2500#

American Petroleum Institute (API) driven:

3,000#

5,000#

10,000#

15,000#

20,000#

These very high pressure API flange ratings are normally associated with wellhead and drilling related piping.

Every single one of these items listed above are built as shapes into the 3D materials catalog database allowing the pipe modeller to bring them into his design of the piping system. Piping valves are normally dimensionally configured to codes written up by the American Society of Mechanical Engineers (ASME) B16.34. Flanges are built to ASME B16.5 while all other components are built to other ASME codes.

To supplement flanged joints that may have 20 or 24 bolts, clamped hubs are also used in piping systems. Hub joints are more expensive to purchase than flange sets but with only 4 bolts for each item irrespective of line size, the maintenance is cheaper taking a fitter less time to dismantle and reassemble the joint.

Material databases are built to supply the piping designer with a wide range of standard materials and standard sizes, assigning a unique commodity code comprised of several characters.

From time to time an unusual size or component might be required by the piper. An example might be a 10″ x 3″ reducing tee. In such cases, the designer shall complete a form called a request for item code (RFIC) and have the signed form forwarded to the materials engineering team for action. The CAD database catalog management team review the request and build the requested component in the catalog, thereby allowing the designer to extract it and place it in the modelled piping. While this approach may appear to be a simple solution, when you're trying to get isometrics out the door it is considered a disruption.

So, for any given line number, the piping designer now knows the materials of construction, the size of the piping, the equipment associated with the piping, where the line runs from and where it finishes.

He also knows what service fluids are running through that piping and the insulation thickness. The designer knows what piping valves and inline control valves are to be modelled.

But what about flexibility? Would the large bore piping design satisfy the flexibility required from any high temperatures that might cause the straight lengths of piping to expand, longitudinally? And with piping connected to a piece of equipment, are there any excessive stresses envisaged at the equipment nozzle?

These early questions in the FEED may be answered by a senior pipe stress engineer who should be able to review the design and provide experienced feedback to the designer.

In detailed design, the stress engineer will receive isometrics from the designer extracted from the 3D model known as stress isometrics or stress sketches and model the piping design in either Caesar II or AutoPipe stress analysis programs. The results from the analyses shall assist the stress engineer and designer in what pipe support welded attachments should be used.

The USA, Canada and Australia based projects do not normally set up a project with a dedicated pipe support team. However, the UK offshore projects do. Large offshore projects executed in London may have a team in excess of thirty pipe supporters. Senior piping designers normally know what type of pipe support to apply to the piping and approximately what position to place it on the line. These days with increasingly less senior pipers on the design team, pipe modellers need some assistance when sorting out the pipe supports. If a junior stress engineer is assigned to an area with junior piping designers being supervised by a junior piping design supervisor then there will be a problem that may not get caught till the piping is fabricated and installed. Unless it's installed by a junior at site!

Shoddy designs that get through design and checking will arrive in the pipe fabricator's shop with, likely, incorrect materials. The pipe fabrication contractor will rub his hands together at the changes to isometrics and additional costs his company will make from the mistakes.

*After all, it's all about making money.*

Unfortunately, poor quality isometrics may not be caught for several months because the contract has not yet been signed. Possibly, after hundreds of isometrics have been issued for construction.

In present day 3D driven projects, the amount of material construction rework from incorrectly modelled piping systems is low.

At various stages of the project it is important that the right project folk get to see the modelled equipment and piping design. A software program called Smart Plant Review (SPR) is used to review modelling by any discipline. It is not the actual CAD platform used to develop the design.

As touched on earlier, three *Model Reviews* are arranged and are often referred to as a 30%, 60% and 90% model review. The first one, conducted at approximately 30% through engineering and after the FEED is completed, will show the entire scope of equipment and locations, with other plot defining criteria like pipe racks, buildings and platform structures. Furthermore, large bore piping will be modelled to prove that the plot plan is achievable.

The second 60% review is more detailed and conducted just beyond the halfway point through the detailed engineering phase. A line by line review against the P&IDs is normally done with the hard copies taped to the walls of the room where the review is conducted. Similar to how the designer yellowed off his own set of P&IDs, the same work process will be used on the drawings hanging on the walls.

Sometimes, a 60% model review can take several weeks to complete due to the sheer size of the scope and areas being reviewed. Any comments raised in the review will be noted as formal model review 'tags' and it is these tags, along with relevant SPR screen shots, that will make up the formally issued Minutes of Meeting notes documented from the weeks of reviews. Some clients are frightened off by such lengthy model reviews but if the Process is critical with licensor involvement, such long reviews are important.

A 60% model review is not ready to be reviewed if other disciplines have not finished their respective modelling, process P&IDs and piping line

251

designation table (LDT) or *line list* have not been issued for construction (IFC). Or, if dimensionally certified data has not yet been received from vendors supplying control system materials like control valves and flow transmitters, mechanical equipment and piping special items.

A few weeks later, the tags should be closed out as the design moves on towards the last review. The lengthy, IFC piping isometric issue program for the larger piping diameters normally commences right after the 60% tags have been closed out *as long as final vendor data is in place.*

In the last review at 90%, all remaining small bore piping modelled and all the outstanding line numbers not yellowed off on the P&IDs will be reviewed. Piping reviewed in previous reviews should not be revisited in the 90%. Do it once.

The 90% model review should not be conducted if certified vendor data is not in place for the remaining piping scope not yellowed off on the P&IDs.

After tag closeout, these remaining isometrics can all be issued.

In summary, there are a dozen steps of piping design:
1.  Knowing the process flow
2.  Understanding the fluid types
3.  The available plot space
4.  Transpositions
5.  Materials of construction
6.  Equipment modelling
7.  Piping design
8.  Piping flexibility and pipe stress analysis
9.  Model reviews and approvals for design
10. Fabrication and construction

That's about it on the subject of piping design.

*Are you still there?*

I exercised my option to expand my private pilot's licence and acquired a South African licence before starting to fly in Joburg and Secunda. I hired an aircraft out of Lanseria International Airport.

Aerodrome facilities included a large terminal and a single runway offering landings and take-offs at 07 and 25 degrees, or generally east north east (ENE) and west south west (WSW). I would take off most often to the east and at altitude, turn left and head north towards the Magaliesburg range of mountains. The blue waters of Hartbeesport Dam looked spectacular below me.

The Magaliesburgs were conceived around three billion years ago when West Ham last won the FA Cup. The configuration was such that there were essentially two sides to the range with slopes dropping down to a bowl. A bit like a cylinder split down the middle.

I would leave the dam and cross the south sides of the range, set the instruments to level flight at two thousand feet AGL and two hundred and seventy degrees west.

Most of these trips would be an absolutely stunning experience but on one such occasion, I was not so fortunate.

I was returning to Lanseria but relying on my flashy Garmin 396 GPS satellite navigation unit. However, before long the battery crapped out and a 1960's Cessna has no charging facility. I was negligent to allow this to happen.

So, I then needed to rely on my flight charts. I had made another fundamental error by putting them in my holdall on the back seat. To a pilot, stowing critical documents out of arm's reach is a step in the wrong direction.

Furthermore, I could not quite understand my position. I radioed in and advised Lanseria. I received no response so tried again. Still no response, so the radios were also now down. Here I was over some spectacular countryside or *feld*, as the South Africans refer to with no satellite navigation hardware, no charts in front of me and no idea how to communicate with air traffic. Lovely.

A pilot cannot simply pull over and climb into the back to retrieve a bag. I thought about quickly clambering into the back to recover my charts but this would mean diving over the headrest and scrambling back. An activity that was not taught in ground school. There's no auto pilot, let go of the wheel and the aircraft dives.

I then recalled one chapter I had been taught at ground school and that was, whenever a pilot is lost, to circle that area in the form of four sides of a square with one minute flying duration on each leg till one of three things happens. The first one was to find out your position using charts and landmarks. If that fails, plan B kicks in to keep trying air traffic control for assistance. The third option is not quite as desirable as the first two:

continue to maintain the flight pattern till you run out of fuel and crash to your death.

The position I chose to circle the airspace in, was not the best position. It was just east of Lanseria but much too close to approaching traffic wanting to land on runway zero seven. I became acutely aware of this when I heard the following message over the comms; *"Lanseria traffic, this is SA356 flight from Cape Town, there is a Cessna circling east of zero seven. Notify the aircraft immediately and have him out of there. Over."* The next message I received was finally, from the Lanseria ATC. They simply asked me to move to a position about twenty minutes away directly above a large shopping centre with a white domed roof.

An acute problem one faces when piloting light aircraft is language. The international language for air flight is English. If you've been abroad you'll note that the signs around all international airports are provided in English. Even if you are in Mali. I never had much of an issue with the Canadian accents but the SA ATC certainly had a bit of a problem with mine.

I finally made contact when my fuel tank was on the red. They brought me in and escorted me up to the tower where I got to meet the controllers. I was remarkably apologetic from dropping the ball and relying solely on a piece of electronics, albeit hugely popular with pilots of light aircraft and not having close at hand a rather important item of reference: a flight chart. The ATC team were very gracious and forgiving and passed it off as something that might occur every day. But the chief instructor at the Lanseria flying club asked if I wouldn't mind going up with him for an hour. On the house.

The following week I was up flying with him as he walked me through several manoeuvres and discussed South African flight ethics. I responded to each manoeuvre or request, perfectly.

The concerns the chief instructor could see were predominantly related to the language barriers between myself and ATC. No-one at the flying club could ever recall having a cockney pilot in their company. But, it was all quickly forgotten and I was found not to be at fault from a flying aspect. Just poor preparation which I learned a lot from.

One of the most common things any piper has to manage on his project, is time. Apprenticeships don't teach you about the planning component, we have to learn along the way. There is always pressure to get things out, quickly, dirty and with often disregard for the quality. The lead piper is often asked to compromise quality against cost and schedule. It's a fine balance between setting high standards and retaining a 'fit for purpose' approach to satisfy the bean counters. Over the years I have come unstuck from applying too much attention to the quality and jeopardised my position as a lead when my managers are all being squeezed by the client to deliver on time, within budget. More of this, later.

Let's take an estimate of piping manhours to complete the piping effort on a $10bn project.

The supporting documents I would need would be P&IDs, plot plan, line list and a level III schedule. It would take me a couple of weeks to pull something together that was reliable and a plus or minus 15% level of accuracy. But often, I'm not given the time to do the estimate properly. So, crap in… crap out and the estimate proves to be flawed as the project proceeds for project management to discover later that the project is going to cost the client much more in estimated manhours… and therefore, cost.

Likewise, piping designers are encouraged to rush through a layout and model the piping much too quickly. Youngsters panic and are not comfortable when telling their supervisor he or she need more time. They accept the demands and without time to review the modelling thirty folk sit in at the model review only to see hundreds of comments where the design is incorrectly perceived as flawed. In truth, the piping designer just didn't have that opportunity to put his stamp on it and complete the modelling.

Construction had started on the Secunda refinery and I had started to take a look at some of the piping spools that were being erected. Each year, one or more units had to be shut down for maintenance. This generally consisted of changing out stuff like mechanical equipment, piping, instrumentation and electrical components. A three week window for a shutdown would be planned for as far as three years earlier. All materials like piping, elbows, flanges, valves and other parts must be ready for installation the day that process unit is brought down and isolated.

On a refinery, there are a number of operating units or plants that require regular maintenance consideration demanding the replacement of poor quality materials that have either corroded or been found to be inefficient. Interconnecting pipe racks snake through the core of the refinery and off to each side are process units. Towards one end of each process unit is an area commonly known as a battery limit. The battery limit consists of access platforms and stairways up to one or more levels of piping and isolation valves. This area is made accessible to operations folk who need to shut down the unit by closing all the valves in that one common area, making the plant 'safe' to work. Once the unit is shut down and isolated, work can commence on the replacement of materials.

The beauty of working on the client sides of the fence are numerous. One of them is that you can set out your own levels of auditable activities, stroll around a jobsite with a stack of drawings under your arm and, in your own time and space, take a look at the quality of workmanship and make notes accordingly, before talking to the piping lead about anything you've noticed that wasn't kosher.

After making notes in the field, back at the office a formal report would be prepared.

The timing of this particular Sasol shutdown was not what I really wanted. I was about to tie the knot for a third time, to Erica, a lovely South African born and raised girl.

With the October 1st wedding approaching I had arranged a stag night at Al's Grill House in Sandton, a couple of weeks prior to the event. With the shutdown fast going pear shaped, I was asked to supervise some of the activities which meant a full weekend, in Secunda and smack in the middle of my stag party forcing me to postpone the stag a week.

The relevant units had been isolated with new piping spools ready to install. These would replace older, at-risk materials where the wall thicknesses had eroded to an inefficient level, or more effective piping designs and valve arrangements had been considered. As mentioned, all considered two or three years back.

As part of the MC team my responsibilities were to step up to the plate, be present on site and organise several field checks and 'punches', or verifying installed arrangements and materials against the engineered construction drawings.

I worked my nuts off for that long weekend, once for eighteen hours on the trot to help get the units back online. There was one particular caged ladder I had used several times a day to access an upper level. On one, tired occasion I had forgotten to look above me before starting my ascent from ground level. Halfway up the ladder I met a heavy chap coming down and almost buried my head up his arse.

The stag party the following week was rescheduled and half a dozen of us enjoyed a good night out at the lovely steak house and then onto the neighbouring Katzy's night club for some port and cigars. I abstained from a cigar but made up for it with far too much port.

Our wedding was indeed a wonderful event. Booked at the River Place estate next to the Hennops River the fifty-three friends and family who attended from a few parts of the globe had a lovely time.

# 2011

I was settling down in an Italian restaurant close to downtown Montreal one Saturday evening over the weekend of the Canadian Grand Prix. Across the room was a long table laid out for twenty persons with McLaren jackets on the back of the chairs. Glancing around the table I strained hard to spot a racing driver and assumed that the diners were all part of the mechanical support team.

I ordered a nice bottle of red wine. Nothing extraordinary, but a good one, nevertheless. On my table was a reasonable sized glass but on the McLaren table were large, *Syrah* style wine glasses.

The French-Canadian waiter brought my wine to the table and began to remove the cork from the bottle. Pointing, I asked him if it might be possible to have a wine glass like the ones over on the long table. The waiter didn't even look up and said, *"I'm afraid not, sir. Not with this wine."*

Back at the Secunda refinery, the Sasol Growth Project was now well into construction activity. Mechanical completion (MC) is one of the construction stages of a project, necessary before handing a unit back over to the client's operations team. The piping systems are engineered, designed, checked, fabricated, installed, welded out, bolted up, hydrotested, punched, insulated and signed off as mechanically complete, ready to go into operation.

As the project drifted towards completion I was called into a meeting and told that by the year end my assignment in South Africa would be finished and I would return to my home office in Calgary. This news came as a surprise but, in truth, it was always going to finish.

Plans were drawn up for Erica and I had to head to Canada!

Fluor had graciously given me about five months to get it all together and on the twenty-ninth day of December, 2011 we headed off to Tambo International airport with a twenty-two-year old cat to catch business class flights back to Calgary.

I had been in South Africa for one thousand, three hundred and eighty-six days and my life had turned around for the better.

# 2012

Leaving sunny skies and temperatures of 30°C, then arriving to temperatures of -30°C was a shock. The amount of snow was a heck of a change.

It was to be a new experience for me actually living downtown in the two bedroom apartment I had bought ten years earlier as a rental project. The location was perfect and right next to Prince's Island Park.

A week into the new year and I walked into Fluor's offices and sat in the reception area where Alan Lawrence greeted me almost four years after I had said goodbye to him. It was great to be back and it looked like he was pleased to see me.

However, since I had been gone the city of Calgary had gone through a serious downturn. Of all the engineering companies in town Fluor had been the hardest hit.

Instead of moving straight onto a new project, things stagnated and I was engaged on a number of audits on projects either in FEED stages or Detailed Design. Some weeks I would have to scratch around for snippets of work. I simply hate having nothing to do in our business.

Alan had suggested that I consider moving into Engineering Management. We both agreed it could be a nice opportunity and I was introduced to a couple of senior managers interested in moving the idea forward.

Two concerns contributed to my decision not to accept this next stage of my life;

a) the Manager of Engineering was a chap called Richard Tweatford. In his interview, he essentially put me in my place and in no uncertain words described to me that any project I would be assigned to would be the size of a mouse's earhole and have next to zero glamour. I would also need to spend between three and five years on a learning curve before being given more responsibility and a project of any substance. I walked away from that interview feeling condescendingly belittled.

b) The other issue I had was that while I was preparing for the transition back to Calgary, a letter had been sent to me by the condominium board of my Eau Claire apartment requesting the sum of $50,250 as a payment to cover construction repairs and legal costs of a Special Assessment recently approved by all five members of our condo board. I was furious with this demand and had no idea how I could make this payment. If I chose to reject the demand the course of action would be quite simple; they would foreclose on me and I would lose my home.

By March 2012 the engineering opportunities were starting to recover in Calgary. Except Fluor, of course, who remained quiet with the exception of work on a new refinery project for a growing oil company called North West Redwater Partnership (NWR).

Another problem was that my salary had stagnated over the past few years at Fluor. I now found myself earning probably a little over half of what I might enjoy elsewhere in town. In truth, my occupational desires were soon driven by the dollars and I cannot deny this. I was never good at seeing the advantage of staying on a company's permanent staff bringing home, after tax, a little more than half of what I could bring in by being contract on a good project. And, of course, not sucking up to chap like Mr Tweatford.

So, after seven consecutive years on two projects, I made the decision to move on from Fluor.

An agent contacted me and asked if I was interested in a lead piping supervisor's position on the brand new Hangingstone project at a Japanese-owned company called, Toyo Engineering.

I was very much interested, of course. Toyo are downtown and about fifteen minutes' walk along the river from home. I went for an interview and was soon offered the position to run the piping team on the Steam Assisted Gravity Drainage (SagD) project for a relatively new Japanese owned client, JACOS.

My hourly rate would be $105 an hour which would equate to approx. $218,400 gross a year. I would be leaving Fluor and a salary 45% lower than this. In truth, Alan was not thrilled with my decision but because of this special assessment I had to make the right moves that might help me pay these exorbitant costs I was starting to lose sleep over. If Fluor had been busy, it may have swayed my decision to stay. I therefore left Fluor in April that year and joined Toyo Engineering, walking to the office and back each day.

Life at Toyo was challenging. On my first day I discovered that the JACOS project I had been assigned to was not yet ready for the FEED phase but actually still working its way through the approval work process between the client and engineering contractor. I was therefore assigned on a temporary basis to a new *Sturgeon County* refinery project for a relatively new oil company, the North West Redwater Partnership. But a Light Ends Recovery and different from the Crude & Vacuum unit that Fluor had been awarded by the same client, NWR.

My duties were to develop manually drawn piping studies of pipe racks, battery limit valve stations and an enclosed building housing three, high pressure, reciprocating compressors.

I had not been involved with detailed piping design for several years and I simply loved this, albeit temporary, position. My office area was not geared up for design work and drawing boards were well gone so I taped clean sheets of A1 size paper to the surface of my desk before using straight edges, scale rules, circle templates and lead-filled, mechanical pencils to study the design. From my studies, a few CAD designers would take the pencil drawings and enter the information into the PDS 3D model. One piping study created in a couple of days could keep a 3D designer busy for three weeks.

Over the next few months I got to work closely with the designers, engineers, managers and several of the NWR client team; particularly one stress engineer, Thatchi. We had worked together at Colt Engineering, eighteen years earlier. A good fella.

Six months later I moved off the NWR project and was finally assigned to the JACOS project I had been hired for.

The Hangingstone project was a 50,000 barrel a day SagD project located in northern Alberta. Steam Assisted Gravity Drainage (SagD) is a process where the pressure of a hydrocarbon reservoir located several thousand feet below ground level and into the earth's crust is insufficient to recover and bring the hydrocarbons up to the surface for processing. This is where boilers are included in the plot development to boil large volumes of water, make the steam then use the pressure of this steam to inject down into the depths of the reservoir and boost the pressure of the oil and gas fluids to bring them up to the surface and recover them.

I had brought on a familiar person to help me get things sorted. Colleen Velcrose and I had worked together at Fluor on the Sipchem project before I'd left for South Africa. Colleen would be a perfect fit for the project as my deputy.

A number of piping designers had also been assigned to my team, a few of whom I had already got to know from the NWR project.

The FEED kicked off and normal piping front end activities got started.

First, the scopes of work, terms and conditions written up in the contract between JACOS and Toyo had to be understood. This couple of weeks led me into a detailed list of deliverables. Plot plans, piping general arrangements, line lists and fabrication isometrics.

Once the deliverables had been identified the project team sat around and discussed an achievable schedule. It was then my task to estimate the amount of hours it would take to complete the FEED phase, followed by the entire number of detailed design engineering hours.

This estimate proved to be something of a catastrophe, for the entire project team.

As usual, I had used historical data, go-bys and experience to establish line counts, drawing counts, engineering activities and include hours covering reviews, piping design and modelling, QA and isometric extraction, checking and IFC issue.

I then submitted this estimate before all hell let loose.

The piping manager, project manager, project engineering manager, Toyo's Director of Engineering and even the company directors all gradually got involved with the Estimate of Piping Engineering hours. The cast of Titanic were all over me!

I spent several days being interviewed and scrutinised for the number of hours I was submitting. Of course, I had included a contingency to cover unforeseen interruptions but nothing out of the ordinary and besides, this is something a piping lead would do anyway.

My estimate of hours for the detailed design equated to 102,416. This included Calgary efforts but also work fronts to be executed in South Korea and Japan.

The Toyo home based offices in Tokyo sent project control folk over to Calgary to add further turmoil to my working days by supplementing the enquiries. It was like I had broken the law.

With the exception of a small percentage of these hours I agreed to reduce I was confident in the fact that my estimate around 97,000 hours was spot on, the numbers of deliverables were spot on and the piping dates supporting my project schedule were also, correct.

After several days of what I can only describe as an interrogative approach where Anglo-Jap translators were also called in to help the cause, I soon discovered the reasons for all these shenanigans.

Toyo Engineering had, essentially, bought the project! Senior management had spent several months wining and dining JACOS owners in an effort to be awarded both FEED and detailed design phases of the SagD project. All the effort and quizzing of my estimate was to get me to bring down the hours from a hundred and two thousand to something closer to a ridiculous twenty thousand!

Of course, this was an impossible and futile exercise. But, more importantly, I was angry and disillusioned by this whole shit show and the fact that Toyo had brought me in as the piping lead without me being told of what I was to go through. A lesson learned there.

Furthermore, I had the pleasure of meeting yet another fine manager in the name of Tony Teddy. A Newfoundlander who was not the full shilling. A smoker who spent more time outside in the back alley than he did in the office, Tony had a fuse as short as a maggot and was absolutely useless as a manager. I'm being kind, here.

Refusing to listen to any of his discipline leads in any meeting Tony was chairing, if he didn't like what he was hearing he would vibrate with anger and almost fall off his chair. Throughout the ordeal of trying to slice up the hours, Tony Teddy was usually at the forefront, sitting there with steam blowing from the ears on his fat head.

# 2013

Needless to say, I was slowly becoming disenchanted with the JACOS Hangingstone project and started to regret leaving Fluor. The Christmas holidays were approaching and a well needed break was in order.

But, just after Christmas and the New Year, a strange thing happened as I returned to the Toyo office on the fourth of January. I received a telephone call from Thatchi.

NWR were looking for a piping guy to oversee some of the refinery scope and would I be available for a chat later that afternoon with his supervisor, Gord Berg at NWR's offices downtown on 4$^{th}$ Street?

Now, the timing of this phone call could not have been any better. I agreed to the interview. No preparation, no homework, I simply walked a few minutes through the downtown streets and arrived in good time for the one p.m. meeting.

Gord and Thatchi sat with me and we talked about the position before Thatchi left me with Gord to discuss some other details.

I was being recruited by NWR to oversee three of the fifteen refinery units Fluor were contracted to engineer. Unit 10 – Crude & Vacuum, Unit 20 – LC Finer and Unit 30 – Hydroprocessing. Gord asked me to forward an email stating my demands and attaching my resume. If the moons lined up, I would be working as a contractor in Fluor's Sundance offices representing the client. A position from the piping heavens.

I skipped back to the still, relatively empty offices of Toyo.

The contract hourly rate I was on at Toyo was $105 when I started in April of 2012. The company had then given me an increase of five bucks just before Christmas. I was just about to go into detailed design, albeit with a forced approach on engineering hours I would have to succumb to.

The following morning I sat down in the office and penned an email back to Gord. I thanked him and Thatchi for the opportunity to meet yesterday and agreed to take the position down at Fluor's offices. I stated that my hourly rate would have to be $140 for me to make the jump.

Now, I'm not sure why I went so high but NWR had asked for me and

264

I did not think this rate for a client-based position was excessive.

I received no reply and a couple of weeks drew on. Toyo's project team returned to work and Tony Teddy was up to his usual tricks, hollering at folk with beads of white liquid flowing from his ears.

Four weeks after my interview with NWR and with no immediate or follow up response, I made the awkward decision to send another email back to Gord.

He called me back almost immediately, apologising for not getting back to me since the interview. He had spent the last three weeks at home with the flu.

He then suggested that the hourly rate I had asked for was more than what some of the NWR project managers were earning and would I be okay accepting $125 or $130 an hour?

I politely told Gord that I would indeed consider this suggestion and get back to him by email, with a modified rate.

An hour later I was happy to forward an email with a revised figure of $130 an hour... instead of $140. If someone offers you $125 or $130 for a salary... who would say $125?

A week later a contract was issued and I was all sorted!


Now, I appreciate the fact that this new position for a growing, client-based company would be a no brainer to accept for most folk. But I did already have a responsible position as a Lead Piping Supervisor working for Toyo Engineering. Yes, I had been approached by NWR, but the real reasons I had accepted a short notice interview was this: I was intrigued to know why someone would want Mitch Jago working on their team. My affiliations with Fluor over the years and knowledge of their considerable work practices and procedures had likely earned me an opportunity for NWR to bring on the right chap. It was these positive considerations that caused me to take things to the next level. The high rate I asked for quite simply reflected my confidence at the time in being able to stay with Toyo and see *Hangingstone* through to its conclusions should the higher rate *not* be accepted.

In conjunction with the offer from NWR, I was very unhappy working at Toyo. It was not easy to forget that folk had been flown in from Japan to question my estimate of manhours and I was getting minimal support from my senior peers at Toyo, while being royally shafted to accept a chunk of hours that wouldn't be enough to build a broom cupboard. And, may I add, estimated by a piper with almost forty years to his credit, thirty of them as Lead Engineer estimating manhours across several different projects. I was getting no frikkin help because guess what: Toyo had bought the bloody *Hangingstone* project and old muggins here had to deliver it in a fifth of the time expected.

On the strength of all this crap making my life at Toyo a misery, I signed the NWR contract, popped it into an envelope and personally walked it down to the agency, a few blocks away.

I wrote out my notice and prepared the email. Before sending it I went in to see my Piping Manager, Joe Stiletto. Joe is a decent chap and I believed, was dragged into the arguments over manhours when he preferred not to be. I sensed that he felt a bit awkward and was probably involved in establishing the twenty thousand hour estimate accepted by JACOS. What department manager would not?

I told him I would be sending an email out shortly. Joe was unhappy that I was leaving but wondered, on what grounds had I given notice? He knew Tony Teddy had been busting my balls and he knew I was disenchanted about the forced cutback of hours. One of those reasons would have been sufficient alone, to move on.

But, although I had tendered my notice of resignation many, many times over the years for reasons that were several fold the task is never easy.

I was calmly elusive in my response to Joe. Returning to my office I hit the send button submitting my notice in writing.

So, I left Toyo. The *Hangingstone* project was about to enter detailed design with around seven hundred and sixty-five piping hours left in the pot that should be six figures.

I was excited about the Sturgeon County refinery project and working for this new client, NWR. Checking in at Fluor's reception I bumped into many guys I knew. Word had got around that I was joining NWR and several familiar faces stopped by and shook my hand wishing me all the best. This was a nice gesture.

Let me tell you, as a piping engineer or designer there is no other project on this earth more rewarding and challenging than a brand new, grass roots refinery. From a piping aspect a refinery has absolutely everything you can think of.

The services that flow through these metallic and non-metallic materials are also numerous; Process gases and oils, hydrogen, oxygen, plant air, instrument air, cooling water supply and return, severe sour service, catalyst slurry, acids, utility water, flare and blowdown, closed hydrocarbon drains, open drains, storm water collection systems, lubricating oil and seal oil, firewater, potable water, raw water, steam, condensate, boiler feed water and deluge for sprinkler systems. Plus amine, refrigerants and other chemicals. Not to forget that hydrogen sulphide is also evident in some process fluids. $H_2S$ is invisible, impossible to detect from smell and is a killer when accidentally emitted.

Furthermore, the types of valve found on a refinery are endless: pipeline valves, gate valves, check valves and globe valves. There are soft seated ball valves and metal seated ball valves. Plug valves and butterfly valves. These valves may have bolted bonnets, welded bonnets, extended spindles and chain operators. The valves might be car seal locked open or closed. Valve ends might be screwed, socket welded, butt welded, flanged or clamped.

Metal seated ball valves have several different types addressing severe service, high solids, high pressures and high temperatures. There are metal seated ball valves where the valve bodies have small bore connections allowing a purging flow of either hydrogen or high pressure oil through the valve to maintain the velocity of the line service that is particularly sticky or *viscous* that could foul up the internal operation of the valve.

Fluor were awarded the Hydroprocessing and Crude & Vacuum units a while ago and only a few months back were also awarded the LC Finer after NWR terminated a complicated contract with Saipem, out of Milan. These were the three largest units on the refinery and all under one engineering house. Clearly NWR felt comfortable in placing a lot of eggs in the same basket.

My position was to support NWR and oversee the quality, cost and scheduling of Fluor's piping activities for all three plants throughout the FEED and detailed design phases.

Halfway through the year a wonderful thing happened. My son Ryan, his then fiancé Michelle (now married) and daughter Ryleigh all emigrated to Calgary where Ryan joined Fluor as a permanent staff piping designer.

A while ago after a heavy boys' night out while alone on an overseas assignment, I returned home to my apartment around ten thirty p.m. and went straight to bed. Waking up the following morning I hopped sprightly out of bed, walked into the bathroom, closed the door and turned on the shower.

Cleaning my teeth while having a whizz, I flushed and stepped into the shower. A few minutes later I was towelling myself off and shaving in front of a steamed up mirror.

A spot of deodorant and a quick splash of after-shave before heading back into the bedroom. I switched on the light, made the bed and grabbed undies and socks from the cupboard. I then sat on the side of the bed to start getting dressed. Heading downstairs to the car park, I stood and waited for the bus that would take me to work. After ten minutes, I glanced at my watch. It was 2.05 a.m.

Now, I have no idea how things like this happen but to someone hearing this story for the first time, it's all probably hilarious. But to me, I clearly have a problem with large quantities of alcohol.

Alcohol can play weird things on the mind and body, and over the years, I've heard some simply amazing stories. Peeing in wardrobes is one but in another, sadder case, peeing on a young daughter in her bed while she slept.

One of my mates, Gerald, stood fifty feet above the river Tyne in Newcastle one Friday night and trying to keep his balance, peed into the raging waters below. One slip and he'd never have been seen again.

On another occasion, a poor chap had hopped onto an underground train sometime after midnight when a few stops later he realised he badly needed to clear his bowels. Getting off the train from the front carriage, John stands there alone on the platform as his train disappears down the tunnel. Lo and behold, evidence of some construction activity and a sandbox at the rear end of the platform. In a moment of despair, John climbs into the box and drops his strides. As a smile appears on his face, there's the downstream wind and howling noise as the next train thunders into the station.

The train pulls up to a stop and John has no option but to continue crouching in the sandbox, the sides of which come up to his knees.

On the back carriage of the train is a group of about eight women returning home from a ladies' night out.

With nowhere to run, and John not quite finished doing what he had set out to do, a couple of the girls spotted him messing around in the sandbox.

Within thirty seconds, all eight girls and several other passengers in that carriage… were all looking at John's squatting techniques in a messed up sandbox.

Thankfully for John, the doors closed and a couple of dozen folk were seen laughing their heads off as the train headed off to the next station. Thankfully for John, these were the days before cell phone cameras!

Two other unfortunate things have happened to me that I'll not forget in a hurry. A bit more embarrassing than getting ready for work at two o'clock in the morning. Both in Calgary. Forgive me, but these stories are not for the squeamish…

A freezing cold Christmas Eve and a nice dinner in town near a wood fire at The Belvedere restaurant. A hundred metres from the restaurant, a number 3 bus would take me home down Elbow Drive to a stop next to Fish Creek Park, just a short walk from my house in Canyon Meadows.

I was the only person on the bus and a couple of minutes into the half hour journey I realised that I might not make it all the way home and would need to find a toilet soon enough. I knew there was a gas station about halfway but that was too far.

I was in a bad way. I knew I had to get off the bus, so pulled the cord. Actually, I pulled the cord about seventeen times.

The driver sensed something not quite right and as the bus screeched to a halt, the doors slammed open and I stepped from the bus thanking the driver. I was about six steps from the sidewalk. I sadly submitted to the fact that I had no control whatsoever over my senses and with each step I took released about a pound of effluent into my trousers.

As the bus headed off into a quiet night I scrambled behind the tall concrete wall surrounding a large apartment block overlooking Elbow Drive. Beneath a hundred-year-old evergreen tree, in below freezing conditions, I stripped down and cleaned up as best as I could. This is where my hundred dollar cashmere scarf came in handy, as pine needles don't help the situation. Dressing, a taxi picked me up at the gas station and took me home, the driver perplexed by a sudden onslaught of acridity to consume his cab. *I still miss that scarf…*

The next story at an Oakridge house warming party in 1995, I had invited about forty people and I prepared canapés and hors d'oeuvres. Something I love to do.

I had also hired a lovely female bartender that night to take care of the guest's drinks.

She had been topping up my glass with chardonnay and, in truth, when someone is topping up your drinks you have no recollection of precisely how much alcohol you have consumed.

A workmate, Dennis, had decided to come to the party and arrived late with his wife. Dennis and I, with a few others had got stuck into tequila shooters. You know, with the salt and the lime wedges. It was well after midnight and I had been drinking non-stop since about six p.m.

After some dancing, the party finished around five a.m. and I went to bed.

I awoke at noon with a bullet train screaming through my head.

I walked downstairs to put the kettle on and as I walked into the newly fitted kitchen I turned one corner of the island and there on the floor right next to the fridge was a two pound pile of shit.

I was gobsmacked and immediately cleaned up the mess.

But, in truth, I was really not sure if it was I whom had laid this down or someone else? There was little evidence to suggest one way or the other.

Sitting down with a cup of tea I started trying to piece together the last half hour of the evening before I had gone to bed. The conversation soon led me to my underpants and more specifically, where were they? *This might offer some clue…*

Back in the bedroom I had neatly placed my shirt and trousers back on the coat hangers. The socks were in the washing basket but my underpants were nowhere to be found. It was turning into a real mystery and one that probably wasn't going to end well.

I managed to get through the day and gradually felt better. Back at work on the Monday, the week started off well and this continued through to Thursday when I drove home from the office.

I then had cause to pop into a bathroom not usually frequented. Pulling back the shower curtain I glanced down at the plug hole.

There, were my soiled underpants from the weekend rolled up tightly. Poking out of the middle of them was a stick of celery. The flower was still on the end. I laughed till I cried before calling the local psychiatric clinic.

I have not touched a drop of tequila since that party.

# 2014

I settled into my position with NWR and gradually got to know all the engineering folk around me, as well as the Fluor team.

The single first thing to address was to review and respond to Fluor's observations that the number of NWR material line classes fell well short of the number of line classes required to build an LC Finer. An additional thirty-two line classes would be required to supplement the hundred and sixty already approved for use on the project. This was a situation where the wheels of a 'big machine' and an engineering contractor like Fluor would annihilate a small, new oil company with re-imbursible claims on a monthly basis.

Plot development on the LC Finer was the next challenge. In the previous five years, Fluor had been developing and implementing a culture known as 'Third Generation', and a form of Modular Design.

Essentially, this concept was meant to support a much more proactive approach to modules resulting in as much as 80% of the unit plot plan.

Maximising the number of modules on any plot has a negative component. More steel is required and therefore will have a restrictive impact on operations, mechanical handling and maintainability of the unit. It's a trade-off against less expensive, site labour hours.

There was an Indian based supplier of pipe fabrication, static mechanical equipment and other scopes of steel materials. Let's call them LNT. I was asked by NWR to join a team from Canada to visit the company's construction facilities near Mumbai in the state of Gujarat.

The firm employ fifteen thousand people in various capacities from sales and marketing to all elements of the fabrication of equipment and pipe spools required on global offshore and onshore installations. The visit was to ascertain whether they were capable of supporting a contract worth about C$50m worth of pipe fabrication work.

Assessments would address competence in pipe fabrication, post weld heat treatment, project management and controls like cost and schedule, materials of construction, packaging and surface freight delivery to the refinery at Redwater, Alberta.

We were treated very well indeed as LNT, eager for the contracts, showed us around.

One evening back at the hotel, a lovely meal was catered for and the outside temperature was up in the high thirties Celsius. Gujarat is a dry state and alcohol free. I was dying for a beer and wasn't afraid of bringing this point up in light hearted conversation. Within twenty minutes, a few chilled, Carlsberg cans suddenly appeared which many of the beer drinkers were grateful for.

On the last morning, the visitors were taken to an area of closely mowed lawns where we were all given a tree to plant. A small ceremony was followed by a plaque positioned in the soil at the foot of each tree. The wooden plaques had the name of the visitor carved on each one. A truly remarkable gesture from the LNT management.

And yes, LNT were awarded the contract!

I was to revisit India three more times over the following two years to follow up on quality checks and balances. And, of course, to check and water my tree.

Each visit, planned by our project management team, was scheduled too early and the checks I was asked to do could not actually be achieved. Due to late deliveries of drawings, the shop floor space that was originally assigned to our project was re-assigned to pipe spools related to another, large Fluor power plant installation located in the southeast United States.

Each of my trips cost NWR around twenty grand. The first visit was timed with empty shop floors where the materials were not yet in place to start fabrication. The second visit was a bit more resourceful and I was fortunate to see pipe spools loaded into purpose built wooden crates. These crates would then slide into a standard forty foot steel container and shipped to Canada.

The idea behind building these wooden crates instead of just dropping the pipe spools into the containers, was smart. Once the units arrived at site, the wooden crates would slide out of the container and allow the wooden boxes to sit on a laydown area and then be unpacked at a more determinate moment in time that would suit the project. The expensive metal containers are then free to be immediately returned to their provider, without costly detainment.

Apart from pipe spool containers arriving at site, the project was building more than a thousand pieces of equipment, piping and electrical modules, equipment skids, electrical buildings and vendor packages. They would be coming into Redwater from various corners of the globe, over a two year window.

Meanwhile, engineering and design was moving forward in Calgary. It was a full blown SmartPlant 3D project and was, supposedly, meant to be 'paperless'.

How did we ever get by in previous years without computers? Take any simple spreadsheet. You would need to have a notebook with horizontal lines and a couple of vertical lines already evident on the sheet, adding more lines as necessary. And a sheet of blue, ink-stained carbon paper would be slipped in between two sheets to get the copy you wanted.

How about making a change? A letter to project management or the client would be required, followed by carbon-copied, interoffice memorandums. Consequently, changes were much less apparent in those earlier years because the work process demanded more attention to hand written letters.

On the contrary, changes are made by anyone and everyone in today's project market. Process drawings like piping and instrumentation diagrams, flow sheets or utility distribution diagrams used to be issued and frozen and the changes would only be seen at the next formal issue several months later. These days, changes are already being drawn up before the drawings are actually issued by the document control and management team.

It has all gotten a bit out of control. Project costs have spiralled upwards predominantly due to the sheer enormity of change. If changes are made in the engineering phase of a project, that's bad enough. But when changes are made after materials are purchased or equipment vendors procured, the costs escalate ten times more than they would if the change was solely, design affected.

And changes also have a serious impact on schedule, too, of course. These days, project schedules no longer are signed by all parties engaged in the development then stamped and published. Engineering teams like Piping are advised by project managers that the schedule is 'live' and it will change next week. For a piping lead, maintaining all the dates and milestones is much like nailing jelly to a wall.

I know this book has touched on many negative issues of our industry regarding the advent of electronics and computers, but there are one or two that have improved because of this transition. Materials management is one; the opportunity to extract material quantities straight from an electronic 3D model saves an extraordinary amount of time when manual material take off (MTO) sheets are considered, as it used to be.

However, it is not all rosy because these days piping leads have little control on their materials. Often, an entire department of material management folk are employed to control and track piping materials. Furthermore, there is opportunity to slip up as one case I recall.

It was an Intergraph PDS platform. One piping designer had to accommodate three large bore, twenty-six inch diameter flanged butterfly valves in his area. These were gear operated valves on a cooling water supply system.

Like most projects these days, prior to every monthly update of the purchase orders, designers are asked to 'clean up' their models and remove any erroneous items. One particular designer had ignored regular calls for cleaning up the integrity of his model and a few weeks back had revisited his piping arrangement. He chose to copy his existing model and placed the copy about a hundred metres directly above the true position of his piping and out of sight from the real models. This is not an unusual work process for designers but they must remember these studies exist.

The designer had rearranged his piping but had completely forgotten to delete the study model sitting in cyber space a hundred metres up. When the model was uploaded to extract quantities the material management team did not check the P&IDs to confirm that only three of these valves were required but instead, purchased twice as many valves, in this case six! The error was missed throughout the project and eventually at site, the six valves were delivered and three sat there for months while supply chain managers scratched their heads.

In truth, valve take-offs should only be conducted directly from the P&IDs. This would eliminate the potential for such expensive errors.

The NWR project was the biggest thing in town. Fluor's three units demanded hundreds of engineers and designers. Existing projects winding down at Fluor were placing their resources on our project. Contractors were coming to Fluor and each Monday morning in the Sundance reception, up to twenty new starters were sitting there waiting for a photo and security badge. Fluor were also hiring permanent staff employees to join their projects of which they now had dozens.

Go forth the project did, as NWR continued to oversee the engineering development of a brand new refinery. Other engineering contractors were also engaged in the process. Jacobs, Worley Parsons and CH2M for some pipeline scope.

Guys I knew in the past were also joining Fluor and it is always good to see decent folk on the same project. Many floors in more than one Fluor building were consumed with NWR project folk.

Model reviews were arranged every few weeks and one of my duties was to support our NWR Operations team by ensuring that enough access and maintenance space was provided in the design that would make their lives easier at site over the next twenty-five plus years. This was not always straightforward. First of all, there are many project engineers in positions that show their authority on any particular issue but who actually know three fifths of nowt about the piping engineering and design, access and maintenance requirements.

The 3D piping designer, when required to place a 20 inch diameter, high pressure rated ball valve into his pipe modelling, he is at the mercy of a team of catalog database specialists who spend their days tucked away in dark corners modelling vendor information and data received from a supplier. The valve that the designer places in the model may be correct in its configuration of one metre in length, but there are other working parts adjacent to the valve that the catalog team know nothing about yet so have not included in the database. Therefore, what is depicted in the 3D models and design often is much smaller than the real thing once delivered to the site.

So, when it's time for this piping system to be reviewed in front of thirty people at the model review, not all the facts are apparent and looking at the model, the available space looks okay.

In these reviews and supporting the subjects of safety, cost, schedule and quality I would often need to raise a hand that design is clearly not to recognised standards. In this case, requirement for more space was apparent due to the size of the air-supplied actuator that manages the opening and closure of the valve may well be three metres in length and sit in a longitudinal plane directly above the valve.

Some of the metal seated ball valves on the LC Finer specified one or more purge connections on the body of the valve. The information on these purge connections was unknown at the time of the model reviews but after some homework discussing the valves with the process and material engineers I was satisfied that there was enough stainless steel purge tubing and valving required around the valve and, given the size of the actuator, this all demanded much more access and maintenance space than was originally stated in the client specification.

It gets a bit awkward when you have to defend something that isn't yet in the model. It was important that we made notes and did not rush into any decision, so the idea was 'parked' and this would allow some further investigation to be done before the model review re-convened the following morning.

Speaking of rushing into things, we are more impulsive when we are younger, I think, than in later years. Once upon a time this impetuosity almost cost me my life.

In the 1980s in Calgary I had rented a vehicle called an AMC Pacer. Looking much like an inverted bathtub the curved rear window suggested it was a poor man's Jensen Interceptor. Far from it.

I would normally take the number 17 express bus into the downtown core from the Ranchlands community but one cold, foggy November morning I needed to take the car into work as I had a five-a-side football match after that evening and a car was more appropriate for me getting home afterwards.

I was running a bit late and, football bag in hand, jumped into the frosted car with a slice of toast and marmite. Without the appropriate checks and balances I started her up and wiped a few inches of windshield with a glove. I had not the slightest idea how to get downtown because I was asleep on the bus most mornings and hadn't taken any notice of the precise route, so I winged it this time. As I started moving away from the house, I got lucky by recalling the bus route: a turn to the left, a turn to the right or straight on at each junction. Maybe a bus stop to be seen. It was dark and the street lights were blinding as I tried to wipe away more frost on the windscreen with one hand and eat my toast with the other hand, while driving.

In Alberta they have an unusual but useful traffic light system at a four-way intersection that included a flashing red light in one direction and a flashing amber light in the other, but only at off-peak times. This essentially means that in the dead of night when a vehicle comes across an intersection flashing red, they may stop, look around and if all clear, they may continue.

In the other direction when flashing amber, the driver does not need to fully stop but slow down and if all clear, he may continue. It means that the driver doesn't need to wait for the green light to proceed. Sensible.

Through a mist-covered windscreen and about two minutes into my journey I came across an intersection with a flashing red light. Stopping and taking a look around me the roads were all clear and I remembered the bus driver going forward at this point in the journey, so I proceeded forward. Gradually accelerating, I continued down a slight incline before all hell let loose. I had hit something hard in the middle of the road. For a few seconds I was tossed around like a ball in the car and split open my forehead on the rear view mirror. The car came to halt in a position where I was still strapped into my seat but was facing the stars. Was it a moose? Was it another car?

It felt like I was having a heart attack and breathing heavily, I opened my door and fell out of the car a few feet. Finding my feet and shaking with terror I soon realised what I had just done.

In Calgary, there are a small number of pits built into the centre of a road. Essentially, these six-foot wide, twenty feet long and four feet deep pits were constructed as a deterrent for vehicles travelling along a bus route. Three large steel bars were positioned from one side of the pit to the other.

These traps were designed to support faster bus times into town where the bus would not get caught up in traffic rush hour issues. The traps were wide enough to deter motorists (most, anyway) from taking that particular road while the wheels of the much wider bus could pass, unobstructed along the outside of the trap before the driver turned onto the highway.

I had seen the flashing red light but there was clearly another reason for this other than an off-peak intersection. Although I had pulled up to the four-way stop, the flashing light was there to deter motorists from driving forward and diving nose first into the trap about fifty metres down the road.

I had missed the warning lights, missed all the signs and there I was standing in the pit, blood and marmite on my cheeks standing next to my car now rested in some grave with its arse pointing up to the sky.

As if things couldn't get much worse, along came a number 17 bus and slowly ground to a halt in front of the pit. Fifty folk had put down their newspapers to gaze out of the misty windows of the bus and marvel at the mess that this nutcake had made, in front of them.

I was still dazed and the driver asked me if he could help. I collected my bag from the car and jumped on feeling a more than mild sense of embarrassment as folk asked me what had happened. The bus driver found a different route into the downtown core and I saw to my wounds at the office before collecting my vehicle from the car pound to where it had been towed.

Looking back, it was unforgivable to risk my life by rushing into things when all the dangers around me had not been fully checked.

Nowadays, the safety culture, at home and in the office or at a jobsite has changed dramatically for the better. Less lives are threatened and we are all more safety conscious.

In my twenties I was totally unaware of such things. I would go out on a Friday night with six mates, all of us squeezed into my dad's Cortina, drink about eight pints of Abbot ale and drive everyone home before falling into my bed.

At the age of eighteen, my best mate Gary and I were inseparable. We would go out pubbing and clubbing most nights of the week. His dad had an old 1959 Austin A40, affectionately known as *The Lady*. It was good for four persons and one late night coming home from the Room At The Top club in Ilford with a couple of girls, Gary took a route away from the main roads to avoid any police stop checks. Mill Road was renowned for a short, narrow, single lane stretch of road about fifty metres long and through a brick tunnel under the railway line, with traffic lights at each end.

It was three in the morning and a real pea souper. Thick fog and I was in the back of the car and acutely aware of our surroundings as we approached Mill Road. The light was red and Gary started to accelerate. With three passengers screaming, we entered Mill Road and silence engulfed *The Lady* for about five seconds. Just enough time in fact, for my short life to flash before me. We came out the other side, no traffic in sight, and all of us sighed with relief. It was an amazing piece of fortune that another car had not entered that tunnel at the same time from the opposite direction! Gary and I still talk about that experience to this day.

# 2015

As the refinery engineering wound down, NWR offered me a position on the post-engineering, construction team up near Edmonton. There was not a whole heck of other choices around in Calgary but to see the refinery take shape and grow from the ground up would be an excellent opportunity and so, accepted the assignment.

The construction side of the project started taking shape as modules were assembled at a number of local yards around the Edmonton area, and below the border in the States. The first six months of my tenure up there was to visit these module yards and check out the module-installed piping.

This was a contentious time, too. Module assembly contractors don't like client reps snooping and crawling around piping systems trying to find errors. But my new position up at site as Technical Acceptance Lead was always to provide audit and oversight for NWR while at the same time reporting any nonsense, safety shortfalls and irregularities with construction.

Dressed like the Michelin Man, walking around steel modules in minus 20°C with howling winds make these exercises all the more difficult. I would find it impossible on some occasions to spend more than an hour and a half outside in the frigid conditions with a backpack full of drawings and tools.

Safety considerations were slips, trips and falls. Objects dropped from height, being close to high pressure hydrotest activity and frostbite from extreme cold temperatures all contributed in wanting to hide from the wind and snow behind a structure and tick all the boxes without actually performing any checks. But much like my similar tasks offshore, that's not the point of a job now, is it.

Other safety concerns are pinch points to nip a finger, lifting heavy loads when ill-prepared and drinking some of the coffee put out on the tables in the trailers.

Avoiding this stuff was hard enough but I also had a job to do. I would first track down the module in the yard. There could be one hundred of these huge structures in various stages of completion but a module number is usually clearly painted on two sides. Some modules would almost be finished while others may just be getting underway. They are normally positioned at an angle of 45° to one another to ease movement into position and then out several months later.

Each module can be a maximum hundred and sixty metres (five hundred and twenty-five feet) long by 7.3m (twenty-four feet) wide and 7.3m tall when considering Alberta transportation guidelines. When finding the right location in the yard to start assembling them it's important to be able to get a trailer in front of each one. How daft would that be if the module was finished but they were all too close to each other to get transportation in between each one! Much like building a boat in your basement.

Once I had found the appropriate module to check out I would then track down the particular section of piping shown on the drawing.

On occasion it was not possible to check the entire section of piping because scaffolding had either been removed too soon or the piping was, simply, inaccessible.

One mandatory safety consideration is that anyone working above 1.4m without a handrail must be 'tied off'. This effectively includes a harness, shackles and belts to tie you back to a fixture so if you did fall, the harness and ties would break your fall and possibly save your life by stopping you hitting the ground. It is therefore important when wearing this arrangement that the length of tie-off is actually shorter than the drop. Sadly, fatalities sometimes occur because this point went unchecked.

There would be a formal team walkdown a couple of days prior to the module's departure to site. Twenty of us would sit in an office discussing an agenda of what we were about to see then follow each other over to the module. Better to do the planning in the warm with a coffee than outside in the cold and noise.

The group would break up into smaller disciplines and look at the more critical areas of the module. Pipers together, sparkies together, etc. Because I was spending time in the weeks ahead of this, I was prepared and made notes in previous walks to raise them at the final walkdown.

And let me tell you, there are so many excuses why an issue or error might be raised. You had to fight hard to get anything rectified as resources at the yard sternly defended the cause.

I was checking out the piping on a large, road bound module. A short section of thirty-six inch diameter piping consisted of a straight length of pipe running along the module and two, ninety degree elbows, one at each end turning away from the module to the plant east direction. Each elbow was fitted with a short length of pipe leaving both ends of the system open. A few pipe supports were separating the piping from the steel but the insulation had not yet been installed.

The fabrication isometric clearly showed that, once installed, this piping system should be sloped in a downward direction at 1:100 from the south area to the north. A total centreline distance of about thirteen metres. Over the entire spool on the module (just three sections of straight piping and two 90° elbows) the 1:100 slope factor would mean that the centreline elevation of the open end to the north of the spooled section would, in truth, be positioned 130mm higher than the open south end. Ten minutes of checks disclosed that no such slope existed as instructed in the drawing. Instead, the north-south straight run was precisely horizontal with no slope at all, while the two short east-west sections were both sloped but both sloping from the straight, north-south section centre of the module down towards the east.

This was a fairly significant cock-up. If left untouched, when arriving at site the mating ends of the 36 inch piping on another module would not match up to this piping so something needed fixing.

At least one thirty-six inch weld would now need to be cut off and the elbow section rotated and repositioned to the correct slope characteristic identified on the isometric. Maybe two days of work for welders and pipe fitters.

When preparing my report, I was under intense scrutiny as this delay might hold up the delivery of the module about to go to site, just an hour's drive away. I was asked to endorse the paperwork and thus the changes were to be addressed at site, resulting in additional costs. This, I refused to do. Site labour costs are more than twice those costs established at a module yard. Hence the reasons for avoiding site 'stick-built' work. If this refinery was in the Middle East, Far East or Africa modularisation would not usually be considered as field labour and individuals are, sadly, a dime a dozen.

Then my project manager got involved. *What a great idea.*

PM's really don't want to hear about reports like this. They would rather pay me for twelve months of module checks without a single report, and keep the number of faults found under wraps because that might administer change, and changes affect critical schedules. These considerations dictate all decision making. He wanted my report to be modified and asked his project engineer to lean on me a bit.

The module was delivered to site with all my findings listed on a 'things to do' punchlist to be addressed at a later date before weld out.

These things happen; I was doing my job and the PM was doing his. But often, a piping lead's decision is overridden by the project. I've learned to anticipate these coming down the line and not to 'die on that hill' trying to get my way. Project or Delivery Managers have many things they oversee but the good ones don't overlook quality.

Field checks by engineering teams on finished construction are extremely important in the build up to a start-up and efforts to release and formally handover the piping systems to the client.

But, eventually it all gets done. At a cost. Delays in schedules when construction teams are at a peak of several thousand people can add up to not millions, but *billions* of dollars. This is essentially why project managers and pipers don't always see eye to eye. From my seat, flush out the irregularities of the piping fabrication and fix them immediately, incurring any additional costs before the issues arrive at site. From the PM's chair, procrastinate, postpone, or even ignore the reports and the risks are greater. But in truth, the good PM's I've worked with over the years are mostly supportive of my approach as a lead piping engineer.

Two years after its conception, when the module program finished and the yards emptied out, hundreds of craft labour were released into the market. Normally, this sort of thing posed little threat to the workforce and they would jump onto another project in Alberta. However, when this transition happened there was simply no work to be found. Welders, scaffolders, steelworkers, pipe fitters, and foremen all went home not knowing where their next paycheque would come from.

I moved to an office at site. I was still inundated with email traffic to look after but now I also needed to be visible in the field helping to resolve construction issues. Fluor's construction team expanded at site and each of the three units I was overseeing grew taller and wider as modules arrived at site and were welded together.

In a perfect world, the delivery of a large 1,000+ tonne module would coincide with its final position being ready to receive the structure. Once through the site gate, it would go straight to its final destination.

This rarely happens. 'Staging' is a term used when establishing a tentative location for modules not yet ready to move into position.

For a long, 500m stretch of pipe rack modules numbered 1 to 30 you don't want number 19 delivered to site first, so timing is incredibly important to avoid monstrous areas on site staging such modules.

On site, purpose built heavy haul roads are identified early and these are used to bring all the larger hardware onto site. If module number 19 arrives early, it will be staged on a large laydown area till it is time to move it that last six hundred metres into position.

Crane leasing and timing is also critical at a jobsite. At its peak, there can be up to a hundred cranes on a jobsite of this size. With some companies charging $150,000 a day for the larger units it is important that they don't sit there idle in the wrong position while the late modules are arriving at site, early.

The Redwater refinery north of Edmonton was a three-hour drive from my Calgary home and my requirements at site demanded a rather cosy arrangement; Work four x ten hour days Monday to Thursday then head back to Calgary late on Thursday afternoon. I would then drive up to my leased apartment in Fort Saskatchewan on a Sunday afternoon and get a good night's sleep before the working week kicked in.

# 2016

Later on, the project expected us all to be in on Fridays. This was changed when demands increased and each discipline was found to be absent on a Friday when a construction contractor had questions. Personally, that extra day up on site had a dramatic change in the quality of my life.

I flew to China where I spent a couple of weeks checking out Gasification Unit 40 modules at a company called Yanda. The Yanda pandas had fallen short furnishing the modules. So much material was missing I couldn't write it all down fast enough. When I presented my report suggesting Yanda complete their work before these modules set sail, the report was noted and ignored. And I was representing the client! After calls between Canada and China it was deemed more important that these modules were transported to the coast and loaded onto ships, half empty. The huge costs of missing a shipping delivery slot would be offset by the much lesser costs of finishing the modules at site. I therefore questioned the reasons for my trip and discovered it was to only tick the boxes.

Just before leaving for China, I had heard that several folk would soon be getting their notice from NWR. The hammer had come down on dozens already and it now appeared that I was not that far away from getting released.

Then, on the last Monday of August, 2016, I was called to the security office and given three days' notice to leave the company. I had been on the project for forty-two months. My chicken-shit overall lead piping engineer Hughie Makeel could not even be bothered to attend the notice meeting or indeed, call me. This act of cowardice simply reinforced his lack of competence while on the Sturgeon Refinery project.

In my site boots I walked slowly back to the office, a heavy sickness in my stomach. I knew there were no piping positions in Calgary and living with Erica and I were her parents I needed to support. Most of my friends and colleagues were out of work, with one or two finding jobs in southern

California. I left the Redwater site on the Thursday and in a short moment of pleasure, started my three-hour drive south from site for the very last time.

I'd been up there one full year and had enjoyed the three and a half years on the project, immensely. During that drive home south on the highway 2A I gave my situation some serious consideration. While unsure of the immediate future I embraced my new situation and, looking in the rear view mirror, I told myself that I would never look back but only forward to a new, exciting era that was about to begin.

I put out some feelers for jobs. Nothing in Calgary, not even a promise it might improve. As the 2016 year kicked off the oil price had dropped to $27 a barrel. Projects had been put on hold or suspended. Those on hold were cancelled six months later.

I was contacted by an agent representing work opportunities in the Middle East. The position was three months on, one week off, in Saudi Arabia. Flights and accommodation included. But the rate was US$3,000 for the three months. I would likely work six hundred hours in that period so the hourly rate was $5. I told the agent he should be jailed and he laughed and told me I'd be calling him back in an hour. I didn't of course, but knew though that someone would take the position because this was a worldwide slump, not just Calgary.

It was dog eat dog and time to re-assess the values in my life.

Values are important and, in truth, should never change. But when you are looking for a job and bleeding money you start to think hard about all sorts of ways to pull out of it.

The GM at Fluor Canada, Simon Buckingham, who came to our wedding in Joburg suggested I get hold of the GM in Kazakhstan, who I knew from South Africa. The Tengiz Chevroil, or TCO project, was underway and they may be looking for a piping lead.

I dropped Mark Dennard an email and followed this up with a telephone call. Mark was quite receptive and dropped into the conversation the lead piping supervisor's name.

I fired off an informative email and didn't hear anything for a week. Then I received a call from the Kazakh agency who told me that the project wanted to interview me for a position as deputy lead piping supervisor. I was to expect an email to confirm the day and time.

A few days later and a Saturday evening around nine p.m., the telephone rang. It was Andy Railing, a Londoner in Atyrau, Kazakhstan. The same chap I had sent an email to. He was expecting to hear a Canadian on the other end of the line and was surprised to hear another cockney voice. Furthermore, he was also a West Ham supporter!

The interview went very well, not just because of the Hammers link. And so, the lengthy work process began to get me out there as Andy's deputy. The interview was followed up with telephone calls and emails regarding my assignment contract, terms and conditions. I would be engaged on a six week on, two week off, rotation. A US hourly rate paid monthly to a bank account and regular, eight-weekly return flights guaranteed to anywhere in the world I choose. Accommodation would be included as would transportation to and from the offices while a per diem expense would also support food and beverage costs. Not a bad deal considering the one in Saudi I had been offered!

I had been through some heavy paperwork before when preparing for my assignment to South Africa but this one took the biscuit. Over the next few weeks I would receive emails, questions and forms while sending back documentation, medical reports and background checks. I was advised that the whole process would take three to four months! I also learned what the word 'apostile' meant when legally guaranteeing qualifications.

Several weeks later I was approved for the project under the KPJV joint venture team, employed by a Kazakh firm, KING through the Bolashak agency system. My flight dates were confirmed for late November and I would be in Kazakhstan over Christmas. Oh joy.

Kazakhstan is the largest land locked country in the world and I have no idea how many football pitches would fit into it. The nation borders five others; China, Russia, Kyrgyzstan, Uzbekistan and Turkmenistan. A large chunk of the Caspian Sea, too, and this is where the huge sturgeon fish live, for sometimes as long as a hundred years, famous for their roe, or *caviar*.

Atyrau is the third largest city and twelve hours ahead of Calgary and five, London. With just one stopover, my flights would take me through Amsterdam.

The Future Growth Project (FGP) on the twenty-five-year Tengiz oil and gas development in western Kazakhstan is an enormous project with a price tag of US$40bn. Over an area that would encompass the Greater London boundary, the flat, barren and desert-like landscape of an area of the country accommodates drilling pads, wellheads, underground pipelines, gathering installations, production facilities and metering stations. There is a new five thousand person camp planned, expansion and twinning of major highways and an upgrade to its airstrip where private, forty-six-seater Dash 8 aircraft would come and go on a daily basis.

Atyrau International Airport is a five hour flight from Amsterdam and there are no duty free expectations or a shop of any kind to be found. You are bussed from the plane out on the tarmac, to the terminal and stand in line to await customs entry by an insufficient number of stern, officious military-like gentlemen wearing forest green uniform and large, daft-looking hats the size of dustbin lids.

An hour later a bus takes you a short twenty-minute ride into town and my smart, single bedroom apartment at the Europa Residence.

Once settled, I get to enjoy a view along the Ural river which happens to bisect two continents; Europe to the west and Asia to the east. My offices at the Worley Parsons building are just a quarter of an hour away.

So, I live in Asia and work in Europe! My two week breaks will take me back to North America. An inter-continental marriage, one could say.

The FGP business case is to double the current production output of two hundred and sixty thousand barrels a day (bbld) to five hundred and twenty thousand by 2023. The project is already a year behind schedule and the costs are mounting, as they always do on such large, mega projects.

My position as a new deputy was to support Andy in his overall lead duties while he would be out on R&R every two weeks and our rotations would not clash. As there was really nothing cast in concrete for the activities I was to engage myself in I prepared a narrative and job description.

I decided to take things one day at a time, suss out the project culture, get to know the team and managers then look at it all again in my second rotation. The timing of my first visit to Atyrau would mean that I would be in-country for Christmas and see the new 2017 year in, too, flying out at the end of the first week of January.

The piping engineering and design team overseeing the Gathering silos of the project consists of fifty-six piping folk, half of which are Kazakh nationals with one or two Russians. The rest are a mix of expat characters with their homes in the UK, Canada, Czech Republic, Canary Islands, Spain, France, South Africa, India, Iran, Australia and The Philippines.

*Gathering*, as the description suggests, consolidates fluids from several areas across the huge Tengiz oil fields. Operating areas associated with drilling, extraction from the ground, movement of fluids through pipelines and large, metering station operating plants with each MS up to eighty thousand square metres in area. The entire area of real estate stretched out thirty kilometres by twenty.

The engineering and design for additional Gathering scope would also be executed in Almaty, a larger city a couple of hours' flight east of Atyrau.

The first six weeks disappeared quickly as I slowly became accustomed to the project's specifications and working procedures. As Christmas Day fell on a Sunday it was the one day off we have each week. Being new to the project and not yet part of any social 'team' as Christmas approached, I thought about what to do with myself. A day at home on the couch watching local telly was not something I looked forward to a month into the assignment, but I was patient to adjust.

I got to hear about a small dinner for ten lonely bastards being arranged in the Gay Bar. After hearing such news, suddenly the idea of sitting at home on my own watching telly, had an infinite appeal. But I soon discovered that the *Gay Bar* was an affectionate term used for the drinking establishment down at the other end of the building that was frequented by mostly men watching football and rugby on any one of three large TVs.

I dropped an email and waited.

On December twenty-first, the organiser of the event, asked me to pop down and see him. It was a bit like joining an exclusive Mayfair men's club. He discussed the arrangements and costs and told me there would be a turkey dinner with all the trimmings. Would I like to come along?

How lovely I thought, thanked him and happily agreed to be there on the twenty-fifth. So, ten chaps turned up, mostly from UK origin and the entire afternoon was absolutely first class.

Getting a tad emotional at the bar later, thanking the others for including me in the luncheon a cheeky Londoner replied:

*"No worries, Mitch. We took a vote and it turned out five–four."*

# 2017

Those first few weeks in Kazakhstan I got to settle well on the project and enjoy the company of a few good folk, either in the office, down at the Gay Bar or other places like the Riverside pub next to the Europa apartments.

As those weeks may have appeared to be a harsh alternative to being at home in Calgary there was nothing, in fact, that would have taken hardship to a higher level by sitting by the telephone hoping and praying for a job.

After a terrific first trip back to Canada and upon my return to the project in late January I started to get more involved in isometric production... or lack of it. Each team had moved through their model reviews and had started issuing fabrication isometrics but they were falling at the first fence.

I soon discovered that the area leads did not really have the correct approach on how to support an isometric issue program. A control level schedule had been set up but there were so many roadblocks when trying to achieve the numbers.

There are a number of things that have to be in place before an isometric in any given area is ready to be issued for construction (IFC):

a.   The area must generally, not be in a state of change.

b.   The process engineering in that area must be finished. This can only be acknowledged if the P&IDs for both Process and Utilities scope have been IFC and do not have any holds or caveats.

c.   Hazardous operations (HAZOP) actions from previous meetings, cleared and acknowledged.

d.   The Process and Utility area Line List must be IFC and does not have any holds or caveats.

e.   The design in that area is finished. This includes having conducted all the 30%, 60% and 90% plus any other model reviews, with the client present and yellowing off the P&IDs against the modelling to ensure items like vents and drain connections have been captured in the modelling, along with all the new and latest changes.

f.    Any 'tags' written up from the model reviews have been addressed and agreed to by the originator and the client.

g.    The drawings for all the 'inline' control systems instrumentation on the piping are designated by the third party vendors as dimensionally certified, meaning they are guaranteed by the vendor not to change.

h.    The drawings for all the control systems instrumentation hanging off to the sides of the piping are designated by the third party vendors as dimensionally certified, meaning once again that they are guaranteed by the vendor not to change.

i.    The materials management activities have been completed and the Bill of Material (BOM) is correct.

j.    The drawings for all the mechanical equipment that piping systems are connected to, are designated by the third party vendors as dimensionally certified, meaning they are guaranteed by the vendor not to change.

k.    The isometric has been checked.

l.    All pipe stress engineering is finished and the stress sketches or isometrics updated with the final loads and pipe support requirements.

m.    The clash detection report reflects a clash-free model and the line is not running through a steel beam.

n.    Pipe supports and other welded attachments are correctly identified both in the model and on the isometric.

o.    The CAD platform catalog database has been finished to reflect the correct dimensions for a designer to use in their 3D model.

p.    Any known 'holds' have been cleared.

q.    The isometric has been signed off by the following signatories:

i.    The piping designer.

ii.    The responsible piping checker.

iii.    The responsible control systems engineer.

iv.    The responsible pipe stress engineer.

v.    The responsible piping materials management or controller.

vi.    The piping area lead.

Of these line items, not all the boxes had been checked but the area leads were preparing the isometrics for issue, anyway. When an isometric is issued for construction this *IFC* designation gives the pipe fabrication contractor the green light he needs to start cutting pipe and commence welding. In a nutshell, expensive piping materials should not be touched unless the checklist items for this listing above are all addressed.

The pipe fabrication team is already in place and if these drawings do not come along when planned, guys sit around doing nothing, thereby costing a fortune to retain.

It really needed one piping person as a coordinator to take on that responsibility. This is the role I assigned myself, with Andy's approval of course, to which he agreed.

In March, with utmost sorrow I lost my dad, whom at the age of almost 88 was ready to go. He had been in a care home with dementia for a few years in The Netherlands and a nice, small service was arranged to celebrate his life. He was a wonderful dad and I shared some lovely moments with him either in the office together, watching West Ham, playing golf and snooker or having a pint down the local. I shall miss his tender persona, non-judgmental approach to all around him and throwing non, non-stick cookware at the wall when not being able to get a Yorkshire pudding out.

Around April, a brand new phase of the project was introduced. To supplement my position as deputy I was now assigned as the lead piping engineer on what was known as Priority 3, or the P3 project. The piping team were already fully engaged in design and isometric production covering the P1 and P2 scopes of work and I was advised, along with the other discipline leads not to even think about staffing up with any of these resources. Instead, I would need to hire new pipers to support the P3 project.

I knew one or two good people from Calgary, out of work. I was advised that there was no problem with endorsing this approach by bringing in resources from Calgary if I was sure the individual would be a good fit. Furthermore, there was no need to go through a tedious interview process.

Names of piping designers I submitted were contacted by the Human Resources team and offered contracts a few days after submitting a resume. Expats with twenty-five plus years of experience were easy to find in the Calgary and London market but bringing onto the project any Kazakh nationals was much more difficult.

I was encouraged to recruit as many local folk as possible but soon discovered that there was an acute lack of experience, in-country. Any pipers with six or seven years behind them were already part of the current

291

team. Management asked that I lower the pre-requisites and instead of looking at resumes with six years or more experience, revisit the discarded CVs with just three years in the business. The solution was to introduce training courses for the SmartPlant 3D (SP3D) piping design program. We would interview, accept, make an offer, go through the lengthy work process then advise them of a start date on the project.

From their first day on the project the first four weeks would be assigned to an SP3D training course. They would then be assigned to an area of P3 where they would sit near an expat mentor who would provide guidance in their design work, while offering help on the CAD side, too.

The trouble with this simplified approach was essentially, quite dangerous. Guys with hardly any 3D design experience would be hired and trained but you cannot train that same person to understand the criticalities and importance of piping design and engineering. This takes decades of design, fabrication and construction experience.

These young fella-me-lads would be designing piping systems and, if any poor design was not caught in the checking system, the materials would be built and commissioned with oils and gases soon running through these piping systems at high pressure and high temperatures.

A true, lethal mix.


The day I returned to the office in early May, my supervisor Andy didn't look too good. He had been suffering from a bad dose of the flu and was coughing, hoarsely. As he sat right behind me this did not go unnoticed and I suggested he pop across the road to a clinic and see a doctor.

He took Tuesday and Wednesday off and came back in on the Thursday but his health had gotten no better. I gave him a royal bollocking and he agreed to let me take him to the medical clinic. It was just two hundred metres and a short walk.

Within a hundred feet from his desk he fell against the wall and could not go any further. I was more than a little concerned. Furthermore, he is a Type two diabetic. Collecting a taxi to go the two hundred metres and checking him into the clinic, I went back to the office.

The following day the clinic advised Fluor of his condition and I went back over to see him. Fluor were to evacuate him back to England on a private medical jet, but first through Berlin where the appropriate physicians were present to see to his poor condition.

He was soon diagnosed with acute pneumonia and spent the next fortnight in Germany undergoing all kinds of tests before completing the second leg of his journey back to London.

It was soon acknowledged that I would step into Andy's position while the poor fella would be off sick. A timeframe that could be two months. This now added a considerable fresh load to my current duties but nevertheless, I pushed forward without too many complaints.

Apart from the day-to-day project concerns on P1, P2 and P3 scopes of work this new responsibility now meant I had to manage personal issues, too.

One such issue raised its head.

There was a piper called Salamat who worked at one end of the office. I had been advised from project engineers sitting near him that he was never there at his desk. He was reporting to one of the P1/P2 lead piping engineers and knowing these lead engineers I knew that Salamat would be left alone to get on with his work. While this approach is acceptable for most piping designers who have respect and integrity, it simply doesn't work for everyone. Salamat was clearly swinging the lead by ducking out of the office on a regular basis and needed to be pulled up for it.

I first contacted security. I wanted to see all the computer readouts from the in/out badging turnstiles. A couple of days later and I could see this guy was royally taking the piss. He was coming in half an hour late each morning, going home three quarters of an hour early and taking a couple of hours for lunch. There were even line items of him checking into the office gym at three in the afternoon! *It was time for a chat...*

I contacted HR and asked for some advice. He was a Fluor permanent staff employee so Fluor HR needed to get involved. The advice I was given was to give him a verbal warning in the presence of others. I set up a meeting with four persons; The HR manager for the local firm, KPJV, the HR manager for Fluor, myself and, of course, Salamat, whom I hadn't really gotten to know that well.

I organised the meeting arrangements and stopped by Salamat's desk, without interrupting his activity advised him of the meeting that afternoon up in the conference room.

I inadvertently walked with him to the room, of which there were two minutes of deaf and dumb sandwiches and not a word was spoken.

Closing the door behind the four of us, we all sat down.

I kicked off the meeting reminding everyone why we were there. I looked across at Salamat who shuffled nervously in his seat. I was twice as nervous.

*"Salamat,"* I said. *"I understand you have been spending an inordinate amount of time away from the office. We have had a look at your badging record and can see you coming in late, going home early and taking far too much time out of the office for lunch. Furthermore, Salamat, you have been going to the gym inside normal working hours. This is not a meeting we all feel comfortable with. Do you have any comments, please?"*

He looks across at me and pauses before saying anything, then gives us his response;

*"I'm not Salamat,"* he says.

Now, this took a few seconds for me to digest what I heard. My heart skipped while everyone shuffled uneasily in their chairs. I had regretfully, come to the horrific conclusion that I had picked the wrong one of the two chaps working together at the other end of the office. I knew them both by sight but not by name and sight, together. I was flabbergasted.

I apologised profusely to each one around the table, especially Yevgeniy whom I had got mixed up with Salamat. To supplement this dire embarrassment, Salamat is a dark haired Kazakh with a goatee while Yevgeniy is a fair haired chap of Russian origin. Another error on my part.

The two HR reps advised that they knew this immediately when we all sat down but did not have the time to tap me on the shoulder and stop me from making a right dick of myself.

Walking back to the office with Yevgeniy, I once again apologised for my inexcusable mistake. He was most understanding and laughing because let's face it, ten minutes before he thought he was being sacked!

It was a few weeks before I told anyone about this *faux pas* and over a few beers in the Gay Bar one evening, the story did get a laughing reception.

P3 moved forward and over a six month period of time, the piping team grew from fifty-five to ninety persons. Andy came back to the office but, unfortunately, fell ill again in October and made a decision to resign from the project and return to his native Fluor office in Farnborough, England.

There were also too many 'clicky' situations on our team. Our stress lead, an Iranian chap called Khosro Abhaghrahamaghratashalah was not exactly supporting the project and signing off stress stuff. The piping leads were anxious about this, except one lead, Andrew Tussle. He was pretty pally with Khosro and between them they played enough games to put the project back several weeks. It is also important that the twelve or so months I had been there in a leadership role was getting in the way of any clicky groups. In truth, most of the piping team in Atyrau were excellent and I enjoyed every minute working alongside them.

But this team spirit was lost among the clicky sets. Things had to change.

One afternoon, Khosro, myself and a couple of other designers had quarrelled in a meeting room. I instructed Khosro to get some stress analyses signed off so that the isometrics could go out. He would not support this and furthermore, that evening was flying back home for a 2 week break.

I then seized an opportunity to bring in another stress lead whom I had already started the paperwork for. Debbie Auld and I had worked together in Calgary and she would be a great fit as an overall stress lead for the team.

Khosro got wind of this while on leave, no doubt care of Mr Tussle, and sent me an awful, threatening email which I escalated. The project never saw Khosro again and soon after Debbie had joined the team, Andrew Tussle left the project. Under Deb's excellent leadership the stress work was getting sorted and she got on with just about everyone.

# 2018

On the sixteenth of January I celebrated my sixtieth birthday with an organised party in the Gay Bar. Where else! Warren, a natural DJ from South Africa, was playing seventies disco music, there was stacks of champagne, beer and Indian food.

Andy's replacement, a long term Fluor Calgary employee (of course) by the name of Darek Sherry, joined the project. As such, I had decided to throw my hat into the ring for a position at site on a twenty-eight day on, twenty-eight day off assignment at the Tengiz field.

After project approval, I was then re-assigned as overall Piping Technical Authority to the Tengiz oilfield on a rotation to oversee the construction activities across the entire project.

Why is it, halfway around the world from home where everyone needs to get on with each other there are always a small percentage of engineers who go out of their way to intimidate and upset the lives of other similar engineering folk working away from home?

We're all just trying to do a good job and get along with others working twenty-eight days in a row often in forty-five degree Celsius July temperatures?

Now, normally I just get on with what I have to do and try to avoid such folk. But, areas of this project were so complicated it took many individuals to close out RFIs (request for information) issued by the construction contractors who, at the time were trying to install a number of underground piping systems.

I reported to two individuals who sadly fell into this category and, soon enough, I was being pressed by these two chaps to sign off construction documents I knew to be incorrect and potentially problematic. The issues around the subject of materials, dimensions of fittings, fabrication, hydrostatic testing and installation of high density polyethylene (HDPE) piping systems, offered several opportunities to trip up.

First, when addressing any specific subject several of the project TCO specifications were not aligned and contradictory to Chevron's owner specifications.

Second, my TCO client representatives on site did not always agree with the engineering contractors, like me. Several weeks passed and a couple of rotations when it all unravelled and I was backed into a corner and asked to endorse a path forward which I vehemently disagreed with. I openly disputed the solution proposed that would certainly end up in a court room.

Unfortunately, the sensible original engineering lead who hired me, Jason, was on leave and his back-to-back, a miserable Californian called Pete Prison was on shift and twas he whom expedited my demise.

This was achieved in the most cowardly manner by getting an HR representative to contact me while I was filling out forms for my annual visa medical, prior to boarding a flight from Atyrau to Amsterdam. By the time I was sitting in my designated seat on the aircraft, the initial shock from being let go so suddenly was behind me and I was looking forward to seeing the back of Kazakhstan and returning to Calgary.

Thankfully, in those twenty-one months I had been away, work opportunities were picking up a bit in the city and this was welcome news. The recession had bit hard into Canada's energy sector and many good pipers were struggling to find work. Since 2013 the issues restricting oil and gas job opportunities in Canada were numerous and not assigned to any one particular item.

Due to a glut in reserves and stored hydrocarbons around the world, oil prices had plummeted adding constraints on energy companies making a profit. OPEC and its nations were forced to cut back on production and non-OPEC countries like Canada and the neighbouring USA were forced to shelve projects that had already passed through successful gate checks on front end business development, prior to detailed engineering and construction activity.

Add to this, the accelerated increase in the demand for hydrocarbon products to support energy needs from countries like China and India. The population of these two countries alone amount to more than one third of the world's peoples.

Liquified natural gas (LNG) projects had started to become popular and it would be a wonderful opportunity to move Canada's resources, refined or not, across the Pacific waters by tanker.

Now, to load up a tanker at any seaport on the north, west or east sides of a country with the world's longest coastline means you have to get the product there, first. The most expeditious way to do this is to provide a well-planned, safe system of pipelines to run across the country. Simple, right? Not quite.

Over the past few decades and not unlike the independent State politics in the USA, Canadian provincial governments had become stronger, diligent, resilient and obstinate. They were not exactly putting the country first before their province.

Alberta is streaks ahead of its nearest provincial competitor when turning fossil fuels into useful energy products for sale. From the northern oilsands regions where the bulk of bitumen and other heavy oils are mined, pipelines are laid throughout Alberta like tentacles to get the products to market.

All well and good but being a landlocked province Alberta relies heavily upon other neighbouring provinces agreeing to support the cause and extend these pipelines across their lands to tide waters and piped to storage tanks on purpose built, seaworthy tankers.

There are four provinces to the east of Alberta before you see the first tidal waters of the massive St Lawrence seaway and Atlantic coastline where tanker opportunities prevail; Saskatchewan, Manitoba, Ontario and Quebec. There are already pipelines in place that move oil and gas products from Alberta but the available volumes are continuously maxed out. The upshot is that these four provinces simply don't want any more pipelines to support the Alberta cause.

To the north lies the North West Territories. Laying pipelines through their land shall require northern coastal installations where sea ice is a problem to move tankers through the Northwest Passage and out to the Pacific.

So, to the west lies just one obstruction between Alberta's rich resources and links to China and India: the Canadian province of British Columbia.

BC and Alberta politics are like chalk and cheese. Alberta with a historically conservative government, fossil fuels and hydrocarbon installations across their landscape. BC with its New Democratic Party (NDP) and support from the environmentalists of the Green Party. The 'tree

298

huggers' of BC want little to do with the supporters of 'dirty' oil and gas from Alberta.

As such, the provinces clash on a regular basis and no-one would be giving in to the other on the subject of moving oil and gas out of Alberta. Much of Canada feels the same way as BC, too. There are so many folk across Canada (and the rest of the world) outside the oil and gas industry who believe that fossil fuel development has had its day and that the world must now support cleaner, alternative fuels. But the trouble with this approach is that Canada has no abundance of alternative energies saturating a market to replace gasoline or diesel powered vehicles.

Furthermore, look around you; most products we consume and use in our lifestyle are made from fossil fuels. Even if electric vehicles were to make a larger dent in the automotive market by supplying cheaper cars to the consumer that can be recharged anywhere you wish, we still need oil and petrochemicals.

It is incredibly naïve to believe that oil and gas has had its day. It most certainly, has not. Yes, we see electric vehicles on the rise, wind turbines scattered overland and solar panels being installed within municipalities and offshore. But the world more than ever, needs to continue to extract and develop fossil fuels and move its stuff to market. And when in Canada, preferably east or west but not south through the US where a strong American government will make mincemeat of Canada's economics.

Putting their foot down and holding steady and refusing to increase new pipelines to their existing infrastructure, the BC government chose to steer clear of endorsing new ones. Alberta was hamstrung.

Rallies and protests in BC show flag waving people with SUVs parked out of sight. One man was recorded as saying:

"Hey, don't have a go at me I didn't drive here. I took the bus." *I think he's a lawyer.*

Another vital component in getting product to a coastline is that a sizeable chunk of Alberta and British Columbia has Indian or First Nation ownership. These peoples have a say in what goes down when pipelines are to be built.

A pipeline that has to run for such a long distance, of course, has more complications than a pipeline that has to be laid for just twenty kilometres.

All things considered, the operations and management team on a $5 billion pipeline project will need to jump through a shitload of hoops before moving the fluids.

Federal and provincial government decision making, energy regulatory policies, First Nation interjection, river crossings, forestry interference, wildlife migration and habitat to name a few.

Then there's the potential rupture to the pipeline from overpressure and the inaccessible location in a wilderness to fly a team in to repair it and the ultimate clean-up costs and court cases.

Consideration for what sections of the pipeline system will run above ground and what will run underground are also studied. Laying pipelines above ground would inhibit movement of wildlife while underground decisions would add cost to the construction, the tracking and ultimate correction of any spills.

It's worth noting here that the Trans Alaskan pipeline commissioned back in the 1970s was raised two metres above ground to support the migration of caribou across the arctic landscape.

Other areas of consideration are maintaining critical fluid temperatures by insulating and electric heat tracing above ground sections of the pipeline. Then there's a question of whether the operating pressure of the product being moved might require a boost in pressure? If so, considerations of where the site for a compressor station (to boost the pressure of a gas) or pumping station (for liquids) will need to be located. The fluid in any eight hundred kilometre pipeline will never get to its destination without introducing several pumping stations for the liquids, or compressor stations for the gases. These facilities command a lot of real estate and, of course, are always visible and above ground.

Then there are maintenance considerations for these pressure boosting stations and the pipelines that include changing out faulty gaskets at flanged connections, valve replacement and corrosion issues requiring changing out piping materials. A gas pipeline may need to collect and dispose of any liquids that have gathered in the long run, prior to being compressed and its journey continued. Liquids entering the blades of a gas compressor will ruin the machinery.

Not to forget damage by construction activity to species of wildlife, plants and fauna with the added potential contamination of local river and lake waters.

While many of these issues can be addressed before a pipeline is built,

300

the others can be addressed during construction. But they all have a place in a conversation.

Prior to any construction, engineering and design activities are contracted out to firms capable of handling a project of this size and magnitude. Budgets and timelines are nailed down along with contracts for the pipe materials, fabrication and construction work ahead.

With all these issues to be addressed, if the existing pipelines and storage facilities in Canada are filled to capacity there is little point in moving forward with upstream (drilling, wellhead) and downstream (upgrading, refining) projects that would extract and refine the bitumen and crude oil when it cannot be moved to market. Why bring something out of the ground if there's nowhere to put it?

This last statement has had a volcanic effect on the energy industry in Alberta. Projects have been shelved or cancelled. Potential projects not yet being considered remain as that... projects that will not be considered. Facebook organizations are now online called 'I Love Canadian Oil' and 'Oil Sands Action' in a show of strength toward the industry.

I was lucky to find something and was assigned a supporting lead role for an engineering firm on a small but critical project. The client, Canadian Natural Resources Limited (CNRL), were having operational problems with some fired heaters on their huge, Horizon facility 75km from Fort McMurray, Alberta. The project was to change out two heaters and, over time, systematically replace them with eight new ones.

I began the first day of my first week by being taken into a private room by the Lead Piping Engineer, John Wallace, and categorically told that the project I was about to embark on was a complete bag of shite and that the client was difficult beyond belief. *Great start to the week.*

As I settled down though, I quite enjoyed the project. After a couple of months it was evident that JW was not enjoying the lead role at all. He was winding himself up at every turn. Whinging about the client, criticizing the engineering management and even moaning about some of his own piping team. Hopefully, not me, whom he personally brought on. I had known John for thirty-seven years when we worked alongside each other on the drawing board at Fluor in 1982 and he has always been a candidate for a meltdown or heart attack.

One day, he asked me if I would consider a transition into his lead role and allow him to retire. I had no issues with this and had managed larger teams and much larger problems in the past. I said, sure.

So, I started to tag along with him to meetings with management and CNRL and get to understand some of the lead piper responsibilities like schedule, budgets and deliverables expected from this project piping group.

Everything was slipping nicely into place except for one thing. Progress. Each Friday I was getting battered for showing a low progress factor. Progress is something that can be described as utter bullshit but nevertheless we all have to play the game.

Here's an example:

I might assign fifty hours to a brand new drawing from start to finish. Let's say I have ten weeks to get it done. Well, if there are no interruptions one of the pipers would spend five hours a week on the document and I would claim 10% progress each week. A no brainer.

Now, let's say that halfway through the work process the client wanted to add stuff to that drawing or change a few things that was on it. These changes could take twenty hours to implement. So, this particular week, instead of claiming 55% progress I would not claim any progress at all and leave it at 50% for a few weeks. Suddenly, I am in danger of missing that ten week finish deadline but I dare not lie and put 70% complete. Telling the truth would be the correct approach.

When the deadline passes and I've used all the hours up but the drawing has not been finished someone will kick my arse around the office. I would then need to claim back from my managers those twenty extra hours I needed and also get CNRL to agree to the extra hours. I then either get overtime approved to catch up, or we miss the deadline.

Well, after getting a bollocking four Fridays in a row, I decided to check out the hours assigned to the project and see why I was constantly being criticised for lack of progress.

I took a look at our entire scope of piping work for the eight new heaters and decommissioning of the two existing ones. I reviewed P&IDs and the Line List to establish how many lines we would have on the project. I then estimated the time it takes to model one single piping system and analyse it for stress and flexibility. I estimated the numbers of drawings required at the end of the project while I included hours in the estimate for field visits, checking, material coordination, pipe supports and supervision.

After a few days of this rather intense work process it was soon apparent that the original budget of piping hours approved by the client fell well short of what we needed to get the job done. To be precise, more than four times the hours we had been approved.

I could not let this go so set the scene and called five of the leadership team into a meeting to discuss my findings. If I had screwed up on my estimate work, going forward, no-one would treat my estimate activities, or any other work, seriously. I would be released by the project for getting it all wrong and giving no-one a warm fuzzy feeling of my piping lead capabilities.

After an hour, the project team present all sat there with their mouths open. They clearly realised there was a dreadful shortfall in the number of piping manhours it would take to get the job finished. After reassurance I was on the right track I went back to my desk and completed the brand new estimate of hours before forwarding it to my managers. Their responsibility was then to react in the only way possible and advise CNRL that the hours that had been submitted by the project and approved by the client several months ago must now be increased by a value of four to one. Furthermore, and equally important, the schedule must be clearly revisited.

This was the only clear path forward to get the project out of the mess it was in.

I also needed more pipers to do the work so hired Trent, a Canadian checker I had also brought out to Kazakhstan two years back. I hired other designers to manage areas of the plot that, to date, had no-one working on them. I brought on a terrific isometric coordinator who had also worked for me in the past, plus other intermediate level piping designers to help get drawings issued.

The project engineering management team were arguably the weakest I'd seen in recent years. Instead of standing up to an aggressive client, they moved the shit downhill and bullied the engineering disciplines. Doesn't the saying go: *"Look after your own team and they'll take care of you"*? Absolute bollocks.

The project manager submitted a meagre trend for extra hours and zero change to the schedule. I was dead in the water and would certainly fail to deliver a project in six weeks that should take closer to twenty. Trying to get three pounds of crap into a two pound bag, something's gotta give.

Over the next several weeks, while the team was in place helping to complete areas of design activity, model reviews to look at the piping design were planned with CNRL. One of these model reviews held in the last two weeks of December 2018 was a catastrophe. With little or ineffective support from my project management in attendance at the MR, changes were made to the plot space and piping design. The one project chap who sat in parts of the reviews, Steve Toms was a complete waste of space and on his cell phone the entire time.

A piping lead facilitating any design review can only really offer piping design related modifications. Any changes that might have an effect on the current schedule must essentially be approved by the project management team. On this occasion in late December, alas, there was no-one to support the cause. Consequently, the changes went ahead but sadly without any interruptions to the project schedule that stayed put. This helped bury the piping group and, with another poor decision made by the project management team to hold the next model review just three weeks after the December review, the writing was on the wall.

# 2019

The bulk of the project was moved to India and to save on costs I was released from my role as lead piping supervisor. I had established a completion date of April when the last isometric would be issued but they wanted it in January. Not really much I could do about it. Russ, my good mate and trusty deputy was moved into the lead role and as he also saw little light at the end of the CNRL tunnel, shortly afterwards made the decision to quickly move on.

For six months I had battled on that CNRL project and had no idea how the remaining team would get it done. What it did need and what all projects need is a much stronger PM team to stand up to what's right, reassure the engineering disciplines that enough time shall be taken to put a quality deliverable together and not bully a piping team into submission. A PM team must be able to push back on an aggressive client, too. The leadership team on that CNRL project were a waste of space; Paul Pastries, Steve Toms and Brian McClacker have no clues how to execute a project.

So, I raised my hand when I couldn't get it done in the timeframe available, instead of sitting quietly at the back of the classroom and waiting till the walls came tumbling down. This has always been my mandate and my work ethos and, as a piping lead, absolutely necessary. In the past, this approach has helped deliver successful projects. Some have come in a bit late but the minimal construction rework in the field has been a testament to a good design project. But, in truth, throughout these past successful projects I was supported by strong project managers and stronger engineering managers.

Sadly, as the world turns, projects are being executed with little or no thought for the timeframe of piping engineering and design in which it takes to get it done.

Later in the year I was informed that the CNRL project actually finished with the last isos going out in June. I rest my case.

I have touched on this subject throughout the book but thought that more narrative related to the Calgary energy situation, is relevant.

When the oil price dropped to below US$40 in 2017, any potential projects in Alberta were cancelled or suspended because it costs $65+ a barrel to develop a project. Engineering houses in Edmonton and Calgary were decimated. First contractors, then permanent staff resources were let go from large engineering companies like Fluor, SNC Lavalin, Jacobs, Worley, AMEC and Bantrel.

The oil price gained a few dollars in 2018 and some of these projects were in part, resurrected. If an oil and gas operator like Shell, Imperial Oil, Suncor, Syncrude, CNRL or another wanted to invest a few hundred million bucks in some improvement project that might increase reliability within their oilsands facility, they had a huge choice of engineering firms to choose from, all with immediately available resources and vacant office space ready to step onto any new project. It's worth noting that each of these companies have satellite offices in India and China that are being kept busy on the execution of other oil and gas projects being commissioned around the world.

With a fresh project to consider, the owner and engineering house would sit together for a few weeks to discuss the cost and schedule. The owner may well go to more than one firm looking for a price and eventually, after agreeing the numbers, a contract is drawn up and the engineering firm recruits key positions for that project. These key positions would be considered as lead discipline roles like piping, supported by individuals with the right experience to head up their team. But these are not the cheapest positions in Calgary and will start eating into any agreed budget.

The next step would be for the lead piping supervisor to recruit a few good 'lieutenants' to support the project. Guys that the lead piper can trust with safety, quality, cost and schedule. On a smaller project the folk that fill this second row of the piping organisation may need to be 'hands on' and get involved with the 3D design. Furthermore, there are the smaller projects where the lead piping supervisor may also be assigned an area to model on the 3D platform.

Again, these senior contract or permanent staff guys on the second tier may be on a sizeable salary.

Depending on the complexity of design areas remaining, instead of expensive seniors the pipe modelling may be covered by who we might refer to as an 'intermediate' designer; or someone who would be able to handle simple areas of piping design like undergrounds, pumps, pipe racks, battery limit valve stations and storage facilities. Although these specific areas also have their unique design criteria to which the designer must have sufficient knowledge and experience.

Finally, the team would be supplemented with stress engineers, materials engineers, materials controllers, piping checkers and isometric coordinators.

I had then established a permanent staff position in Calgary with WOOD. The FEED phase for a petrochemical project for CKPC was up and running. The lead piping engineer, Ryan Delrosa apparently was snowed under and needed some lead support.

I was hired to support a small team with a few detailed design activities in this FEED, a work process quite unusual.

The contracts for a number of tall, vertical vessels had been placed and the nozzle locations had to be established. This approach is most odd when the piping design had not really been understood but one goes with the flow.

I brought on a few extra designers and Ryan had asked me to sit in on meetings with the client. Many of these folk were old NWR personnel and it was a blast being back in touch with them again.

I prepared a schedule with accurate timelines and the team moved forward in the right direction.

In preparing the schedules I could see that the original planning was not easy to support.

*Notice anything familiar, here?*

Ryan had created a schedule and in private conversations had acknowledged its difficulties and suggested I propose an achievable schedule, which I did, before asking me to set up a meeting.

I set up the meeting with my supervisor Ryan, the project engineering manager and my department manager.

The EM, an Egyptian from Zog, Mohammed Mankee, questioned my timelines. When Ryan was asked by the EM if he agreed with my proposal, Ryan said nothing. The DM looked on bewildered not seeing any support but choosing also not to ask questions and intervene.

After several months doing what I believed to be a good job, I was released from the project and Ryan said nothing. In an effort to stay below the radar he had clearly seen the writing on the wall and had brought me in as the fall guy and set me up for failure. Furthermore, his department manager Flyn was equally spineless and with both trying to protect their positions, stayed low. The odd thing about all this was that my CKPC client colleagues I'd worked with for four years at NWR thought I was doing a reasonable job. But they were not working for WOOD.

This new shocker sent another shiver down my spine. With the lack of work and bills coming in, do I scramble for snippets of work in Calgary, or was there an alternative option?

I put property up for sale and took myself off to London for three weeks in search of a permanent position of employment back in the old country. I sat with three companies and each conversation was positive. There was clearly more work opportunity in the UK than Canada due to the broader spectrum of global opportunities. In December I sat the family down to discuss the logistics of moving us all across the pond to England.

Everyone was gung ho for the move including the two dogs!

# 2020

COVID 19 was now getting increasingly uglier by the day and after accepting one of four offers that popped up in the New Year, with Kellogg, Brown & Root (KBR) we all prepared for a move to England.

I chose to move back, first. My position was deputy to the department manager Aron Train and starting work in February I enjoyed the position immensely, writing up audit programs and getting to re-acquaint myself with piping chaps I hadn't seen in 40+ years.

Soon into the position, COVID 19 got much worse and right after moving the family 8,000 kilometres to another continent, the worse thing happened as we all locked down and energy projects were suspended or cancelled in the UK oil and gas market!

Could you believe it. *Beam me up, Scotty.*

I wondered if I had made the right decision but stayed positive and carried on.

I worked from home every day and with lack of energy projects and audit programs I was moved onto an offshore Caspian Sea project called UMID-2 for SOCAR, an Azerbaijan client and, again, deputy to a good lead piper, Matt. I enjoyed the experience working from home, as most engineering resources were now doing. And once more getting involved in offshore stuff was a treat.

# 2021

Then, with the Caspian project coming down, I too was released from KBR before securing a position with Worley in their Brentford offices and balancing the working from home component.

There is no question that working from home has dominated the engineering office scene. With the COVID downturn companies had relinquished control over expensive office and parking space and cut back their Greater London operations, considerably. The compromise was trying to maintain a strong enough workforce where staff could now choose from the two options. In 2021 it was definitely a win-win situation all round.

The FEED phase of the SHAHEEN project for S-OIL proved to be exciting as I built up a team of nineteen piping resources in the home office and ninety-two in Mumbai, while engaging a small team of seven in Charleston, West Virginia, who had experience in polymerisation design capabilities, but more knowledge on the process engineering side. With a budget of a hundred and twenty-three thousand manhours and a year to prepare an Estimate for detailed design bidders to move it forward there were challenging components of the project to overcome during the FEED.

After a twelve month postponement when COVID struck, the FEED project was resurrected. Our South Korean client S-OIL were a tough team to deal with regarding cost and schedule. But in their credit, they wanted to be hands on and offered close support in the Brentford offices.

Furthermore, they had moved thirty folk from South Korea to a London-based assignment. The facilities on the Dusan south coast included an expansion to an existing refinery, a tank farm and a polymer facility producing polypropylene and polyethylene. There was a Steam Cracker facility and a secret squirrel Thermal Crude to Chemicals plant.

There were utilities and offsite scope, and a five kilometre network of underground interconnecting piping, assigned to a third party, in-country. Plenty of secret squirrel stuff too on the process so we'll leave it at that.

# 2022

The S-OIL project continued through to the June as deliverables were wrapped up and the client reps returned to their homes in Korea. Worley continue to support the fresh EPC phase as a project management team (PMT).

I then joined a Swedish electrification project with Worley for a client, Northvolt. Essentially making large batteries from minerals like cobalt, lithium and cadmium. A visit to Skelleftea was scheduled in the July and as the aircraft descended it was just like being back in Alberta again. Forests of evergreen trees and lakes. A clean environment without dark smokes filling the sky from unwanted carbon gases.

Worley then started to build up their project teams once more and encourage all work force to consider being present more in the office. As such the company are making a concerted effort to offer the employee an office/home balance that satisfies both alternatives.

What has been evident in this WFH culture is that it has worked very well with employees taking the responsibility to cover their quota of 8 or 9 hours a day but also enjoying the flexibilities of a WFH environment. The teams of pipers that have worked for me at Worley are not swinging the lead but turning out good stuff day in, day out without the distractions an office based culture may have.

Meetings are now arranged in the office but as they are always set up in a TEAMS format too, the employee has that opportunity to attend the meeting in the office or attend it from home while sitting in shorts, scoffing down a cup of tea and a slice of toast and marmalade. The occasions when a meeting room has been arranged at the office, six engineers might attend but six will be at home. The folk attending in the office sit there listening to two hours of stuff not really relevant to his or her discipline until their ten minutes pops up toward the end of the meeting.

The folk at home who are waiting to be brought into the discussions have their headphones on but are actually managing to get a couple of hours of other work achieved, but discreetly. The evidence of this culture is now seeing folk attending a TEAMS meeting when nine of the twelve may all be in the office but all are now dialling in from their desk!

On 24 February 2022 thousands of Russian soldiers entered Ukraine and starting decimating large areas of the country while cutting short the lives of thousands of patriotic Ukrainians. At first, no-one had any idea on the back of COVID that the oil and gas sector would be affected but in just a few months, the isolation valves of Russian pipelines serving European nations were switched off. Economic sanctions were enforced and without much notice the price of oil and the price of gas, skyrocketed.

It was soon apparent that the world landscape had changed and suddenly, we need more oil and gas! New licences for North Sea development were being issued by the UK government, the *Just Stop Oil* campaigners were climbing all over our motorway structures, putting lives at risk and halting the commuting and transportation in everyday life.

Inland fracking is now back on the table while shortages in vehicle battery production offer temporary hiccups to the electric vehicle revolution.

# 2023

The Northvolt project rolls along and a great team of designers and engineers out of Sweden and offices in India and the UK continue to support the EPC efforts with project startup planned for 2024.

My life in the piping game has been a fantastic ride with many more stories I haven't had time to share. I am now at an age where I try to cut the years of a resume instead of adding them on as I did in my teens.

I have reached this moment without too many hiccups in my life and proud of the fact that I have never smoked a cigarette, taken any drugs, spent a night in hospital or broken a bone in my body. I have other vices, of course like not ever knowing when to leave a great party, throwing in too much money on other people's social events and not making enough effort to understand more about home improvement throughout my life, preferring instead to pay for someone else who would probably do a better job.

I have been fortunate to have seen a fair bit of our world. Thirty-four countries is not a vast number but have worked in England, Scotland, Norway, Venezuela, Canada, the United States, Ivory Coast, South Africa, India and China.

I have toured a fair bit of Australia, China, India, Thailand, Vietnam, Malaysia and Indonesia. Other places include Spain, France, Portugal, Italy, Sicily, Sweden, The Netherlands, Germany, Belgium, Mozambique, Zambia, Kenya, Egypt and the USA.

Yeah, I've been married three times and it is what it is. In my wife Erica, though, I've found someone very special whom has filled a void in my life I didn't have in the past and fulfils everything I ever wanted in a partner. Our life is anything but boring and mundane and she is a loving, supportive wife.

Live life.
    Be liked.
        Help others.
            Act on a few dreams.
                Have no regrets!